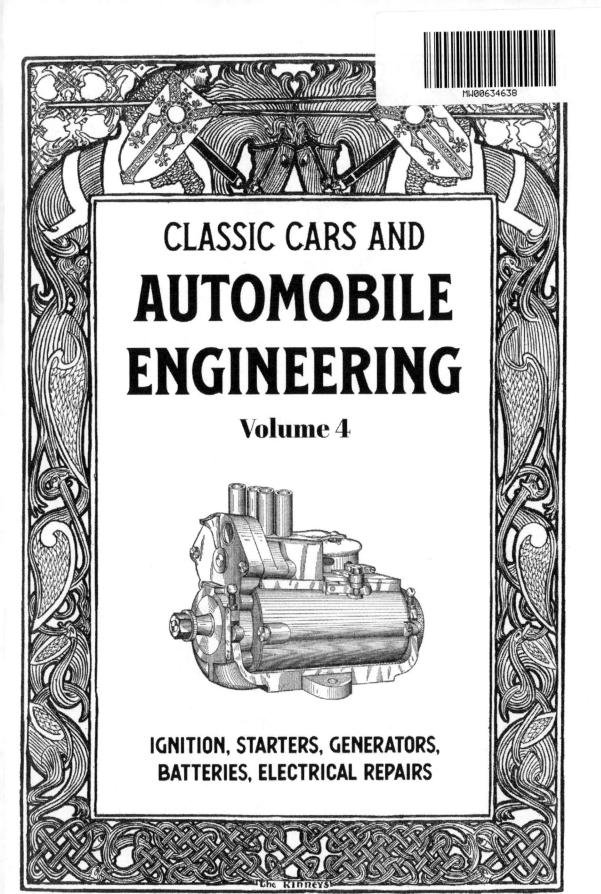

CLASSIC CARS AND
AUTOMOBILE
ENGINEERING
Volume 4

**IGNITION, STARTERS, GENERATORS,
BATTERIES, ELECTRICAL REPAIRS**

Classic Cars and Automobile Engineering: Volume 4

Ignition, Starters, Generators, Batteries, Electrical Repairs

Restored by Mark Bussler

More books at
CGRpublishing.com

The Complete Ford Model T
Guide: Enlarged Illustrated
Special Edition

The American Railway:
The Trains, Railroads, and People
Who Ran the Rails

Antique Cars and Motor Vehicles:
Illustrated Guide to Operation,
Maintenance, and Repair

Automobile Engineering

A General Reference Work

FOR REPAIR MEN, CHAUFFEURS, AND OWNERS; COVERING THE CONSTRUCTION,
CARE, AND REPAIR OF PLEASURE CARS, COMMERCIAL CARS, AND
MOTORCYCLES, WITH SPECIAL ATTENTION TO IGNITION, START-
ING, AND LIGHTING SYSTEMS, GARAGE EQUIPMENT,
WELDING, FORD CONSTRUCTION AND REPAIR,
AND OTHER REPAIR METHODS

Prepared by a Staff of

AUTOMOBILE EXPERTS, CONSULTING ENGINEERS, AND DESIGNERS OF THE
HIGHEST PROFESSIONAL STANDING

Illustrated with over Fifteen Hundred Engravings

FIVE VOLUMES

PACKARD SIX-CYLINDER SEDAN

Table of Contents

VOLUME IV

Electrical Equipment

By Charles B. Hayward   Revised by Tom C. Plumridge

Elementary Electrical Principles . . . . Page * 7
Knowledge of Principles Necessary. Magnetism. Poles. Laws. Magnetic Substances. Magnetic Field. Lines of Force. Solenoids. Effect of Iron Core. Current. Circuit. Conductors. Voltage Drop. Non-Conductors. Generators. Dynamo. Commutators. Armature Windings. Field Magnets

Ignition Fundamentals . . . . Page 41
Induction. Self-Induction. Faulty Ignition. Low and High Tension. Source of Current. Magnetos. Working Principle. Low-Tension Magneto. High-Tension Magneto. Inductor Type. Dixie. Multi-Cylinder Magnetos. Ford Magneto.

Ignition Systems . . . . Page 71
Hydraulic Analogy. Condenser. Spark Plugs. Atwater-Kent System. Connecticut System. Induction Coils. Coils and Vibrators. Resistance Unit. Spark Control. Changes. Timers. Ignition Failure, Causes, Effect, and Cures.

Ignition Operations . . . . Page 101
Spark Timing. Irregular Sparking. Advance and Retard. Power Strokes. Magneto Speeds. Fixed Timing Point. Automatically-Timed Systems. Ignition Setting Point. Typical Firing Orders. Indications and Causes of Late Spark.

Motors . . . . Page 125
Theory of Operation. Counter E.M.F. Types of Motors. Dynamotors. Starting Motors. Modern System. Requirements. Speed Variation. Voltage. Windings and Poles. Installation. Driving Connections. Automatic Engagement. Clutches. Back-Kick Releases. Switches. Troubles. Causes and Cures. Types of Wiring Systems. Single-Wire System. Double-Wire System.

Generators . . . . Page 159
Principles. Application. Control of Output. Constant-Current Type. Regulation. Protective Devices. Battery Cut-out. Ward-Leonard Type. Relay Adjustments. Troubles. Circuit Breaker. Adjustments. Automatic Switches. Fuses.

Storage Batteries . . . . Page 177
Importance. Requires Careful Attention. Function. Parts of Cell. Capacity. Construction Details. Edison Cell. Care. Adding Water. Adding Acid. Hydrometer. Adjusting Specific Gravity. Gassing. Winter Care. Higher Charge Needed. Hard Starting. Sulphating. Restoring Sulphated Battery. High Specific Gravity. Internal Damage. Readings. Protecting Deranged Cells. Temperature Variations. Tests. Troubles and Cures. Cleaning a Battery. Replacing a Jar. Overhauling. Lead Burning. Installing New Battery. Storing. Charging. Equalizing Charges. Methods. Series Charging. Motor-Generator. Constant-Potential. A.C. Rectifiers. Discharge Rate. Charging Rate. Voltage Tests. Cleaning Repair Parts.

Electrical Repairs . . . . Page 256
Testing Equipment. Growler Armature Tester. Undercutting Machine. Magneto Test Stand. Generator Test Stand. Test Bench. Ignition Switchboard. Bearing Puller. Work Bench. Wash Rack. Small Tools. Ohm's Law. Wiring. Wire Gage. Capacity of Wires. Ford Magneto. Capacity. Testing. Recharging. Repairing Magneto Coils. Charging Magnets. Testing Magneto Armatures. Coil. Condenser Tests. Locating Grounds. Shorts. Breaks. Grounds in Circuits. Short-Circuited Tests. Localizing Short Circuit. Cautions. Lamp Troubles. Testing Cut-out. Testing Circuit Breaker. Armatures. Winding. Commutator Maintenance. Seating Brushes. Brushholder Tests and Troubles. Field Coils.

Ford Car Electrical System . . . . Page 350
Ignition. Induction Coils. Magneto. Output at Various Speeds. Circuit. Testing Dash Coils. Spark Plugs. Care. Timer Wires. Generator. Regulation. Third-Brush. Shunt-Wound Generator. Cut-out. Removing Generator. Armature. Wiring Diagrams. Troubles. Testing Armature. Fields. Starter. Construction. Principle of Operation. Brushes. Removing Motor. Dismantling. Troubles. Bendix. Switch. Bulbs. Horn. Charging System. Battery Core.

Ohm's Law . . . . Page 399
Simple Method of Expression. Applications. Electrical Indicating Volt-Ammeter. Ampere-Hour Meter.

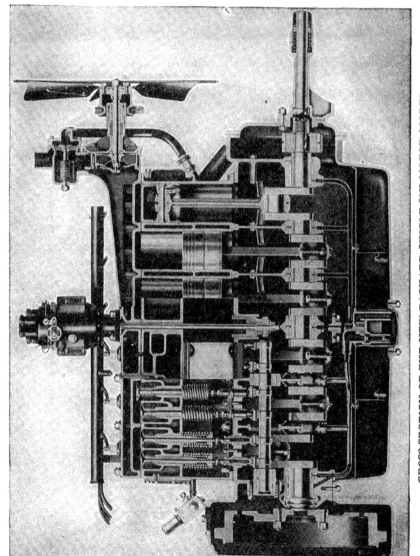

CROSS-SECTION OF THE NEW PACKARD SINGLE-SIX MOTOR MODEL,
SHOWING THE METHOD OF DRIVE OF THE IGNITION SYSTEM

ELEMENTARY ELECTRICAL PRINCIPLES

Knowledge of Principles Necessary. To acquire a good practical working knowledge of electricity as applied to the automobile today, it is essential not merely to find out *how* things are done, either by watching the other fellow do them or by studying "pictures in a book", but also to learn *why* certain things are done and *why* they are carried out in just such a way. In other words, the man whose knowledge is based upon theory and principles applies knowingly the cause to produce the effect and is certain that the desired effect will be produced. On the other hand, the man who works only with his hands aimlessly goes from one thing to another trusting chiefly to luck to accomplish two things. One of these is to strike upon the remedy for the trouble the cause of which is sought, and the other is to deceive the spectator—usually the owner of the car—into believing that the fumbler really knows what he is about.

There are accordingly two distinct classes of knowledge as regards the electrical equipment of an automobile—one which is picked up by rote, an isolated point at a time, and applied in the same manner, and the other which is based upon a clear insight into the underlying reasons for the various actions and reactions that make up the different electrical phenomena involved. If we want to know what is wrong with an electric motor, it is essential that we should know what makes an electric motor operate when everything is right. In the same way, it would be groping in the dark to attempt to investigate the reasons for the failure of a dynamo to generate current, or a storage battery to give up its charge, if we had no knowledge of why a dynamo, when run by an outside source of energy, normally produces a current, or why an accumulator literally "gives back" what has been put into it when its circuit is closed after charging.

It will accordingly be the function of this introductory chapter to give a brief résumé of the principles underlying the operation of what has come to be the most important auxiliary of the gasoline motor as applied to the automobile—its electrical equipment. A thorough understanding of these principles will go a long way toward enabling one to remedy the various minor ills that afflict the apparatus, and to recognize at once those of a nature serious enough to be beyond the first aid which even the best equipped garage is capable of giving. It is worse than a waste of time to hunt for a short circuit or a ground as the cause of failure of the dynamo to generate, when an inspection of its parts reveals the fact that its armature winding has been burned out. Again, one can hardly expect the motor to continue starting the gasoline engine when the owner's neglect of the storage battery has permitted the plates to sulphate so badly that they are practically worthless. Contempt of "book knowledge" is not wholly a thing of the past, and many men consider themselves "practical" in insisting upon learning how to do things with their hands alone. The best-paid man, however, and he who can instruct others how things should be done, is the man who uses his head to acquire a knowledge of the theory upon which practice is based, and then employs his hands to much better effect by letting his brain guide them.

MAGNETISM

Natural and Artificial Magnets. It has been known for many centuries that some specimens of the ore known as magnetite (Fe_3O_4)

Fig 1. Natural Magnet or Lodestone

have the property of attracting small bits of iron and steel, Fig. 1. This ore probably received its name from the fact that it is abundant in the province of Magnesia in Thessaly, although the Latin writer Pliny says that the word magnet is derived from the name of the Greek shepherd Magnes, who, on the top of Mount Ida, observed the attraction of a large stone for his iron crook. Pieces of ore which exhibit this attractive property for iron or steel are known as natural magnets.

It was also known to the ancients that artificial magnets could be made by stroking pieces of steel with natural magnets, but it was not until the twelfth century that the discovery was made that a suspended magnet would assume a north-and-south position. Because of this property, natural magnets came to be known as lodestones (leading stones); and magnets, either artificial or natural, began to be used for determining directions. The first mention of the use of

Fig. 2. Bar Magnet

a compass in Europe was in 1190. It is thought to have been introduced from China.

Artificial magnets are now made either by repeatedly stroking a bar of steel, first from the middle to one extremity with one of the ends, or poles, of a magnet, and then from the mid-

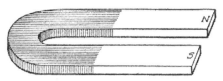

Fig. 3. Horseshoe Magnet

dle to the other extremity with the other pole; or else by passing electric currents about the bar in a manner to be described later. The form shown in Fig. 2 is called a bar magnet, that shown in Fig. 3 is a horseshoe magnet.

Poles of a Magnet. If a magnet is dipped into iron filings, the filings are observed to cling in tufts near the ends, but scarcely at all near the middle, Fig. 4. These places near the ends of the magnet, in which its strength seems to be concentrated, are called the poles of the magnet. It has been decided to call the end of a freely suspended magnet which points to the north, the north-seeking, or north pole, and it is commonly designated by the letter N. The other end is called the south-seeking, or

Fig. 4. Location of Poles of a Magnet

south pole, and is designated by the letter S. The direction in which the compass needle points is called the *magnetic meridian*.

Laws of Magnetic Attraction and Repulsion. In the experiment with the iron filings no particular difference was observed between the action of the two poles. That there is a difference, however, may be shown by experimenting with two magnets, either of which may be suspended, Fig. 5. If two N poles are brought near each other, each is found to repel the other. The S poles likewise are found to act in the same way. But the N pole of one magnet is found to be attracted by the S pole of the other. The results of these experiments may be summarized in the general law: *Magnet poles of like kind repel each other, while poles of unlike kind attract.*

This force of attraction or repulsion between poles is found, like gravitation, to vary inversely as the square of the distance between the poles; that is, separating two poles to twice their original distance reduces the force acting between them to one-fourth its original value, and separating them three times their original distance reduces the force to one-ninth its original value, etc.

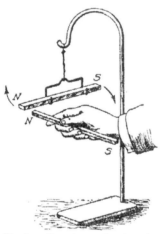

Fig. 5. Experiment Proving the Law of Magnetic Attraction and Repulsion

Magnetic Substances. Iron and steel are the only common substances which exhibit magnetic properties to a marked degree. Nickel and cobalt, however, are also attracted appreciably by strong magnets. Bismuth, antimony, and a number of other substances are actually repelled instead of attracted, but the repulsion is very small. Until quite recently, iron and steel were the only substances whose magnetic properties were sufficiently strong to make them of any value as magnets. Recently, however, it has been discovered that it is possible to make rather strongly magnetic alloys out of non-magnetic materials. For example, a mixture of 65 per cent copper, 27 per cent manganese, and 8 per cent aluminum is rather strongly magnetic. These are known as the *Heussler alloys.*

Electromagnets. The identity of magnetism with electricity is readily established by some very simple experiments that have been repeated so often as to become classics. By taking a bar of iron and winding some insulated wire around it in the form of a coil and then connecting the terminals of this coil with a battery or other source of current, the bar becomes magnetic. One end of it is the positive, plus, or north pole of the magnet, and the other the negative, minus, or south pole. Break the connections or otherwise "open the circuit" and the magnetism instantly disappears. Reverse the connections to the battery by attaching the wire previously at the positive pole to the negative, and vice versa, complete the circuit again, and the bar is once more magnetic, but now the pole that was previously north or positive is south. The bar is once more a magnet, but its polarity has been reversed by reversing the direction of flow of the magnetizing current. This bar of iron with a coil of wire wound around it is known as an electromagnet because it becomes magnetic only when a current is passing through the coil. If a rod of hard steel is substituted for the bar of soft iron and the current passed through it, the bar will be found to be strongly magnetic after the current has been shut off. That is, the bar of steel has, through the action of the current, become a permanent magnet like that shown in Fig. 2. This method is often used for making permanent magnets from hardened steel.

To determine the polarity of a magnet it is only necessary to hold a small pocket compass near it; let the compass needle come to rest normally and then bring the compass near to one end of the magnet. If the needle continues to point in the same direction and gives evidences of being strongly attracted to the magnet, the end to which it is being held is the south pole. Bring the compass near to the other end of the magnet, and the needle will turn away sharply, showing that like poles repel each other.

Magnetic Field. If a bar magnet is placed on a sheet of glass and a handful of fine iron filings thrown around it, they will automatically assume the position shown by Fig. 6. As originally dropped on the glass some of the filings may not be within reach of the influence of the magnet, but if the glass be gently tapped and tilted slightly, first one way and then another, they will arrange themselves in the symmetrical pattern shown. This gives a graphic illustration of the *field of influence* of the magnet, usually termed the magnetic field. This field is most powerful at the poles, as will be noted by the attraction of the filings at the N and S points, representing the north and south poles of the magnet. At intermediate points along the length of the magnet the filings will be seen to have placed themselves as if to indicate a circular movement of the lines of force. This is the magnetic circuit and these concentric circles represent the magnetic flux, or flow. If the magnet is then removed from the glass and the north pole extension of it placed

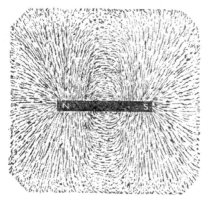

Fig. 6.   Field of Force about a Bar
Magnet

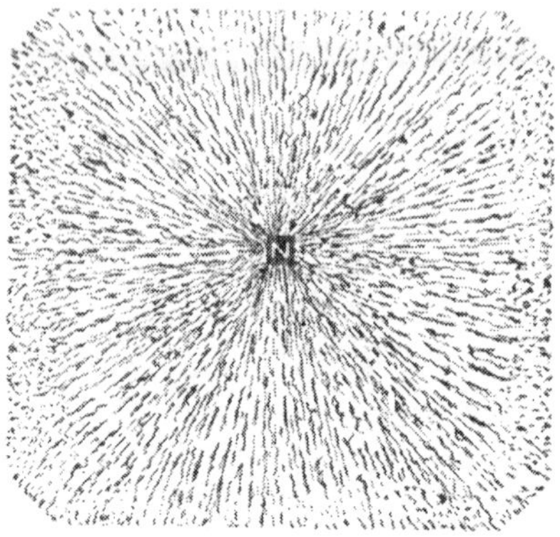

Fig. 7.   Field of Force about a Single
Pole

centrally under the glass, a striking illustration is given of the magnetic field around the pole, Fig. 7. A bar magnet has been shown here for purposes of simplicity, but a common horseshoe magnet such as can be had for a few cents will serve equally well for the experiments.

By carrying the experiments a little further, the identity of magnetism and electricity is strikingly shown. Take a piece of

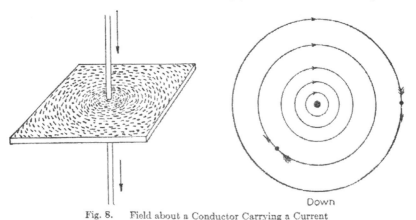

Down

Fig. 8.   Field about a Conductor Carrying a Current

cardboard or heavy paper, punch a hole through its center and pass through this hole a wire connected to two or three dry cells. Scatter on the paper the filings used in the previous experiments, then complete the circuit by touching the end of the wire to the other terminal of the battery. The filings will immediately arrange themselves as shown in Fig. 8, illustrating the magnetic field which is always present around any current-carrying conductor.

Lines of Magnetic Force. Punch another hole through the cardboard and rearrange the circuit of the dry cells so that the wire passes from the positive battery terminal up through one hole of the cardboard and down through the other hole to the zinc or negative. Scatter the filings as before and touch the loose end of the wire to the negative terminal. The arrangement of the filings will then be that shown in Fig. 9, the positive field being at the left and the negative at the right. The fact that the mag-netic fields overlap in the curious alignment indicated is simply due to the proximity of the con-ductors carrying the current.

Another simple method of demonstrating the identity of electricity and magnetism is to place an ordinary pocket com-pass above or below a wire which is running north and south and is carrying a current. If this is a direct current the needle of the

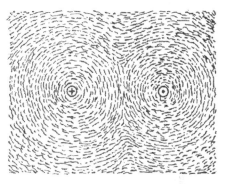

Fig. 9.   Field about a Coil

compass will tend to set its axis at right angles to the wire, that is parallel to the lines of force; the direction of the deflection will depend upon the direction of the current. This test, therefore, not only indicates the magnetic field about the wire bearing a current, but shows its direction.

All of the arrangements which the filings assume under the influence of either a magnet or a current, as shown by the various llustrations, indicate that the stresses in the medium surrounding a magnet or current-carrying conductor follow certain definite lines, the lines showing the direction of stress at any point. These are termed lines of force.

Solenoids. It has been determined that the direction of the current and that of the resulting magnetic force are related to one another as the rotation and travel of an ordinary, or right-hand, screw thread. Consequently, if the conductor be looped instead of straight, the lines of magnetic force will surround it as shown in Fig. 10. The field of such a loop, if outlined with the aid of filings or explored with a compass needle, will be seen to retain

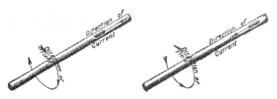

Fig. 10. Direction of Magnetic Lines about a Conductor

the general character of the field surrounding a straight conductor, so that all the lines will leave by one face and return by the other, the entire number passing through the loop. Hence one face of the loop will be equivalent to the north pole of a magnet and the other face to the south pole. In fact, the loop will act exactly as if it were a thin disk magnetized perpendicularly to the plane. By winding a number of these loops to make a hollow coil, there is formed a solenoid, Fig. 11. Exploring its field shows that the lines of force pass directly through the center or opening of the hollow coil, leaving by one end and returning by the opposite end, as indicated.

If such a solenoid is held vertically and a bar of soft iron placed so that it extends for an inch or so into the lower end of the solenoid, a current passed through the latter will cause the iron to be violently drawn up into the coil and held there. As long as the current flows, this rod is strongly magnetic and has all the properties already

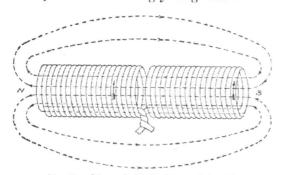

Fig. 11. Magnetic Field about a Solenoid

described. But the moment the current is shut off, the magnetism practically disappears and the rod immediately drops out of the coil by its own weight. Reversing the direction of the current reverses the polarity of the solenoid but makes the effect the same; increasing or decreasing the amount of current sent through it increases or decreases correspondingly the strength of its magnetic field. The principle of the solenoid is used in starting systems to operate electromagnetic starting switches.

ELECTRICAL EQUIPMENT

Effect of Iron Core on Strength of Solenoid. The magnet flux or flow of lines of force through a solenoid is much greater when an iron core is present than when the coil is empty or a core of wood is inserted. The magnetism flows through the iron as a current would. Soft iron is used because it can be magnetized or demagnetized very quickly.

The magnet permeability of air (or a vacuum) is taken as unity, and other substances are rated accordingly—for very soft iron it may be as high as 2500. Substances such as silk, cotton, wood, glass, brass, copper, and lead are said to be non-magnetic. All insulators are likewise non-magnetic.

Permanent magnets are used in magnetos and where permanent magnetic fields are needed. Electromagnets are used for pieces of generators and starting motors. They are also used in induction coils and in automatic switches, such as battery cut-outs, relays, and in circuit breakers.

THE ELECTRICAL CIRCUIT

Current. Electricity is an all important factor in the operation of the automobile but before it can be used its qualities must be understood. Electricity is found practically in everything and is one of nature's strongest forces. All objects do not contain the same amount of electrical force or energy. Electrical energy or force is spoken of as a current and the term used to indicate this force is represented by the letters e.m.f., meaning electromotive force.

Whenever an object is moved, energy is used or pressure exerted. Pressure must also be used to make an electrical force move or flow. This unit of electrical pressure is called a *volt*. In the automobile we have a battery which is used for lighting purposes and it is spoken of as being a six-volt battery (or one of whatever strength the manufacturer uses in a particular make of car). This means that the pressure behind the current which is given out by the battery is six volts. If the bulb used in the headlight of an automobile is a six-volt bulb, it means that this bulb will stand a pressure of six volts.

The gallon is the unit of measure for liquids, just so the *ampere* is the unit of measure for electricity. The quantity of current contained in a six-volt battery is sixty amperes, which means that this battery will deliver sixty amperes (quantity) at six volts (pressure). The bulbs used in the headlights on many automobiles are six-volt three-ampere; this means that these lamps will use three amperes and stand a pressure of six volts.

When an automobile is being driven, a certain amount of resistance must be overcome, such as friction of engine parts, resistance of air, road, etc. An electric current also must overcome resistance when flowing in its allotted path, but in this case only one resistance must be overcome—the resistance of the conductor.

When a manufacturer chooses a wire for a conductor of an electric current, he takes into consideration the resistance of the wire. To correctly measure this resistance there must be a unit on which to base his work. This unit is known as the *ohm*. When we state that a wire has two-ohm resistance, we mean that this wire has a resistance the strength of which is two ohms. These three units are included in a definite statement which is known as "Ohm's Law."

It would be well to consider here the effect of resistance on an electric current. To illustrate, let us use a practical automobile application, that of the starting motor and battery connection. We will suppose that we have two pieces of wire, both of the same length but one smaller in diameter than the other. A connection is made between the starting motor and the battery with the small wire. After a few moments the wire is found to be getting warm, and the longer the connection is maintained the greater the increase in heat. This indicates that the wire has too much resistance to the current flowing in it. As the heat increases so does the resistance, and vice versa; as the resistance increases so does the heat. If the wire is too small, the starting motor will not get the proper amount of current and therefore will not operate correctly.

If the larger wire is used, it will be found that it keeps perfectly cool, and the starting motor operates correctly and up to the desired speed. We learn from this that as the size of the wire becomes smaller the resistance of the wire to the flow of electric current increases.

This property of resistance in a conductor to electric current is often taken advantage of, being used to protect certain units in the ignition system, such as the breaker points and coils. You have no doubt seen the headlights of an automobile burn dim. In order to bring this about a resistance unit is inserted in the headlight circuit. This unit has a certain amount of resistance to the current flowing in the circuit and only allows enough current to pass to make the lamps burn dimly.

This property in wire is used to control and regulate the output of generators and thereby protects both the generator and battery from damage. Resistance has a large controlling influence in the operation, design, and manufacture of electrical apparatus.

It would be well to firmly fix in your mind the three quantities or units of measure used in electrical work and place them as follows: Volts—Units of Pressure; Amperes—Units of Quantity; Ohms—Units of Resistance.

Circuits. Before electrical energy can be used, there must be a path for it to travel in. This path through which the current flows is termed a "circuit." The electric current in a circuit always travels from the positive side around the circuit to the negative side, and it does not make any difference how many units or what apparatus there may be in the circuit to this characteristic of an electrical current.

From this statement it will be seen that an electric current must always return to its source. This is a fact worth remembering as it is the first principle in tracing trouble in electric circuits. The current used to operate trolley cars is fed to the motors of the car from the overhead wire and returns through the tracks to the generators in the power house. This is known as a ground-return circuit. In some systems the positive side is attached to the frame and this is often called a ground return but in reality it is not, because there cannot be a return on the positive side if the current flows to the unit from the positive.

In the single-wire electric system of an automobile, current from the storage battery reaches the starting motor through the starting switch and a single cable of heavy copper wire and returns through the frame and other metal parts of the car itself, or vice versa. This is another instance of a ground-return circuit. Both the primary and the secondary windings of the ignition system of an automobile are also simple grounded circuits. In contrast with this, the circuit may be composed of copper cables directly connecting both poles of the battery and switch with the starting motor. The highly insulated cable employed for both ignition and starting systems is expensive and the use of a single wire greatly simplifies the connections, considerations which account for the general use of this type of circuit. A circuit is said to be open when there is a break in it which prevents the current from flowing, as

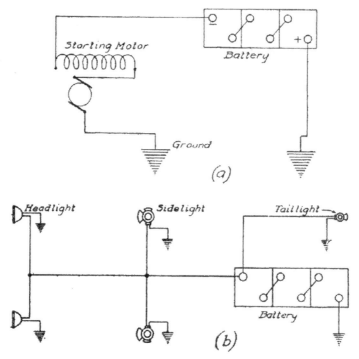

Fig. 12. Typical Starting-Lighting Wiring Diagrams. (a) Series Circuit of Starting Motor; (b) Multiple Circuit of Lamps

when the switch is opened, or when a connection or the wire itself is broken.

Series Circuit. The connections between a storage battery, switch, and starting motor, comprise the simplest form of circuit, in which the motor is said to be in series with the battery, and the cells of the battery are in series with one another. This is termed a series circuit and a break in it at any point opens the entire circuit. The starting motor, Fig. 12 (a), requires the entire output of the storage battery for its operation.

ELECTRICAL EQUIPMENT

To make clear the distinction between this and other forms of circuit, it must be borne in mind that, in equalizing a potential difference, electric current flows from the positive or plus side of the source of supply, whether a battery or generator, to the negative or minus side (plus and minus being arbitrary signs employed to distinguish the positive and negative sides of a circuit or of an instrument). The current is said to flow out on the positive side of the circuit and to return on the negative side. In the case of a series circuit as described, the current flows through each piece of apparatus in turn; each receives all the current in the circuit at a potential proportioned to the resistance of the apparatus in question. For example, in the simple starter circuit referred to above the starting motor receives the entire output of the 3-cell storage battery at its full voltage of 6 volts, less the drop in voltage due to the resistance of the circuit. If there were two starting motors instead of one in the circuit, both in series, both would receive all the current but at only half the voltage.

Multiple or Shunt Circuit. As opposed to this, in a multiple circuit, Fig. 12 (b), in which every piece of apparatus is connected to both sides of the circuit "in parallel", each piece of apparatus in the circuit receives current at the same voltage but draws from the circuit the current determined by its resistance. The failure or withdrawal of any one or more instruments in a multiple or parallel circuit has no effect on those remaining. The lighting circuits of an automobile equipped with a 6-volt starting system are an example of this. Each lamp is designed to burn to its maximum illumination at 6 volts, but the 25-candle-power headlights take more current than the 5-candle-power side lights or the 2-candle-power taillight, owing to the difference in the size and resistance of their filaments. Removing any one of the bulbs has no effect on any of the others, because all are in parallel.

Series-Multiple Circuit. A combination of the two forms of circuits is sometimes necessary to accommodate different devices designed for varying voltages. For example, it is usually found expedient to burn 6-volt lamps on the 12-volt starting systems. In such a case, the starting motor is in series with the battery and receives the full voltage as well as the full current. The lamps are divided into two groups, each group comprising a parallel or multiple circuit of its own, and these two groups are connected in series so that the lamps in each circuit receive 6 volts, but the circuit as a whole takes the battery current at 12 volts. Such a combination

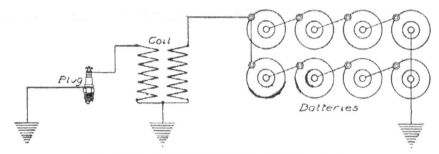

Fig. 13. Dry Cells in Series-Multiple for Ignition Circuit

is known as a series-parallel or series-multiple circuit and is more or less commonly used for connecting dry cells for ignition use, Fig. 13.

Circuits may also be in parallel, that is, practically a circuit on a circuit. The method of connecting up the voltmeter that is mounted on the dash of the car is an instance of this, a wire being led from each side of the main circuit to the instrument. The instrument is then said to be *in shunt*, Fig. 14, and the amount of current that is diverted to it is entirely dependent on the resistance. As a voltmeter is wound to a high resistance, Fig. 15, it is designed to take very little current for its operation. The

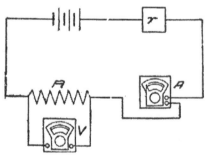

Fig. 14. Diagram Showing How Voltmeter Is
Shunted in the Circuit

ammeter, Fig. 16, on the other hand, is intended to indicate the entire current output of the generator on charge or discharge, and is connected in series so that all the current passes through it.

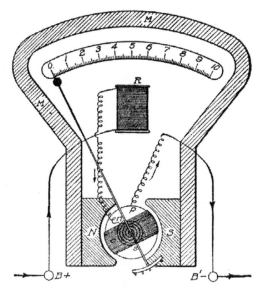

Fig. 15.   Diagram of Voltmeter Principle

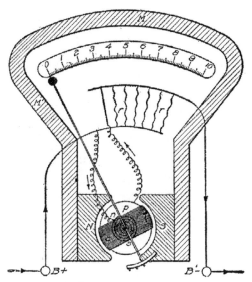

Fig. 16.   Diagram of Ammeter Principle

ELECTRICAL EQUIPMENT

Conductors. To lead steam or air under pressure from a boiler or compressed-air reservoir to the point at which it is to be utilized as energy, it is desirable to use a conductor that will not waste too much of this energy in useless friction. That is, the conductor must be of ample size in proportion to the volume to be conveyed, smooth in bore, and free from sharp turns or bends. The transmission of electrical energy involves some of the same factors. While neither the smoothness of the bore nor the presence of bends and turns has any effect, they have their counterpart in the conductivity of the material of which the wire is made, the size of the wire in proportion to the amount of current to be carried being also a matter of prime importance.

Resistance of Materials. Materials differ greatly in their ability to conduct an electric current, or, to put it the other way around, they differ in the amount of resistance that they offer to the passage of the current. Silver in its pure state heads the list in the table of relative conductivities, and it is accordingly said to possess a relative resistance of one, or unity; the resistance of every other material may be expressed by a number which represents the resistance of that particular substance as compared with pure silver. Naturally silver does not represent a great possibility for commercial use, and so copper, which is second on the list, is almost universally employed. Pure copper is very soft and is lacking in tensile strength; it is therefore alloyed, and it is also hardened in the drawing process; both of these processes increase its resistance slightly over the factor usually accorded it in the standard table of specific conductivities of materials. In this table, German silver (which is an alloy containing no silver whatever and having but a few of its properties), cast iron, steel, carbon, and similar substances will be found well down toward the end. They are known as "high-resistance" conductors and are usually used where a certain amount of resistance to the current is desirable.

It must be borne in mind that ability to conduct a given amount of current without undue loss through resistance depends upon the size and the length of the conductor quite as much as upon the material. In other words, if a steel rail is only one-thirtieth as good a conductor as a copper cable, it will require a cross-section of steel thirty times as great as that of a copper cable in order to conduct the current with the same ease—that is, to make a conductor of equal resistance. An illustration of this may be seen in the overhead copper wire of the usual trolley system. This wire of about one-half inch diameter forms one of the conductors, while the two steel rails form the "return". A similar example may be found in what is known as the single-wire system of installation for an electric starter in automobiles. A single copper cable conducts the current from the battery to the starting motor, while the steel frame of the automobile is the return side of the circuit, or vice versa.

Voltage Drop. It is evident that the resistance of a circuit varies inversely as the size of the conductor—the larger the cross-section of a conductor, the less its resistance—and increases directly as its length, besides depending upon the specific resistance of the material. The specific resistance of the metals constituting electrical circuits on the automobile are (silver being 1.0); copper 1.13, varying more or less with its hardness; aluminum 2.0; soft iron 7.40; and hard steel 21.0. Thus, 9.35 feet of No. 30 copper wire are required for a resistance of one ohm, while only 5.9 inches of hard steel wire of the same gage are required to present the same amount of resistance to the current. If the length of the conductor is doubled, its resistance is doubled, which accounts for the placing of the storage battery as close as possible to the starting motor. Furthermore, the heavy starting currents which are required by the motor demand the use of heavy copper cable for this circuit. If two wires are of the same length but one has a cross-section three times that of the other, the resistance of the former is but one-third that of the latter. If a circuit is made up of several different materials of different sizes joined in series with one another, the total resistance will be the sum of the resistance of the various parts.

In addition to being affected by the cross-section and the length, the resistance is also influenced by the temperature. All metals increase in resistance with an increase in temperature, that of copper increasing approximately .22 per cent per degree Fahrenheit. The change of resistance of one ohm per degree change in temperature for a substance is termed its *temperature coefficient*. Metals have a positive temperature coefficient; some materials, like carbon, have a negative temperature coefficient, that is, they decrease in resistance with an increase in temperature.

It is consequently necessary to employ wires of proper size to carry the amount of current required by the apparatus in circuit —such as lamps—without undue heating, which would cut down the amount of current flowing. For the same reason it is also desirable to make the circuits as short as practicable, since in addition to cutting down the current, the resistance also cuts down the effective voltage. That is, there is a fall of potential, or drop in voltage, between the source of current supply and the apparatus utilizing it, due to the resistance of the conductors between them. This voltage drop is further increased by joints in the wiring and by switches. It is apparent that the lower the voltage of the source of supply, the more important it becomes to minimize the loss, or voltage drop, in the various circuits. For this reason lighting or other circuits on the automobile should never be lengthened where avoidable. When necessary to extend a circuit for any reason, wire of the same diameter and character of insulation as that forming the original circuit must be employed, and the joints should be as few as possible, all mechanically tight, and well soldered. The voltages employed in the electrical systems of automobiles are so low—varying from 6 to 24 volts, with a strong tendency to standardize the 6-volt system—that any increased resistance is likely to cause unsatisfactory operation.

Non=Conductors. In going down through a table of specific conductivities of various materials, the vanishing point is reached with those that cease to be conductors at all. Such materials are known as nonconductors or insulators, and some substances vary in the degree of insulation they afford quite as much as other materials do in their ability to conduct a current. Glass, rubber, shellac, oil, paraffin wax, wood, and fabrics are all good insulators when perfectly dry. Distilled water has such a high resistance as to be almost an insulator, but in its natural state water contains alkaline salts or other impurities that make it a conductor. Consequently, when any otherwise good insulating substance is wet, the current is likely to leak across the wet surface of the insulator. This is particularly the case with a current of high potential, or high tension, and explains why it is of the greatest importance

ELECTRICAL EQUIPMENT

to keep all parts of the secondary side of the ignition system perfectly dry. The potential which causes the current to arc across the gap of the spark plug is so high that it will leak across even slightly damp surfaces, such as the porcelains of the plugs. This leakage is often visible, especially in the dark, and it may also be detected by placing the bare hand on the porcelain.

Just as the amount of current to be carried determines the size of the conductor to be employed, so the potential or pressure under which this current is transmitted determines the amount of insulation that will be necessary. The latter is also affected, however, by mechanical reasons, for example, by the liability of the conductor to chafing or abrasion. The best grades of copper cable employed for both ignition and starting-lighting systems on automobiles today are stranded, that is, composed of a number of fine wires, to make them flexible. The stranded cable is then tinned to prevent corrosion due to the sulphur in the insulation, after which it is covered with a soft-rubber compound of a thickness dependent upon the purpose for which the wire is intended. For high-tension ignition wire this rubber covering is about three-sixteenth inch thick. This covering is vulcanized and is then further protected by braided linen, or silk-cotton thread which is made waterproof by being impregnated with shellac or some other insulating compound.

When it becomes necessary to renew the wiring on an automobile, care should be taken to obtain wire that is, as nearly as possible, the same as that installed by the manufacturers of the car, so that no undue resistance is offered to the current. There are two kinds of wire or cable—high and low tension. High tension is for secondary current, and low tension is for primary current. They can be easily recognized, because low-tension cable has only a few strands and the insulation is usually thin; while high tension cable has a large number of strands and the insulation is thick.

It is often necessary to install or replace terminals on the electrical cables of automobiles. The terminals on all wires should be well soldered to the wires for a good joint cuts down resistance.

Corrosion of any kind on the wires or terminals will cause resistance and an inspection of joints will often disclose the trouble in the circuit. A connection may be mechanically tight but not electrically tight because of corrosion, therefore, corrosion should be considered as a non-conductor. It is a wise precaution to scrape and clean all terminals before replacing them.

GENERATOR PRINCIPLES

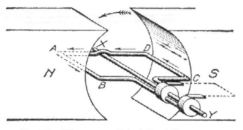

Fig. 17.   Elementary Principle of Generator

Classification. All dynamo-electric machines are commercial applications of Faraday's discovery of induced currents in 1831. They are all designed to transform the mechanical energy of a steam engine, a waterfall, a gasoline engine, etc., into the energy of an electric current. Whenever large currents are required—for example, in running street cars; in systems of lighting and heating; in the smelting, welding, and refining of metals; in the charging of storage batteries; in the making of electric castings, etc.—these currents are always produced by dynamo-electric machines.

There are two kinds of generators (1) direct current, or those producing a unidirectional (direct) current, that is, one which always flows in the same direction in the external circuit, and (2) alternating current, or those producing an alternating current, that is, one which reverses in direction continuously throughout the entire circuit.

Elementary Dynamo. Whenever lines of magnetic flux are cut by a conductor, for example, by a wire passing through them, an e.m.f. (electromotive force) is produced in the conductor, and the strength of this e.m.f. is entirely dependent upon the speed at which the conductor passes through the magnetic field. If, at the time that this is done, the ends of the wire are brought together to form a circuit, a current will be induced in the conductor. The simplest form of generator would consist of a single loop of wire *ABCD* arranged to rotate in a magnetic field, as shown by Fig. 17. Having its plane parallel to the direction of the magnetic flux, the loop, if it be rotated to the left as shown, will have an e.m.f. induced in it that will tend to cause a current to flow in the direction shown by the arrows. The e.m.f.'s induced in *AB* and *CD* for the position shown will have their maximum values since the wires are then cutting the magnetic flux at right angles and are consequently cutting more lines of force per second than in any other part of the revolution. Note that as *CD* moves up, *AB* moves down (and vice versa) across the magnetic flux so that the induced currents in all parts of the loop at any instant are flowing in one direction. The value of this e.m.f. depends upon the speed, and as the loop approaches the 90-degree, or vertical, position, the e.m.f. decreases because the rate of cutting is diminishing, until when the loop is vertical both the cutting

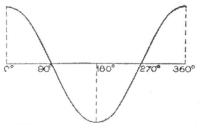

Fig. 18. Dynamo E. M. F. Curve

of the magnetic flux and the generated e.m.f. are at zero. If the rotation is continued, the rate again gradually increases, until at 180 degrees it is once more a maximum. The cutting, however, in the two quadrants following the 90-degree position has been in the opposite direction to that occurring in the first quadrant, so that the direction

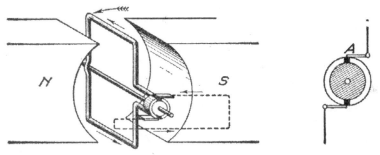

Fig. 19. Simple Form of Generator Showing Arrangement of Brushes in Contact with Commutator

of the e.m.f. generated is reversed. Plotting this through an entire rotation gives the curve shown in Fig. 18. Such an e.m.f. is termed alternating because of its reversal from positive to negative values, first in one direction and then in the other, through the circuit. It cannot be utilized for charging a storage battery, and hence it is not employed in connection with starting and lighting dynamos and motors. To convert an alternating current into a direct or continuous current, a commutator must be added.

Commutators. Fig. 19 illustrates a commutator in its simplest form. It may be imagined as consisting of a small brass tube which has been sawed in two longitudinally, the halves being mounted on a wooden rod. The wood and the two cuts in the tube insulate the halves from each other. Each one of these halves is connected to one terminal of the loop, as shown in the illustration, Fig. 20. Against this commutator, Fig. 19, two brushes bear at opposite points and lead the current due to the generated e.m.f. to the external circuit. If these brushes are so set that each half of the split tube moves out of contact with one brush and into contact with another at the instant when the loop is passing through the

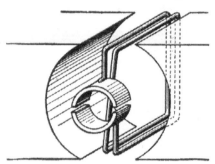

Fig. 20.   Commutator with Double Turn

positions where the rate of cutting is minimum (as indicated in the enlarged end view of the commutator shown at A), a unidirectional current will be produced, but it will be of the pulsating character as indicated by the curve for one cycle shown in Fig. 21.

This would also be the case, if instead of the single loop, a coil wound on an iron ring be substituted, as in Fig. 22, the only effect of this being to increase the e.m.f. by increasing the number of times

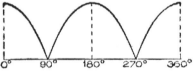

Fig. 21.   E. M. F. Curve with Commutator

the electrical circuit cuts the magnetic flux. Now assume that two coils are connected to the commutator bars, instead of the single loop, shown in Fig. 22. This arrangement will give the simple device shown in Fig. 23, called an armature. The two coils are

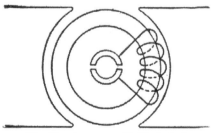

Fig. 22.   Armature with Single Coil

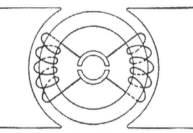

Fig. 23.   Two-Coil Armature

in parallel and while the voltage generated by revolving this winding with two coils is no greater than with one coil, the current-carrying capacity of the winding is doubled. The current generated by this form of armature would still have the disadvantage, however, of being pulsating. As in the case of the automobile motor, the number of cylinders must be increased to make the power output

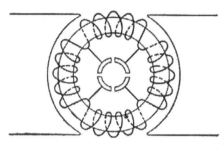

Fig. 24. Four-Coil Armature

a continuous unbroken line, so armature coils and their corresponding commutator brushes must be added that one set may come into action before the other "goes dead". By placing an extra pair of coils on the armature, at right angles to the first, as shown in Fig. 24, one set will be in the position of maximum activity when the other is at the point of least action. While this armature would produce a continuous current, it would not be steady, having four pulsations per revolution, and it is consequently necessary to increase the number of coils and commutator segments still further to generate a steady, continuous current. This is what is done in practice.

A commutator consists of a number of copper bars or segments, equal to the number of sections in the armature. These bars are separated by sheets of insulating material, usually mica, and are

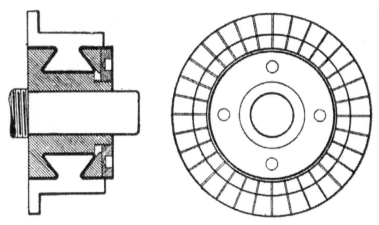

Fig. 25. Sectional and End Views of a Commutator
Courtesy of Horseless Age

firmly held together by a clamping device consisting of a metal sleeve with a head having its inner side undercut at an angle, a washer similar in shape to the head of the sleeve, and a nut that screws over the end of the sleeve, as shown in the left-hand or sectional view of Fig. 25. The sleeve is surrounded by a bushing of insulating material, and washers of the same material are placed between the assembly of commutator bars and the two clamping heads. Each bar is then completely insulated from every other bar and from the clamping sleeve. Commutators are also made by pressing the entire assembly of copper segments together, or molding them, in insulating material (Bakelite), which thus forms the hub or mounting of the commutator as well as the insulating material between the segments. After assembling, the commutator is turned down in a lathe to a true-running cylinder and then sandpapered on its outer cylindrical surface to present a smooth bearing surface for the brushes. At the inner end of the commutator which is closest to the armature windings, the commutator bars are provided with lugs as shown in the sectional view; these lugs are slotted and the armature leads are soldered to them. At the right, Fig. 25, is shown an end view of the same commutator.

From the repair man's point of view, the commutator is the most important part of the generator or the motor, since it is one of the first with whose shortcomings he makes acquaintance. Practically all lighting and starting motors now have their armature shafts mounted on annular ball bearings, so that the commutator and the brushes are the only parts that are subject to wear. If the time devoted in the garage to the maintenance of automobile electric systems were to be divided according to the units demanding attention, the battery would naturally come first, brushes and commutators next, then switches, regulating instruments, connections, and wiring, about in the order named. After all of these come, of course, burnt-out armatures or other internal derangements which necessitate returning the units to the manufacturer; but troubles of this nature are quite rare. While this list gives the order of precedence, it has no bearing on the relative importance of the troubles; with respect to the total time taken by each, the battery is responsible for not far from 90 per cent, the commutator for about 5 per cent, all other causes comprising the remaining 5 per cent.

Armature Windings. In the simple illustrations given to show the method of generating e.m.f. in the armature and leading the current to the external circuit, what is known as the ring type of winding is shown. This is inefficient because half the length of the conductor—the portion inside the ring—does not cut any lines of force and hence does not aid in generating the current. The design, moreover, does not lend itself to compactness, so that it would not be adapted to automobile work even if there were no objection to it on the score of inefficiency. A slotted type of armature core is very generally employed for the small generators and starting motors used on automobiles and the wire is either wound directly in the slots, or is "form wound", that is, the wire is placed on a wooden form shaped to correspond to the position the coil will take when in place on the armature. After winding the necessary length of conductor on this foundation, the wire is taped together, and varnished or impregnated with an insulating compound, and baked.

Owing to its high magnetic permeability, iron is universally employed for the core of the armature, since the function of the core is to carry the magnetic flux across from pole to pole of the field magnets, as well as to form a foundation for the coils. However, when a mass of iron is rotated in the field of a magnet what are known as "eddy currents" are set up in the metal itself, and these prevent the inner parts of the mass from becoming magnetized as rapidly as the outer and also cause the interior to retain its magnetism longer. As the efficiency of the generator depends upon the rapidity with which the sections of the armature become magnetized and demagnetized as they revolve, the lag due to these eddy currents is a detriment. To reduce this effect to the minimum, the armature cores are always laminated, that is, built up of thin disks of very soft iron or mild steel, these disks having the necessary slots punched in them to accommodate the windings when assembled on the shaft. The disks are insulated from one another either by varnishing them or by inserting paper disks between them. They are assembled on the shaft and are put together under considerable pressure, various means being employed to hold them in place. These disks are so thin that hundreds of them are required to make an armature core only a few inches long, and when pressed together in place they are to all intents and purposes a solid mass.

Armature winding, however, is something that is entirely beyond the province of either the car owner or the repair man, no matter how well equipped a shop he has. It is a job for the expert in that particular line, and on the rare occasions when an armature does go wrong, it should always be returned to the manufacturer, if possible, if not, to a shop making a speciality of such work.

Field Magnets. In the foregoing explanation of the generation of an e.m.f. in a conductor when rotated in a magnetic field and the leading out of the current through a commutator, the presence of the field has been assumed and nothing has been said regarding the method of providing it. The term field is applied interchangeably to the magnetic flux between the pole faces of the field magnets and to the magnets themselves, but it is more generally understood to refer to the latter directly and to the former by inference. There are various methods of maintaining

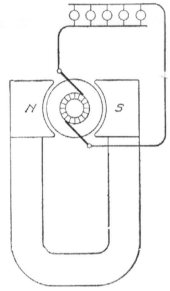

Fig. 26. Diagram of Magneto

the flux, usually described as "field magnet excitation", but only two of them are applicable to the electric generators employed on the automobile.

Permanent Field Used in Magneto. The simplest of these, and the first to be designed, employed permanent magnets, from which such a generator takes its name, *magneto.* Fig. 26 is a diagrammatic representation of an early form of the magneto-generator. Since magnetism cannot be maintained permanently at the high flux-density or strength which can be produced by an exciting coil fed by a current, this method is only employed in very small generators, as its bulk for large powers would be excessive. Its

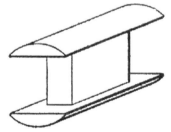

Fig. 27. Sketch Showing Shape of Armature Core
Courtesy of Horseless Age

great advantage is its simplicity and constancy. The magneto-generator shown in Fig. 26, however, is designed to produce a continuous current, and is not the type in general use on the automobile today.

The type usually installed is made with a two-pole armature, as shown by Fig. 27. This figure illustrates the core known as a "shuttle" type because the wire is wound around the center of the core in much the same manner as thread is put on a shuttle. These cores are laminated as already described, in all well-built magnetos. The space on the core is filled with a single coil of comparatively coarse wire on the majority of magnetos, which generate a low voltage current that is subsequently stepped up through an outside transformer. In some instances, in what may be termed the true high-tension type of magneto, there is a second winding of fine wire on the core so that the magneto generates a current

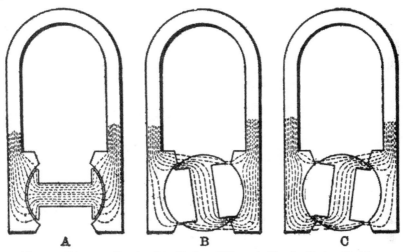

Fig. 28. Diagrams Showing Distribution of Magnetic Flux for Various Positions
Courtesy of Horseless Age

and steps it up without the aid of any outside devices. In either case, one end of the winding is "grounded on the core", that is, connected to it electrically, so that the core and other metal parts of the machine form one side of the circuit, while the other end is connected to a stud against which a spring-controlled carbon brush bears, to collect the current. Detailed descriptions of various types of magnetos are given later so that nothing further concerning the construction need be added here.

Principle of Operation of Magneto. Under "Generator Principles", the principle of the operation of the magneto has already been explained, the method by which the rotation of the conductors in the magnetic field generates an e.m.f. and a current is induced in them. But as the actual operation of the magneto as designed for ignition purposes is radically different from any other form of generator, it is given here. If unrestricted, the armature of the magneto will always assume the position shown at *A*, Fig. 28, and considerable effort will be required to turn it from this position as the magnetic flux through the armature is then a maximum. When the armature is rotated a little over 90 degrees from this horizontal position so that the armature poles leave the field poles, as at *B* in the same figure, the flux decreases, and when in a vertical position no lines of force pass through it. At this point, the direction

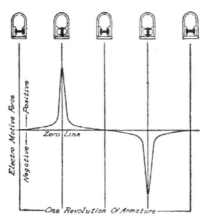

Fig. 29. Curve of Primary E. M. F. in Magneto on Open Circuit
Courtesy of Horseless Age

of the magnetic flux through the armature core reverses, that is, changes from the influence of one pole to the other, and it is at this time that the impulse is given. In the two-pole armature the vertical position is reached twice in one revolution and, therefore, two impulses are given in one revolution, Fig. 29. Having a two-pole armature, the magneto produces an alternating current of one complete cycle per revolution, as shown by the curve, Fig. 29, which illustrates the electromotive force generated at the different positions in the rotation of the armature. The similarity between this curve and the one generated by the elementary dynamo, Fig. 18, will be noted. With the armature in the horizontal position there is a dead point, the e.m.f. curve only starting as the pole pieces of the armature begin to cut the edges of the field magnet poles. It then rises very sharply to a peak, and as sharply drops away to zero again, thus forming one-half cycle, which is then repeated in the opposite direction. As the present discussion comprises only an introduction to elementary principles and theories, further details of construction and operation of the magneto are given later in the section on "Ignition".

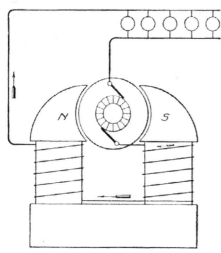

Fig. 30.   Diagram Showing Series Generator

Self-Excited Fields. In a machine of the magneto type, the only method of varying the current output is to vary the speed of the armature, and it is therefore not well adapted to the majority of uses for which a generator is employed. Consequently, other methods of exciting the fields have been developed, which may be roughly divided into two classes: *first*, those separately excited, in which current from an independent source is supplied to the field windings. This is now practically restricted to large alternating-current generators and so need not be considered further here. *Second,* self-excited fields, which are now characteristic of all continuous current generators. In this method all or a part of the current induced in the armature windings is passed through the field coils, the amount depending on the type of generator.

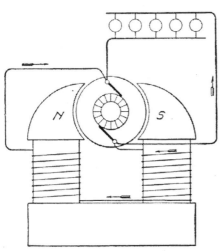

Fig. 31.   Diagram Showing Shunt-Wound Generator

Series Generator. Where the entire current output is utilized for this purpose, the dynamo is of the series type, and a reference to the section on "Circuits", in connection with the illustration, Fig. 30, will make this plain. There is but a single circuit on such a dynamo and while it has the advantage of simplicity, it does not generate a current until a fairly high speed is reached, or unless the resistance in the external circuit is below a certain limit. It is also likely to have its polarity reversed so that it is not fitted for charging storage batteries. As the only series generators put into commercial use have been for supplying arc lamps in series for street lighting, they need not be considered further.

Shunt-Wound Generator. By winding the generator with two circuits instead of one and giving that of the fields a relatively high resistance as compared with the outside circuit on which the generator is to work, a machine that is self-regulating within certain limits is produced. As shown by Fig. 31, the main circuit of the generator is that through the armature with which the field winding is in shunt. The current accordingly divides inversely as the resistance and only a small part of it flows through the field coils, while the main output of the generator flows through the external circuit to light the lamps, to charge a battery, or the like, the resistance of this external circuit being much less than that of the fields. But in this type,

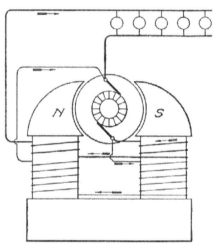

Fig. 32. Diagram Showing Compound-Wound Generator

as well as in the simple series form, the e.m.f. generated varies more or less with the load, and as the latter is constantly changing, it is necessary to provide some means of varying the e.m.f. generated to suit the load, in other words, to make the generator self-regulating. Of the several available methods of doing this, the only one applicable to the small direct-current generators used in automobile lighting and starting systems, is that of varying the magnetic flux through the armature.

Compound-Wound Generator. There are also several methods of effecting this variation of the magnetic flux, but the most advantageous and consequently the most generally used, is to vary the amount of current in the energizing coils on the field magnets.

By adding to the shunt winding a few turns of heavy wire in series with the armature so that all the current passes through them, the magnetic flux may be made to increase with the load as it is directly affected by the current demanded by the latter. This combination of the shunt and series is termed a compound winding, and the usual method of affecting it is shown by Fig. 32. Such a machine

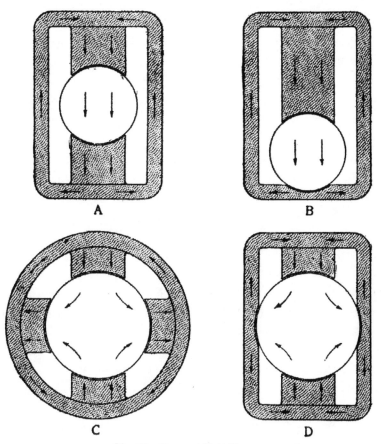

Fig. 33. Forms of Field Frames

is called a compound generator, and is sometimes used for lighting and for charging the storage batteries of automobiles.

In view of the great range of speed variation required of the automobile motor, the series wiring is sometimes reversed so as to act against the shunt instead of with it, in order to prevent an excessive amount of flux and a current that would be dangerous to the windings themselves due to a very high speed. The compound winding then opposes the shunt-winding and is termed a *bucking-coil* or winding. This is referred to later in connection with the discussion of methods of regulating the generator on the automobile.

Forms of Field Magnets. For greater simplicity, all of the illustrations shown in connection with the explanation of the various types of generators are of the old bipolar type in a form long since obsolete. The field frame, as it is designated may, however, take a number of different forms depending entirely upon the designer's conception of what best meets the requirements of ample power in the minimum of space and with the minimum weight. Fig. 33 shows some typical forms of field frames in general use on automobile generators, and it will be noted that in addition to providing a magnetic circuit the field frame also serves to enclose the windings. These are known as "ironclad" types from the fact that all parts are thoroughly enclosed and protected. The arrows in each case indicate the paths of the magnetic circuits, the number of the circuits varying with the number of pole pieces. The form at *A* has two opposed poles, each of which is designed to carry an exciting coil or winding. This is a bipolar machine. Field frame *B* is also of the bipolar type but only one pole carries an exciting winding, the other being known as a consequent pole. In both of these field frames, it will be noted that the magnetic circuits are long, which adds to the magnetic reluctance and tends to decrease the efficiency. To overcome this, multipolar types of field frames are very generally employed. One of these, with two wound or salient poles and two consequent poles, is shown at *D*, the extra poles making four short instead of two long magnetic circuits. *C* is a multipolar type with four salient poles.

Brushes. Brushes serve to conduct the current generated by the armature to the outer circuit and to the field coils in order that the excitation of the latter may correspond with the demand upon the generator. The brushes originally employed were strips of copper which bore on the commutator; as generators increased in size these brushes were built up of thin laminations of copper. Plain copper brushes in any form, however, cause an excessive amount of sparking which is ruinous to the smooth surface and true running of a commutator. Built-up copper gauze brushes were then adopted, and they were fitted to bear against the commutator. Though an improvement, these did not meet all the requirements and were in turn superseded by carbon brushes, which are now practically universal. The carbon brushes usually bear directly against the face of the commutator, either through a blunt, squared end, or one that is slightly beveled. The brush holders are generally attached to rocker rings, which allow adjustments to prevent sparking; in these holders are small helical springs under compression, which serve to press the brush against the commutator. Ordinarily, the brushes are composed of a uniformly smooth and homogeneous compound of carbon that soon acquires a glazed surface at its bearing end and wears indefinitely without requiring any attention, but at times a gritty brush will be found. Such a brush scratches the commutator surface, wears unevenly, and is generally a source of trouble.

Badly worn commutators frequently result from the use of improper brushes, or too heavy a spring pressure—also from too light a spring pressure. The manufacturer has found out by experiment and study just what character of brush is best adapted to his particular generator or starting motor and also the exact amount of spring pressure that is necessary to insure the best results. Consequently, much trouble will be avoided if brushes are replaced only with those supplied by the manufacturer of that particular machine, in connection with the brush springs that were designed for it. There are electrical as well as mechanical reasons for this, since both the resistance and current-carrying capacity of carbon brushes vary. This has been taken into consideration by the manufacturer who has provided a brush especially adapted to his machine.

MARMON FIVE-PASSENGER SEDAN DE LUXE

IGNITION FUNDAMENTALS

INDUCTION PRINCIPLES

Induction. There are many things in connection with electricity and its operation that are hard to understand as to why they operate in a certain way. An electrical current has the property of being able to set up a field about its conductor and when a current suddenly flows in a wire placed close to another wire, a delicate measuring instrument such as a galvanometer will indicate a momentary current in the second wire. When the current in the first wire ceases, that in the second will likewise cease immediately. This phenomenon is known as induction, and a current is said to have been induced in the second wire. This property, induction, is used to obtain the high voltage necessary to jump the gap in the spark plug for ignition purposes.

Winding the first wire in the form of a coil and bringing this coil close to the second wire will give the induced current considerably greater strength. The induced effect is still further increased in three other ways: *first*, by inserting an iron core in the coil; *second*, by winding the second wire in the form of a coil; and *third*, by bringing these coils as close together as possible by winding one directly over the other.

Transformer Principle. The arrangement just discussed is termed an induction coil or transformer (step-up) and is universally employed in connection with ignition systems. The character of the induced current depends upon the relation that the first coil, termed the *primary*, bears to the second coil, known as the *secondary*.

In the usual ignition coil the primary consists of a few turns of comparatively heavy wire, and a current of about 2 amperes (4 to 5 on starting) is sent through it at a low voltage, seldom exceeding 6 volts. The secondary coil, however, consists of a great number of turns of exceedingly fine wire, and the current induced in this is proportional to the relative number of turns between the two and the value of the current in the primary. The secondary current is accordingly of extremely high potential but of low current value.

In the commercial step-down transformer, the relations described above are reversed, the primary being a coil of many turns of fine wire, while the secondary is a comparatively small coil of few turns. In this case, the current is received at the transformer at high voltage and correspondingly reduced amperage, and it steps the voltage down to the standard generally employed, 110 or 220 volts, and increases the amount of current proportionately.

Self=Induction. It has already been pointed out that electricity may be put under pressure or potential, and that the greater this pressure, the greater the amount of work a certain amperage of current will perform, thus affording a direct analogy with steam, water, or air under pressure. An electric current also possesses other characteristics corresponding to mechanical equivalents. Chief among these is inertia and it is the latter that is responsible for what is known as self-induction.

When a current is passed through a coil of wire, a strong magnetic field is set up in the coil owing to the concentration of a great many turns of wire in a small compass. By inserting a core of soft iron wires into this coil, the magnetic field is greatly strengthened, since the permeability of the iron affords a path of slight resistance for the magnetic circuit. There is, of course, a magnetic field surrounding every conductor in a circuit when the current is passing, but the iron core of the solenoid converts a certain part of this current into magnetism. An appreciable time is necessary after the circuit is closed for such a coil "to build up". This "building up" consists of saturating the core with magnetism.

When the circuit is suddenly opened, the current that has been stored in this core in the form of magnetism is as quickly retransformed and its value is impressed upon the circuit, causing a flash at the break. The flash is also aggravated by a certain amount of inertia which the current possesses. We may illustrate this by a stream of water flowing in a pipe. If the water is suddenly shut off by the closing of a valve, it tends to keep on flowing and momentarily causes a great increase in the pressure against the face of the valve, resulting in the familiar "water hammer". The same thing happens when a circuit is suddenly broken, and the higher the potential the more marked this effect will be. The current tends to keep on flowing, and the extra potential which this self-induction gives it will cause it to arc, or bridge, the gap at the break, unless a condenser is provided to take care of this. Every circuit possesses self-induction, but it is only marked in circuits having considerable inductance, that is, in coils, and especially those with iron cores, such as induction coils, circuit breakers, etc.

FUNDAMENTAL IGNITION PRINCIPLES

Faulty Ignition Cause of Much Early Trouble. More than half of the troubles encountered by the designers and the drivers of the early automobiles were the direct results of the extremely crude ignition systems at first adopted. With knowledge of gasoline-motor operation, generally scant at that time, much of this trouble was attributed to causes entirely foreign to its real source or, on general principles, the motor was roundly "cussed" as a deep and unfathomable mystery. Subsequently it became plain that much of this inexplicable tendency to balk was due to the elusiveness of the electric current. Crude insulation and contacts, inherently defective spark plugs, and extremely wasteful current-handling devices, fed from a weak source such as dry cells and partly discharged batteries, were the causes.

Distinctions between Low Tension and High Tension. A low-tension ignition system uses a low-tension current—i.e., the

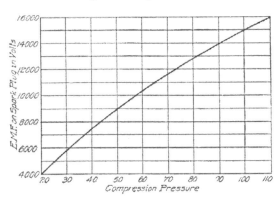

Fig. 1. Voltage Required to Force a Spark across a .020-Inch Gap under Different Compression Pressures

output of a battery or small generator, employed at the voltage at which it was produced, or, in other words, a primary current. A high-tension uses a high-voltage current produced by passing the output of the battery or other source of supply through a step-up transformer (induction coil). As this is taken from the secondary winding of the coil, it is sometimes referred to as a secondary current. It is the result of induction and is commonly termed a high-tension current owing to its great voltage or potential. The battery produced current of high amperage value at 6 to 8 volts, which after being passed through the coil became a current of microscopic amperage value at anywhere from 10,000 to 25,000 volts, according to what the designer of the coil thought was sufficient potential to produce a good spark, that is, to enable it to readily jump the gap in the points of the plug. The curve, Fig. 1, shows the voltage necessary to force a spark across a given distance in air under various pressures.

As the low-tension current will not jump an air gap, a further distinction between the two systems is the employment of totally

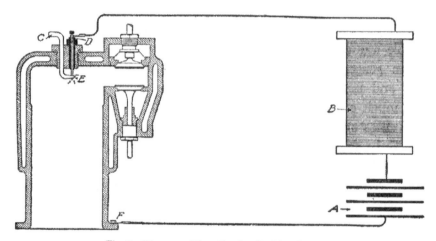

Fig. 2. Diagram of Low-Tension Ignition System

different types of spark plugs. In the former, a mechanically operated plug, i.e., one that is held closed until the maximum current is passing through it and is then suddenly opened by being mechanically tripped by a cam or rod operated by the engine, is essential. Such a plug produces a spark that is immensely superior in heating value and, consequently, in igniting ability, to the usual thin spark that bridges the gap of a high-tension spark plug. But this most desirable quality is likewise quickly destructive of the contact points, necessitating frequent readjustment of the mechanically operated plugs. Moreover, the mechanical lag or time element of operation, due to the inertia of the numerous moving parts, rendered it difficult to make a low-tension spark plug suitable for a high-speed engine without resorting to the most expensive machine work, and much greater skill was necessary for their proper adjustment.

The shortcomings of the original high-tension systems were so glaring, however, that some of the most successful automobiles of earlier days were fitted with low-tension ignition.

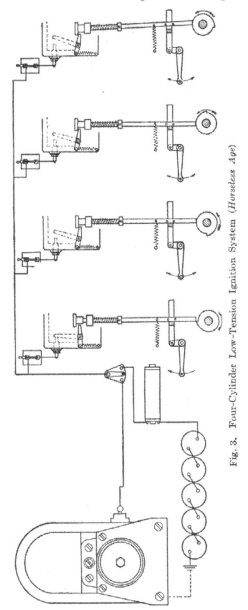

Fig. 3. Four-Cylinder Low-Tension Ignition System (*Horseless Age*)

Low=Tension System. Fig. 2 shows diagrammatically the essentials of a low-tension system for a single-cylinder motor, while Fig. 3 shows a complete low-tension system for a four-cylinder motor. The details of the operating mechanism and the plug are shown in Figs. 4 and 5. Referring to Fig. 2, A is the battery, B is a spark coil (a single coil which by its self-induction develops a high-voltage spark), and C, D, and E are the elements of a make-and-break device that is mechanically actuated at regular intervals by the motor itself to produce the sparks within the cylinder. As shown in the drawing, the circuit is completed by grounding the wires from one side of the battery on the cylinder base, or any other portion of the machine, as at F. In this figure D is a small insulated plug entering the interior of the cylinder, usually through one of the valve caps, while C is a movable arm (see also Fig. 4), that makes and breaks contact with B, at the point E, when it is given a slight rocking movement. For the best results this rocking movement must be very sharp and rapid, in the nature of a snap, and it must, of course, be correctly timed to occur in proper relation to the moment when the spark is required. (See also Fig. 5.

The chief advantage of low-tension ignition is its immunity from troubles caused by short-circuiting by leakage of the current through poor insulation or across moistened terminals. This led to its almost universal employment on motor boats for a number of years, but it has since been generally abandoned even for marine use so that it is now only to be found on stationary engines, the low rotative speeds of which make it practical. So far as the automobile is concerned, the low-tension system is only of historical interest as it is already several years since it was wholly discarded.

High=Tension System. High-tension ignition systems are based on the fact that when a sufficiently high potential is impressed upon a current of electricity, it will leap an air gap or other break in the circuit of a width dependent upon the potential or voltage itself. In bridging such a gap, the current becomes visible in the form of an arc, flash, or spark, depending upon its duration and intensity, and it will readily ignite a gasoline or other gaseous fuel mixture Its

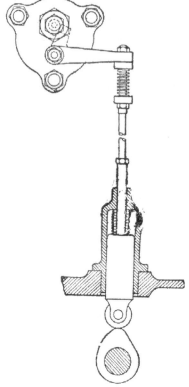

Fig. 4. Make-and-Break Mechanism

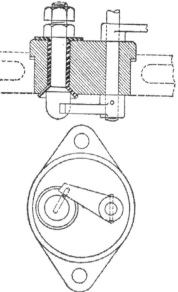

Fig. 5.   Low-Tension Spark **Plug**
(*Horseless Age*)

very ability to do so, however, was one of the most prolific sources of trouble in the early days, as the designer's conception of the insulation required to conduct such a current without grounding or short-circuiting was far from approaching the reality.

The essentials of a high-tension system are shown diagrammatically in Fig. 6. A is the source of current, usually a battery in earlier days, as indicated by the conventional sign, placed in a primary circuit that also includes the contact maker C, the primary winding of the coil B, and the vibrator G. The contact maker C is positively driven by a connection with some revolving part of the motor, so that it makes contact at the exact time ignition is required in each cylinder.

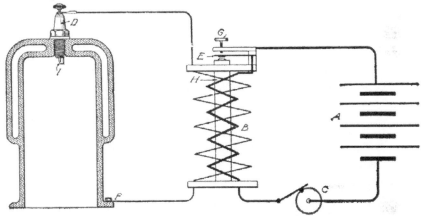

Fig. 6. Diagram of High-Tension Ignition System

With a system of the type described, when contact is made the first result is attraction of the vibrator blade E by the magnetized core H of the coil. This, by drawing E away from the contact screw G, at once breaks the primary circuit again, and this demagnetizes H, with the result that E again springs into contact with G. The effect of this is to cause a rapid series of current surges through the coil B, as long as the contact maker C maintains the contact.

Each time a surge of primary current passes through a coil, a secondary current of very high voltage is induced in the secondary circuit, which is grounded on the cylinder at F and connected at B with the spark plug. This plug, for high-tension ignition, has an open gap of about $\frac{1}{32}$ inch at I, across the resistance of which gap the current will jump, because of its high tension. Ignition is thus effected by a rapid succession of sparks across I.

ELECTRICAL EQUIPMENT

This briefly describes what may be termed the rudiments of a high-tension ignition system and the diagram shows their relation to one another. Of course, this simply has reference to a single-cylinder motor. For each extra cylinder in an ignition system of the type illustrated, there is another contact point on the timer and another coil. The timer or contact maker is sometimes referred to as an interrupter, though this is not technically correct as its function is first to close the circuit.

Source of Ignition Current. The battery system which has come into permanent use in recent years is the original system used for ignition purposes. Formerly generators were not thought of as a part of automotive equipment. Therefore it was necessary to periodically charge the batteries that were used for ignition purposes. In the early days of the automobile, the driver never knew when the battery was going to give out. Manufacturers cast around for some other means of ignition-current source, and the magneto came into permanent use.

MAGNETOS

Owing to the failure of either dry cells or storage batteries to supply sufficient current to operate the wasteful contact devices at first employed, mechanically driven current generators were adopted. American practice at first favored the small, high-speed direct-current dynamo, but as proper regulating devices had not then been developed, it was not successful, chiefly because its speed range was so limited. Few of these little dynamos generated sufficient current at less than 1200 r.p.m. to ignite the charge in the cylinder, so that at slow speeds they would not run the motor. If run much faster, they burned out and were accordingly abandoned.

Working Principle. The magneto is simply a small dynamo in which the fields consist of permanent magnets, instead of electromagnets, the cores of which only become magnetic when a current is passed through their windings. Hard steel, particularly when alloyed with tungsten, retains a very substantial percentage of its magnetism, after having been once magnetized by contact with a powerful electromagnet. Its retaining power is further increased by placing a "keeper", or armature, across the poles, or ends. The advantage of a permanent field for magneto use is that it is at its maximum intensity regardless of how slowly the armature is revolving so that a good spark is produced at very low speeds; while its initial value cannot be exceeded no matter how fast the machine is run, so that the armature winding cannot be burned out. All magnetos generate an alternating current so that when used with a coil there is no necessity of frequently making and breaking the circuit, as is done by the vibrator of a coil handling direct current, the alternate surges of current from zero to maximum of opposite polarity producing the same effect more efficiently.

Fig. 7. Remy Magneto Contact Breaker

Low=Tension Magneto. A low-tension magneto is nothing more or less than the simple instrument which formed part of the thousands of telephones of the hand-ringing type still to be found in rural districts. Built with more powerful magnets and wound to give a greater current output at a lower voltage, it was employed in connection with low-tension ignition systems.

Fig. 8. Contact Breaker of High-Tension Magneto (Bosch)

As the mechanically operated make-and-break plug circuits are timed, the magneto is simply revolved continuously without reference to the motor timing, the current being constantly delivered to the circuit through the usual collector ring and brushes. Magnetos

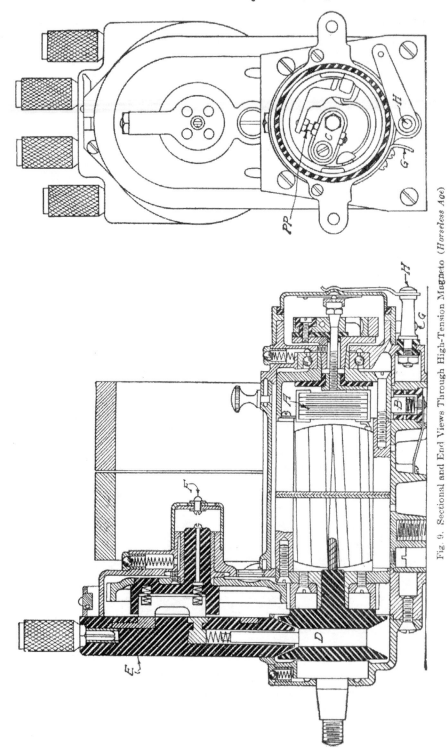

Fig. 9. Sectional and End Views Through High-Tension Magneto (*Horseless Age*)

of this type are still used to a greater or less extent on large, slow-speed stationary engines.

High=Tension Magneto. Essentially all magnetos are the same: that is, they have a permanent magnet field and a two-pole armature. In what may be best identified by terming it the *true high-tension type*, there are two windings on this armature, a primary winding of comparatively coarse wire in which the current is generated, and a secondary winding of fine wire, the same as an induction coil. A magneto of this type is timed with the motor according to the number of cylinders, being driven at crankshaft speed in the case of a four-cylinder motor and at one and a half times crankshaft speed in the case of a six. In addition to the usual current-collecting device, it is equipped with a contact breaker or interrupter, such as that shown in Fig. 7, which is part of a Remy magneto. Fig. 8 shows the same essential of a Bosch light-car type magneto. Except at the point in the revolution at which the spark is to occur in the cylinder, the armature circuit is normally short-circuited upon itself. This permits it to "build up", so to speak; that is, as the armature poles come within the most intense part of the field, the current in the armature winding reaches its maximum value and, at this moment, the contact points of the breaker are opened and a strong current is induced in the secondary winding. As the distributor runs synchronously with the contact breaker, the circuit to one of the plugs is closed at the same time the spark occurs at it.

Description of True High-Tension Type. A sectional view of a true high-tension magneto is shown in Fig. 9. In this the primary and the secondary windings on the shuttle armature are entirely separate to insure better insulation. These windings are not shown in section in the illustration, the usual insulating tape winding being indicated on the armature. Twice during every revolution of the armature, the primary circuit is opened at the platinum points PP of the circuit breaker, the interruption occurring substantially at the moment when the primary current is at its maximum. From the primary winding, the current is conducted to the stationary member of the contact breaker C through the terminal B. A is the condenser. One terminal of the secondary winding is connected to the end of the primary winding, as in a coil, and the other connects with the high-tension collector ring D, from which it is conducted through a carbon brush to the brush of the distributor above it for distribution to the four brass segments in the distributor plate *E*. These segments are connected to the four terminals shown extending above the magneto in the end view at the right and from them the usual high-tension cables are led to the plugs. The distributor is driven from the armature shaft of the magneto through 2 to 1 gearing so that it only makes one revolution for two turns of the crankshaft in the case of four-cylinder four-cycle motor, as in the latter but two explosions occur per revolution. To vary the time of occurrence of the spark in

the cylinders, the contact breaker may be turned through part of a revolution by means of a rod and linkage fastened to one of the extensions of the contact breaker box, as shown in the end view. This connects with the spark timing lever on the steering wheel and, to stop the action of the magneto, it is only necessary to move this lever to the extreme retard position, which brings the spring *G* in contact with the bolt *H* and short-circuits the primary winding.

Fig. 10. Eisemann Magneto Generator for Four-Cylinder Cars

This instrument, Fig. 10, differs from Fig. 8, as it is a magneto and a generator combined. Ignition and battery charging are accomplished by this unit.

Typical High-Tension Magneto Circuit. Fig. 11 is the wiring diagram for a high-tension system, using a true high-tension type magneto. *B* is a wire of the primary circuit. A primary generating coil is in this circuit, being wound on the shuttle type armature; there is also a contact breaker, *E*, which is carried on the same revolving spindle that bears the armature. *C* is a high tension coil wound on the armature, being located in the circuit. The dotted lines indicate the return ground.

High-Tension Type with Coil. This is not actually a high-tension magneto, properly so-called, as it only generates a low-tension current, which is subsequently stepped up through a transformer or non-vibrator coil, but it is commonly so termed as it is always used in connection with a high-tension ignition system. In this case there is only a single winding on the armature and the current is led from the latter through the usual contact breaker and then to an independent coil, generally located on the dash. The condenser is combined with the coil, and from the latter the high-tension current is led back to the magneto to be distributed. Owing to its lower cost, this type of

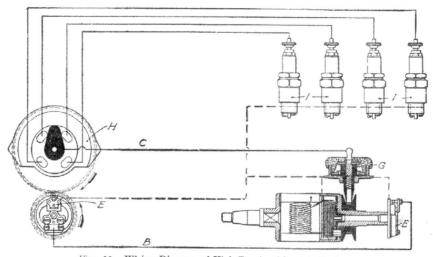

Fig. 11. Wiring Diagram of High-Tension Magneto System

magneto is probably more generally employed, especially on medium-priced American cars, than any other.

Safety Gap. If the current induced in the secondary winding of an induction coil meet with a resistance in the outer circuit in which the coil is connected, greater than the resistance presented by the insulation of its own windings, it will puncture this insulation and the expensive coil will be ruined. The placing of such a resistance in the high-tension circuit occurs when the connection of a spark plug is removed from the plug terminal and is allowed to dangle in the air beside the motor and, unless this were guarded against, it would result in the breakdown of the ignition system. The precaution takes the form of a safety gap. This is an opening inserted in the circuit, and its length is based on the safe maximum distance that the coil can bridge in normally dry air. A safety gap of this kind is shown at *F* in Fig. 9. In the type of magneto just described above it is embodied in the coil. When an opening at any point in the high-tension circuit exceeds the length of this gap, the current takes the path thus provided, thus preventing the imposition of an excessive strain upon the insulation of the secondary windings.

Wiring Connections. For the actual operation of an induction coil, there is no necessity for any electrical connection between the primary and the secondary windings, the electrical energy being transferred from one to the other entirely by induction, i.e., through the intermediary of the magnetic lines of force which interlink both. However, for the sake of simplicity of external connections, the beginning of the secondary winding is usually connected to the end of the primary. Both the primary and the secondary circuits have a "ground return", which necessitates that one end of both the primary and the secondary winding of the coil be placed in positive metallic connection with the engine or car frame. By connecting the two windings, as mentioned, a single wire serves to ground both. The average coil, therefore, has only three terminals, i.e., one primary, one secondary, and one common ground connection.

On cars that are provided with magneto ignition alone, as is the case with French taxicabs and many other French light cars, there would be only two connections between the magneto and the coil, one primary and one secondary; one connection from the coil to a ground, as the motor or frame; and four connections direct from the magneto distributor to the spark plugs. This represents an ignition system reduced to its lowest terms of simplicity. As a matter of fact, it is even more simple in reality, as most French cars use the true high-tension type of magneto so that the four leads from the magneto to the plugs are the only external wires in evidence. Unless a magneto is in excellent condition, however—and the magnets lose their strength more or less rapidly under the influence of the heat and vibration—too much effort is required to start the motor. American manufacturers accordingly supply a battery for starting purposes, and on some of the high-priced cars this takes the form of an entirely independent battery ignition system, i.e., having a battery, coil, timer, distributor, and a separate set of spark plugs. It also constitutes an emergency system that may be resorted to in case of a

ELECTRICAL EQUIPMENT

breakdown of the magneto, but the latter is so rare and the cost and complication of the extra system are such that the latter is not generally used. Instead, the magneto coil, contact breaker, and distributor are utilized with the battery as the source of current.

Inductor=Type Magneto. Mention has been made in the introductory of the fact that if a coil of wire be moved so as to cut the lines of force of a magnetic field, an e.m.f. will be induced in the wire. If, instead of moving the wire, a magnetic flux be made to pass through it first in one direction and then in the other, the same result will be obtained, i.e., an alternating e.m.f. will be produced,

Fig. 12. Rotor and Winding of K-W Inductor Magneto
Courtesy of K. W. Ignition Company, Cleveland, Ohio

and, if the wires be connected to an outside resistance, a current will flow. This is the principle of the *inductor magneto* which is so termed because the current is induced in its winding instead of being directly generated in the latter.

Typical Construction Details and Current Production. The magnetic field is produced by permanent magnets in the same manner as on other types of magnetos and a mass of laminated soft iron is rotated between the pole pieces while the winding is stationary. The moving element is termed the rotor, and this part of the K-W high-tension magneto is shown in Fig. 12. The stationary

55

winding in the center is mounted on the shaft of the rotor and consists of a primary and secondary coil.

There is no mechanical or electrical connection between the windings and the rotor shaft, nor between the laminated blocks of the rotor and the windings. As shown in the illustration these are placed at right angles to one another and are riveted to the shaft. It will be evident that in the position shown in the illustration the right-hand member of the rotor will be bridging the pole pieces of

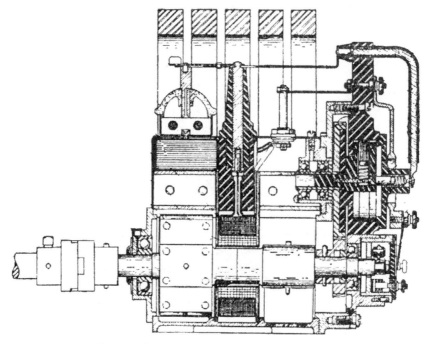

Fig. 13. Section through K-W Inductor Magneto
Courtesy of K. W. Ignition Company, Cleveland, Ohio

the magnetic field; by giving the shaft a quarter turn the two rotor members will have their ends facing opposite poles of the magnetic field, thus completing the magnetic circuit through the center of the windings. Consequently, a current wave will be produced each time the rotor revolves through a quarter-turn, or 90 degrees, so that this inductor magneto produces four impulses per revolution instead of two as in the ordinary type having a wound bipolar armature of H form. Apart from the method of producing the current, the remaining essentials of the magneto are the same, except that no collector brush is necessary as is the case where the current is generated in a revolving winding on an armature.

The details of construction of the K-W high-tension magneto are shown in Fig. 13. While, from an external view of the rotor, it apparently consists of two independent parts, it will be seen in the section that it is practically one piece, the connecting part passing through the center of the winding so that the magnetic circuit is completed through the latter. The primary winding, consisting of four layers of comparatively coarse wire, will be noted close to the rotor; just outside of this is the secondary winding of many layers of fine wire and from the latter the connection is carried upward to a horizontal strip of copper termed a bus bar. At the right, this bar connects with the distributor for the high-tension current; at the left it connects with the safety gap, directly beneath which is the condenser.

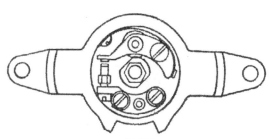

Fig. 14. K-W Interrupter

Timing. The magneto is timed by an interrupter operated by a cam on the rotor shaft in the usual manner; the details of this interrupter are shown in Fig. 14. As is the case with all ignition magnetos, these points remain closed, thus short-circuiting the primary winding, until the current reaches its maximum, and then are opened suddenly, thereby inducing a current in the secondary winding. The firing point of the magneto is just as the contact points begin to separate, as shown in Fig. 14, which is exaggerated to make this clear. At the same moment, the distributor arm is passing one of the segments connected to a spark plug, as shown in Fig. 15, the firing order of the motor in this case being 1, 2, 4, 3. While the magneto produces four waves per revolution, these are not necessarily all utilized; the cam (c in Fig. 15) opens the interrupter twice per revolution, giving two sparks for each turn of the crankshaft, as required by a four-cylinder four-cycle motor. In a four-cylinder two-cycle motor, a four-sided cam would be employed thus producing four sparks per revolution.

The letters on the illustration are: *A* contact breaker box; *c* cam;

P contact points of interrupter; *R* cam roller to lessen friction at that point; *B* distributor arm; *S* distributor segments; *R H* and *L H* referring to the direction of rotation, as either right hand—also termed "clockwise" or from left to right—and left hand, anti-clockwise.

Dixie Magneto. *Essential Elements; Circuits.* While based on the inductor principle, this differs from an inductor type of magneto in that the pole pieces themselves are revolved and they do not reverse their polarity as in the case of an inductor or an armature.

The rotating element of the Dixie is shown in Fig. 16; *B* is a brass block which prevents any magnetic flux flowing directly from

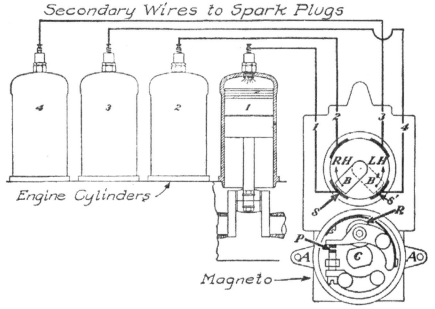

Fig. 15. Wiring Diagram for K-W Magneto Circuits

N to *S*, which are the rotating pole pieces. The coil with its primary and secondary windings is placed directly above this rotating element, in the hollow of the magnets, as shown in Fig. 17. At the right in the same figure is shown the relation between the rotor, the magnets, and the coil. It will be noted that the core of the coil *C* bridges the stationary pole pieces *F* and *G* and that the shaft of the rotor passes through the magnets in a plane at right angles to that of the usual magneto. The reversal of the magnetic flux, with varying positions of the rotor, is shown in the right-hand sketch of Fig. 17, and in Fig. 18.

The primary circuit of the Dixie is shown in Fig. 19; A being the core of the coil, P the primary winding, R the condenser, X and

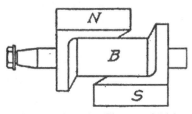

Fig. 16.   Rotating Element of Dixie Magneto

Y the points of the interrupter or contact breaker. The terminal D is a screw on the head of the coil, and the wire Z connects directly with the contact Y of the interrupter. Fig. 20 shows the details of this interrupter, the housing of which is attached to the mounting of the windings, while the details of the secondary circuit are shown in Fig. 21. C is the end of the high-tension, or secondary winding of

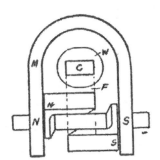

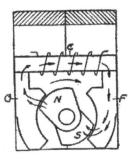

Fig. 17.   Details of Dixie Magneto
Courtesy of Splitdorf Electrical Company, Newark, N. J.

the coil, which is connected to a metal plate D embedded in the hard-rubber end piece of the coil A. A small coil spring holds the

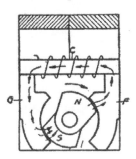

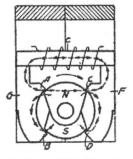

Fig. 18.   Diagram Showing Reversal of Magnetic Flux in Dixie Magneto

connection F in contact with D and at its outer end F connects with J which is the distributor brush. The latter revolves, successively passing over the segments leading to the corresponding spark plugs.

ELECTRICAL EQUIPMENT

But one of these segments is indicated by *L*, the dotted lines indicating the completion of the circuit through the ground connections.

Timing. As the contact-breaker box is attached to the mounting of the coil, the latter moves with it when the former is partly

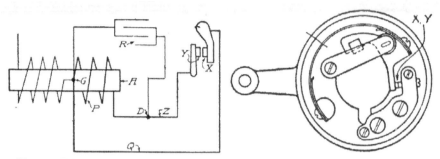

Fig. 19. Primary Circuit of Dixie Magneto   Fig. 20. Dixie Interrupter

rotated to advance or retard the occurrence of the spark in the cylinders, so that the opening of the contact points always takes place at the point of maximum current. This is shown diagrammatically in Fig. 22. As the contact points are opened by the revolution of the cam, it will be apparent that a movement of the mounting of these points with relation to the cam will alter the time at which they will operate. For example, assuming that the

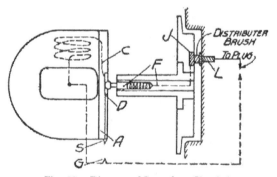

Fig. 21. Diagram of Secondary Circuit in Dixie Magneto

magneto is designed to run clockwise, moving the interrupter in the same direction as the rotation will cause the spark to occur later, as shown by the retarded position in the sketch. Moving the interrupter against the direction of rotation of the cam accordingly would cause the spark to occur earlier. The range of movement is approximately 15 degrees each side of the neutral point indicated by the horizontal position of the lever on the breaker box; the dotted lines show how the firing point may be advanced 15 degrees or retarded an equal amount. The lever in question is connected by means of linked rods to the spark lever on the steering wheel.

Magnetos for Eight=Cylinder and Twelve=Cylinder Motors. It will be evident that, regardless of the number of cylinders to be fired, the principles of current generation, transformation (to high tension) and distribution remain the same, so that a reference to

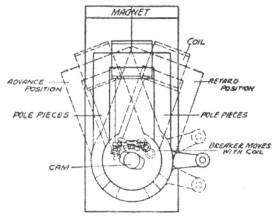

Fig. 22. Diagram Showing Method of Timing Dixie Magneto
Courtesy of Splitdorf Electrical Company, Newark, N. J.

the models of the Dixie for eight-cylinder and twelve-cylinder motors will suffice to cover the modifications required by the increased number of cylinders. To keep the speed of the magneto down, the rotor is provided with four poles instead of two, so that four impulses are generated in the windings per revolution. This permits of

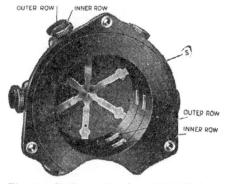

Fig. 23. Stationary Member of 12-Cylinder
Splitdorf Distributor

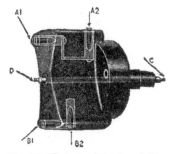

Fig. 24. Rotating Member of 12-
Cylinder Distributor

running the magneto at crankshaft speed for an eight-cylinder motor and at 1½ times crankshaft speed for a twelve-cylinder motor.

Compound Distributor. The contact breaker opens every quarter revolution instead of every half revolution—a cam with four lifting faces being provided for this purpose—and the distributor is provided with twice as many segments and spark-plug leads as a magneto designed for four-cylinder or six-cylinder motors. But as the contact segments of the distributor must be sufficiently long to permit of the distributor brush being in contact with them, regardless of the point to which the ignition timing is advanced or retarded, it is impossible to place more than six contact segments in a circle without reducing the insulation between them to a point where there would be danger of the high-tension current jumping the gap and thus deranging the ignition. To avoid this a compound distributor is employed, i.e., two distributors are combined, but instead of being placed on a flat surface as in the magnetos for a smaller number of cylinders, the segments are spaced around the inner periphery of a hollow cylinder. Two radial contact brushes are carried by the revolving member of the distributor, each of which makes contact with one of the sets of segments. Fig. 23 illustrates the distributor itself, while Fig. 24 is the revolving member. The radial brushes $A2$ and $B2$ of Fig. 24 are electrically connected to contact brushes extending laterally ($A1$ and $B1$) from the revolving member. These brushes make contact alternately with the arms of a metal spider sunk flush in the end wall of the distributor, S in Fig. 23, with which the central pin of the distributor rotor D, Fig. 24, also connects. The high-tension current from the windings is fed to this distributor rotor through the spring brush contact C.

Path of Current. The path followed by the current is accordingly as follows: from the high-tension winding of the coil (not shown here) to the distributor rotor through the brush C; from brush D to the spider S; from S alternately through brushes $A1$ and $B1$ to the distributor segments representing the inner and outer row of spark-plug leads, through the brushes $A2$ and $B2$. Brushes $A1$ and $B1$ are so spaced that, when one is centrally in contact with an arm of the spider S, the other is midway between the second and third arms from the one with which contact is being made.

The relation of the various members of the Dixie magneto will be clear upon reference to the sectional view, Fig. 25, showing one of the four-cylinder models. The contact breaker or interrupter is at the left-hand end of the rotor shaft; just above the rotor itself is the coil, while to the left of this is the distributor.

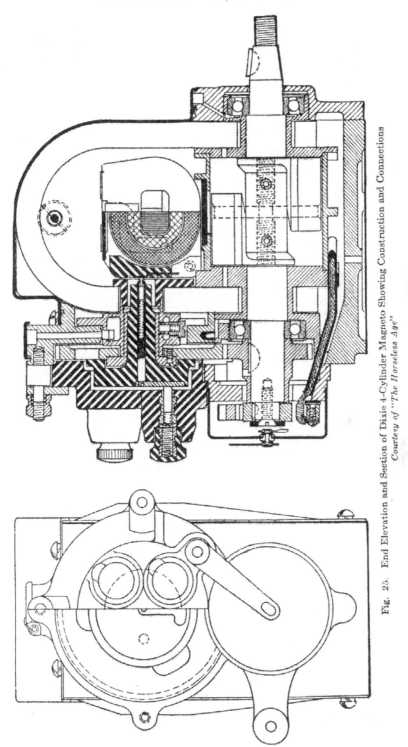

Fig. 25.   End Elevation and Section of Dixie 4-Cylinder Magneto Showing Construction and Connections
Courtesy of "The Horseless Age"

The Mea magneto, shown in Fig. 26 is of the shuttle-type but the magnets used are not the same. In magnetos—such as the Bosch and Dixie—a horseshoe shaped magnet is used. In the Mea, a bell-shaped one is mounted on trunnions, allowing the whole

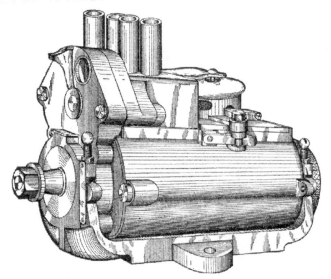

Fig. 26. Mea Magneto in Trunnion Mounting

magneto to oscillate from one side to the other. This has a distinct advantage with regard to the advance and retard spark position. This feature will be explained and compared with other magnetos and methods used for spark advance and retard.

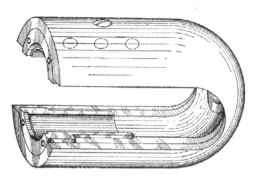

Fig. 27. Bell-Shaped Magnets of Mea
Magneto

Fig. 27 shows the shape of the magnets used in the Mea magneto. The armature revolves inside this bell-shaped magnet.

To enable a magnet to give a spark at high speed there must be a quick and positive change from the magnetized to the demagnetized condition of the armature. This is accomplished by using a core of soft iron in laminated form. Hard spots are often found in armatures and this causes *polarization*. This condition retards the magnetic change and causes missing. A missfire caused by this condition is hard to locate and gives the impression that it is the fault of the cams in the breaker-box because the miss occurs only on one side of the magneto.

The only remedy is to install a new armature—this applies to the shuttle-type magneto.

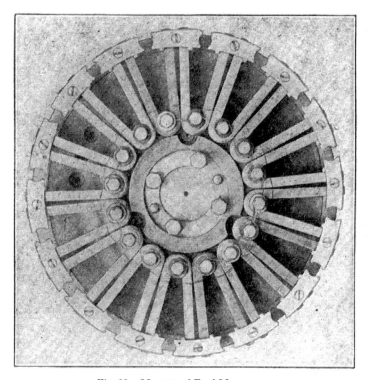

Fig. 28. Magnets of Ford Magneto

Ford Magneto. The Ford magneto is *sui generis*. What the patent lawyers term the "prior art" shows nothing even vaguely resembling it and no ignition current generator used on either American or foreign cars, past or present, can lay claim to any family ties. Not that its principles differ in any way, but their application is very unusual, and as this magneto is now employed on more than a million cars, it is of particular interest. Instead of the two or three horseshoe permanent magnets employed on the ordinary magneto, the Ford has sixteen magnets arranged radially with their

Fig. 29. Ford Magneto as Installed

poles outward, and all are bolted directly to the flywheel, as shown in Fig. 28. Directly in front of them and separated by a very small clearance are sixteen coils, wound of copper strip or ribbon and attached to a spider which is bolted to the crankcase of the motor

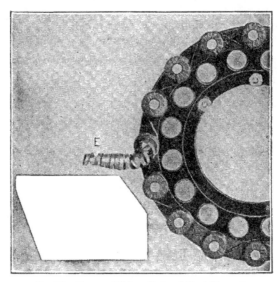

Fig. 30. Copper Ribbon Coils of Ford Magneto

just forward of the flywheel, as shown by Fig. 29. The spider itself and the coils are illustrated by Fig. 30, which shows one of the coils partly unwound at E. The spider and its coils remain stationary while the magnets are rotated in close proximity to them at high speed by the flywheel, thus inducing a current in the coil windings. The current is taken from the collector ring *B*, through the single brush *C*, the other side of the magneto circuit being grounded. Fig. 31 shows the complete ignition system as installed on the motor. The magneto coils are shown marked "generator"; at its upper center is the collecting brush mentioned, connected to the four-unit coil, which in practice is mounted on the dash.   From the coil, four

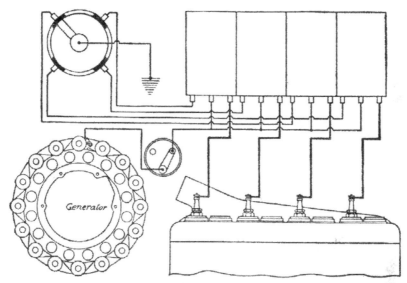

Fig. 31.   Wiring Diagram for Ford Ignition System

primary connections are made to the low-tension timer mounted at the forward end of the motor and driven from the camshaft, and the four high-tension cables for the spark plugs will be noted just below the primary connections.   The other two binding posts on the back of the coil are for the current from the magneto and the ground connection.   While a battery is ordinarily fitted in addition to facilitate starting, this can be accomplished on the magneto alone, as the latter is very powerful.

After a period of service the magnets on a magneto need recharging and the magneto should be overhauled.   The repairman should be familiar with the position of the armature in relation to the pole pieces when the spark takes place in the cylinder.   There is a definite relation between the position of the armature, the distributor brush, and the opening of the contact points. The armature should be placed as shown in Fig. 32, and with it in this position the contact points should be just opening with the distributor brush full width on one of the segments of the distributor board.

Care should be taken when putting the magnets back to see that all the north poles are on one side and all the south poles on the other. There will be a split polarity if this is not done, which will cause a weak spark. This applies to all types of magnetos. In the Ford magneto the magnets should be put back so that the two poles

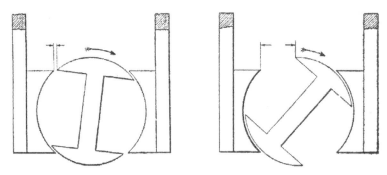

Fig. 32. Position of Magneto Armature for "Advanced" and "Retarded" Ignition

next to each other do not attract. When the magnets are placed in this alternate position on the flywheel there will be an alternate attraction and repulsion all the way around.

The chief cause of magnets becoming demagnetized is heat. Therefore, in installing, do not install a magneto near the exhaust pipe if it can be avoided. Magnets are also demagnetized by vibration; consequently, magnets should not be allowed to lie around on a bench where other pieces of iron can fall on them. Magnetos should be protected from oil, dirt, and water by the use of a cover when on the car.

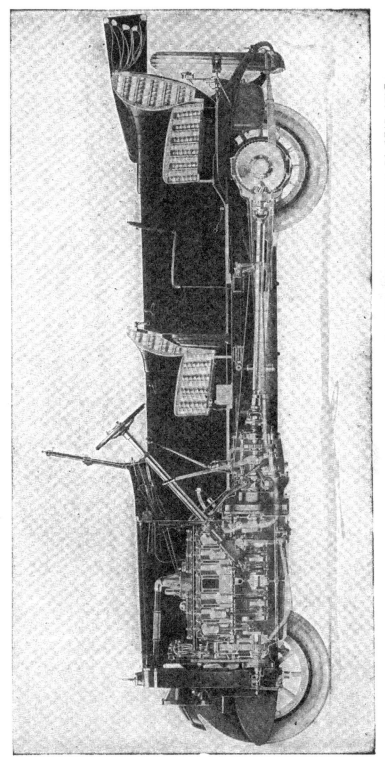

SECTIONAL VIEW OF PACKARD "TWIN SIX", SHOWING POWER UNIT AND TRANSMISSION TO REAR AXLE

Courtesy of Packard Motor Car Company, Detroit, Michigan

HUPMOBILE SIX-CYLINDER SEDAN

IGNITION SYSTEMS

Hydraulic Analogy in an Ignition System. A comparison of the workings of an ignition system with the action of an hydraulic system having similarly related parts will serve to make clear the operation of the former. It must first be borne in mind that a high-tension ignition system consists of a source of current; an interrupter, or method of automatically breaking the circuit of this current supply, timed with relation to the revolution of the engine crankshaft; a condenser to suppress the arc at the interrupter contacts; a transforming device, or induction coil, to transform a current of comparatively high amperage at a low potential to one of high voltage; a device for distributing this high-tension current to the spark plugs, also timed with relation to the crankshaft; and the spark plugs themselves.

Current. The electric current in the ignition system may be represented by water flowing in a pipe from a source of supply which puts it under pressure, corresponding to the storage battery. A certain amount of frictional resistance must be overcome by the water in flowing through the pipe and this is equivalent to the electrical resistance of the wiring in the ignition circuit. The rate of water flow in the pipe corresponds to the current in the coil, and the inertia of the water to the inductance of the primary winding of the induction coil. Now, if the flow of water be suddenly stopped, there will be an enormous increase in the pressure, due to the inertia of the water. This effect, known as *water hammer*, is commonly noticed in the larger sizes of pipes carrying water under considerable pressure. It corresponds to the great increase in the pressure, or voltage, which takes place when the flow of current in the primary of the ignition circuit is opened suddenly by the interrupter. This is due to the inductance in the coil. A quick-closing valve in the water system would accordingly correspond to the timer contacts which interrupt the current in the primary of the induction coil.

Condenser. The condenser is technically known as an electrical "capacity" in that it has the ability to absorb a quantity of electricity proportioned to the area of its conducting surfaces and to the nature of the dielectric employed. This property is utilized to absorb the excess current passing at the moment the primary circuit of the ignition system is opened by a vibrator, thus bringing about a quick cessation of the current flow and preventing the destructive arcing or burning that would otherwise occur at the contact points. The charge thus absorbed is immediately returned to the circuit in the form of a discharge, when the points come together again and a higher potential value is impressed upon the current. A condenser consists of conducting surfaces placed between insulating surfaces, known as the dielectric. For ignition work, the conducting surfaces

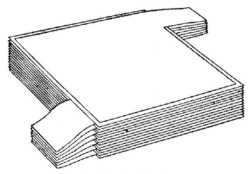

Fig. 1. Sketch of Condenser

are sheets of thin tinfoil cut with conducting tabs which project beyond the ends of sheets of paraffined paper on which the tinfoil is placed. Between each two sheets of paraffined paper is placed a sheet of tinfoil, the latter being arranged so that the tabs project at alternate ends, Fig. 1. The paraffined paper overlaps the tinfoil all around to the extent of an inch or more to prevent a discharge over the edges of the sheets. The capacity of the condenser depends upon the number and the size of the sheets of tinfoil and the thinness and the character of the dielectric separating them; and, when a sufficient number have been assembled, the projecting tabs at each end are riveted or clamped together and a flexible wire lead connected to each. It is then connected in multiple with the vibrator, and, in the case of a coil is inserted in the containing case of the latter and further insulated as well as held in place by having molten paraffine poured around it so as to fill the space. A condenser practically eliminates sparking at the contact points and is also used with the contact breaker of a magneto.

If a strong bright spark is seen at the contact points, it is an indication that the condenser is faulty or punctured.

ELECTRICAL EQUIPMENT

Condensers are made in several forms. Some manufacturers make them in flat form inclosed by a separate housing and attached to the outside of the ignition unit, as in the Packard installation; while others are in rolled form and inclosed inside the ignition unit close to the contact points, as in the Buick installation.

If the condenser is removed at any time for inspection or test, care should be taken to see that the connections are clean and that when it is put back the screws, which hold it in position, are tight. Condensers are very much affected by moisture and this is often the cause of their failure and imperfect operation.

Office of Condenser. There is one peculiar tendency of timer contacts which must be mentioned here to make the analogy more complete. Unless protected by a condenser, they are apt to burn away very rapidly, due to the arc produced by the current at the moment of separation. (This is also true of the contacts of the battery cut-out and of the regulator employed in connection with starting and lighting systems; the condenser does not eliminate this tendency to burn away but reduces it to a minimum.) This failing on the part of the timer contacts would correspond in the hydraulic system to a valve with a very thin edge which would be liable to bend under the sudden rise in pressure before it is fully closed. In the case of both systems, therefore, it is necessary to arrange for some protection, and a condenser is supplied for this purpose in the ignition system.

In the hydraulic system, it takes the form of a surge chamber, as shown in Fig. 2. This chamber has an elastic diaphragm centrally placed in it, and the chamber itself is shunted, or connected, around the valve in the same manner as the condenser is connected to the contact points. When the valve begins to close, this surge chamber relieves the pressure to some extent during the operation of closing the valve and so protects the thin edge of the valve from bending. After the valve is fully closed, there is, of course, no further danger of its being bent over. In the electrical system, the condenser supplies similar protection, reducing the voltage at the timer contacts at the moment of separation and keeping this voltage reduced until they are fully open, thus preventing the current from bridging the gap, or *arcing*. Once the contacts are fully separated, the low-tension current cannot jump the air gap, so that there is no further danger of their burning.

ELECTRICAL EQUIPMENT

Transformer. In order to utilize the pressure produced by tl sudden closing of the valve, it is necessary to provide some tran forming device, such as a pressure chamber. This is illustrated Fig. 2, and it will be noted that it is of a much larger diameter thɛ the pipe. As the pressure in the chamber and the pressure in tl pipe will both have some unit value (measured in pounds per squa inch), the total pressure on the piston will be to the pressure in tl pipe as the area of the piston is to the area of the pipe. By the u of a pressure chamber of large diameter, compared to that of tl pipe, a very considerable force is applied to the piston, but tl

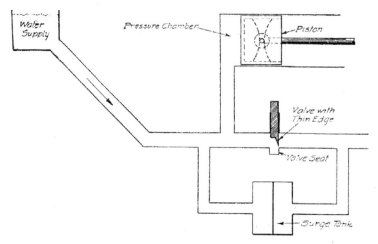

Fig. 2. Diagram Showing Hydraulic Analogy of Ignition System

distance it will travel is very slight. (To simplify matters, the weigl of the piston is disregarded in this connection.)

It is likewise necessary to provide a transforming device in tl ignition system, and, in the case of both magneto and modern batter systems, this is the induction coil, having a relatively large numb of turns in the secondary winding and a comparatively small numb of turns in the primary. (In the earlier battery system, a vibratiɪ coil is used for each cylinder and there is no distributor, while in tl true high-tension magneto, the coil is part of the armature winding Just as in the hydraulic system the increased area of the piston responsible for the increased total pressure on it, so the large numb of turns in the secondary of the coil give the very high voltaᵧ required to enable the current to bridge the air gap at the spark plug

This high voltage is accompanied by a very small amount of current, just as in the hydraulic system the greatly increased pressure on the piston produces but a very slight movement of the latter. This rise in the voltage and decrease in the current can be made clear by a brief explanation. By the principles of induction, a current flowing in the primary coil will induce a current in the secondary coil. The energy of these currents in watts is equal to the electromotive force in volts times the current in amperes. Now, as the transformer cannot create electrical energy, the energy of the transformed current must equal the energy of the current before it is transformed, barring a small loss within the transformer. This means that if the voltage of the current is raised from 6 volts, say, in the primary to 6000 volts in the secondary (that is, made one thousand times greater), the amperage of the primary current must be correspondingly reduced from 2 amperes, say, to .002.

Condenser Troubles. The usual faults of condensers are punctured insulation or leakage of current because of moisture.

Effect of Faulty Condenser on Ignition. When the condenser is operating correctly, the current that is absorbed is discharged back into the primary winding of the coil in an opposite direction to which it was charged. This gives a very rapid change of magnetism in the coil which greatly increases the secondary current or high-tension current necessary to jump the spark-plug gap under compression. If the condenser is not working properly, a weak spark will be found at the spark plugs and in some cases none.

Test for Faulty Condenser. If there is any doubt as to the correct operation of the device, the best plan is to try another condenser in the outfit. If the engine operation is improved at once, it proves that the condenser is at fault. In testing, use 110-volt direct current with a 110-volt lamp in series. Place the ends of the wires on each of the condenser terminals and, if the lamp lights, it shows that the condenser is faulty. A test for open circuit can be made using alternating current. Place one test terminal in contact with one condenser terminal and then lightly touch the other test terminal to the other condenser lead. If there is a slight spark given, the condenser is in good condition.

Spark Plugs. No small part of the trouble experienced with early ignition systems was due to the defective design of the spark plugs employed. Where an over-rich mixture is delivered by the carbureter, i.e., one containing too much gasoline in proportion to the air, a certain amount of the carbon is unburned and remains in the

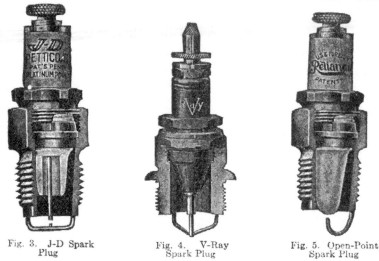

Fig. 3. J-D Spark
Plug

Fig. 4. V-Ray
Spark Plug

Fig. 5. Open-Point
Spark Plug

cylinder in the form of soot. This is greatly increased by an excess of lubricating oil finding its way into the combustion chamber. The heavier carbons of this burn to the same consistency and are also

Fig. 6. Multi-
Point Spark
Plug

Fig. 7. Chambered-
End Spark
Plug

deposited on the piston head, cylinder walls, valves, and other exposed surfaces in the form of a flint-hard coating. The end of the spark plug receives its share and, as the carbon is an excellent conductor, the plug is accordingly short-circuited, so that the current, instead of jumping the gap between the points, takes a path of lower resistance across the carbon-coated insulating surfaces.

Fundamental Requisite. The spark plug is the "business end" of the ignition system and no matter how elaborate or efficient the essentials of the latter may be, its successful operation is governed entirely by that of the plug. As originally designed, the insulating material filled the shell at the sparking end, affording a direct path for the current as soon as this small surface became covered with carbon. Failure was accordingly frequent, it being nothing unusual to have to clean such a plug in less than fifty miles of running. To overcome this, a recess was allowed between the insulation of the central electrode and the outer shell. This simple expedient constitutes a basic patent (Canfield) under which all spark plugs are manufactured. Porcelain, mica, or artificial stone is used as the insulating material, the first-named being most generally employed. This is made in various forms, as shown by the sections, Figs. 3 and 4, and it will be noted that the smaller diameter of the insulated

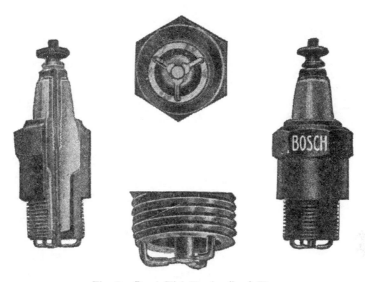

Fig. 8. Bosch High-Tension Spark Plug

electrode in the center greatly increases the area of the surface of both shell and porcelain that must be coated with carbon before a path is formed for the current.

Electrode Arrangement. Practice also varies considerably in the arrangement of the electrodes, taking the form of open points as in Fig. 5, a bridge as in Fig. 3, or a number of points as shown in Figs. 4 and 6. In some instances, the central electrode is enclosed in a chamber, the gas entering through a small hole in the shell, as shown in Fig. 7. Considerable advantage is claimed for the type of plug having a plurality of gaps, the number usually being three, as shown in Fig. 8, or four as in Fig. 6. It is more theoretical than actual, however, as the current always takes the shortest path and the bridging of any one of the gaps by a particle of conducting material, such as carbon, short-circuits all of them.

Series Plugs. As shown in the various wiring diagrams, the

Fig. 9. Series-Type
Spark Plug

shell of the plug is one of the electrodes and forms a part of the circuit by being screwed into the cylinder, the latter constituting part of the common ground return for both the primary and the secondary circuits of all ignition systems. Experiment has shown a slightly increased power resulting from the simultaneous occurrence of two sparks in different parts of the combustion chamber of the cylinder, especially with the T-head type of cylinder in which the two plugs can be located in the oppositely placed valve ports. This is termed double-spark ignition and the type of magneto designed for this purpose is described in the section on "Magnetos". To obtain the same result with the standard ignition circuit designed to produce but one spark in each cylinder, what

is known as a "series" type of plug has been developed. One of these is shown in Fig. 9. In this the spark occurs between two central

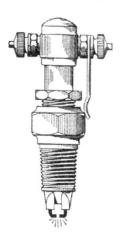

Fig. 10. Method of
Converting Series Plug

electrodes, as shown, the shell not forming a connection with the cylinder. The lead from the distributor is attached to one of the binding posts of this plug and a second wire connected to the other binding post is led to a standard type of plug, thus completing the circuit and placing both plugs in series so that a spark occurs simultaneously in both. By means of an attachment as shown in Fig. 10, this type of plug can be used with a grounded return, the arm shown connecting the shell in the circuit. As the majority of motors now in use have L-head cylinders, and even at the best the advantage gained is very slight, the use of series plugs has not a great deal to recommend it.

Magnetic Plugs. With a view to overcoming the defects of the mechanically operated make-and-break plug as used on low-tension ignition systems, an automatic plug was developed. As shown by the section, Fig. 11, this is simply a solenoid A and plunger C, the latter being held in contact at D by a spring B. The current passing through the winding A lifts the plunger and the spark occurs at D. The remainder of the system consists of a low-tension magneto or other source of current supply and a timer. Such plugs have been used to some extent on stationary engines, but have not proved practical on the automobile motor, as the high temperatures drew the temper of the plunger spring and often burned out the insulation of the winding.

Priming Plugs. For low-priced motors, such as the Ford, which have no pet cocks or compression-release cocks on the cylinders, a spark plug combined with a pet cock, such as that shown in

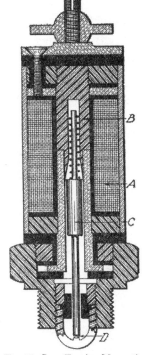

Fig. 11. Low-Tension Magnetic Spark Plug

Fig. 12, can be had. These are usually known as "priming" plugs in that they permit of priming the cylinder with gasoline to render starting easy in cold weather.

Waterproof Plugs. Ignition systems, on motor-boat engines in particular, are apt to suffer short-circuiting from spray or dampness, though this often happens on the automobile as well in heavy rainstorms. To guard against this a so-called waterproof type of plug is provided. The precaution usually takes the form of a hood of hard rubber or other insulating material placed over the connection, as shown in Fig. 13.

Plug Threads. European practice has standardized a straight-threaded plug, the thread itself usually being of fine pitch. A plug of this kind is screwed home on a gasket

Fig. 12. Priming Type Spark Plug

of copper and asbestos or of the latter material alone, which is relied upon to prevent leakage. Foreign types are usually referred to as "metric" plugs, as the thread dimensions are based on the metric standard. As developed at first in this country, all spark plugs were made with an "iron-pipe" thread. This has a taper of three-fourths inch to the foot and the plug is screwed into the cylinder as far as the taper will permit, no other provision being made to hold the compression. As this is a crude expedient, adopted chiefly because of its cheapness, and the metric standard is not employed here, an S.A.E. standard plug has been developed along the same lines, both the plug diameter and the thread itself being made somewhat larger than those used abroad.

Fig. 13. Spark Plug, with Waterproof Connections

Spark Plug Troubles. Trouble that causes misfiring in spark plugs can be traced to three things: excess oil, causing short-circuit at the points; cracked porcelain or insulation, allowing the high tension current to jump to ground and thus prevent it from reaching the spark-plug points; and loose electrodes, either in the spark-plug body on the ground side or at the central electrode. In the first case, cleaning the plug will often clear the trouble. In the second case, where the insulating part can be taken out, as in Fig. 5, and examined, the crack can usually be seen. The crack is often found at the radius where the insulation fits into the spark-plug body or where the packing holds it in position. In the third case, the altering of the spark-plug gap in service, after a short time of running, will indicate loose electrodes.

Atwater=Kent System. The Atwater-Kent system is based on a "single spark" interrupter and was the pioneer in making battery ignition successful on the modern automobile before the advent of the perfected lighting generator, the current source usually being a dry-cell battery. It was considered an advantage in earlier years to produce a series of high-tension sparks in the cylinder on the theory that, if the first failed to explode the charge, it would be fired by the subsequent sparks. The fallacy of this long since became apparent and the reason therefor has been dwelt upon already. The Atwater-Kent interrupter is typical of devices of this class which have been developed since and as it is fitted on thousands of cars which come to the repairman's attention at one time or another, a detailed description of its working is given here. Another type of single-spark contact breaker is shown in Fig. 14.

Operation of "Unisparker." The ratchet A, Fig. 15, has as many notches as there are cylinders to be fired. It is mounted on the central vertical shaft of the device which also carries a distributor, and in this combined form is known as a "Unisparker." On four-

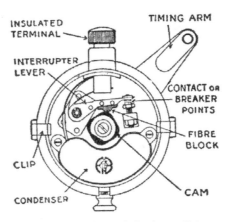

Fig. 14. Breaker and Condenser Unit

cycle engines it is driven at half crankshaft speed, and at crankshaft speed on two-cycle engines (motor boats). The ratchet A engages the lifter B, and, as A rotates, its teeth or notches successively tend to draw B with them, against the tension of the spring C. In doing so, the head of B strikes the swinging lever or "hammer" D, whose motion in both directions is limited as shown, and the hammer communicates the blow to the contact spring E, bringing the contact points together momentarily. E is a compound spring, the straight member of which carries the movable contact, while the stationary contact F is mounted opposite it. The second member of this compound spring is curved at its end to engage the straight member. Ordinarily the straight spring blade is held under the tension of the curved blade and the contact points are held apart.

When the curved blade is struck by the hammer D the points contact. The curved blade, however, is thrown over farther by the impact and its hook leaves the straight blade. Upon reaching the

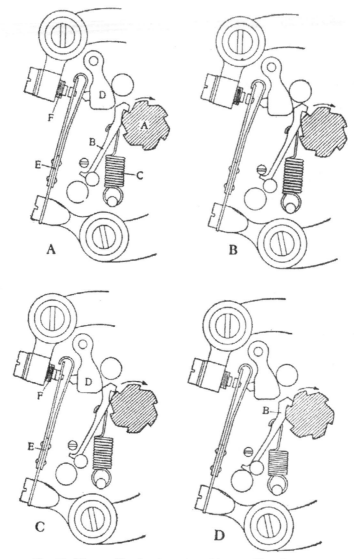

Fig. 15. Diagram Showing Operation of Atwater-Kent Interrupter
Courtesy of "The Horseless Age"

limit of its movement it flies back and strikes the end of the straight blade a blow causing a very sharp break of the circuit. This movement is so extremely rapid that it cannot be detected by the unaided eye, so that its working cannot be tested simply by watching the operation of the contacts as in the case of a magneto interrupter. *B*, *C*, and *D*, of Fig. 15, show the successive movements of the parts during a single phase. In *A*, a notch of the ratchet has engaged *B* and is drawing it against the tension of the spring *C*. In the second sketch *B*, the hook is released. In *C*, the lifter is riding back over the rounded portion of the ratchet and striking the hammer *D*, which in turn pushes *E* for a brief instant against *F*. The return of *B* to the position shown in sketch *D* is so rapid that the eye cannot follow the movement of the parts *D* and *E*, which to all appearances remain stationary.

Adjustment of the contact points is made by removing one of the thin washers from under the head of the contact screw *F*, and the gap should be .010 to .012 inch, never exceeding the latter. Where more accurate means of determining this distance are not available, it may be gaged with a piece of manila wrapping paper which should be perfectly smooth. With the aid of a "mike" (micrometer) a sheet of paper of the proper thickness can be selected. The contacts are of tungsten and as the moving parts are all of glass-hard steel, very accurately machined, the wear is negligible so that adjust-

Fig. 16. Connecticut Interrupter

ment is not required oftener than once in 10,000 miles running and replacement only after 50,000 miles.

With this interrupter it is impossible to run the battery down by leaving the switch closed inadvertently, as the contacts are never together when the moving parts are idle. The remainder of the system comprises an induction coil (nonvibrator) and a high-tension distributor.

Connecticut Battery System. While this system also employs a single-spark interrupter, it is what is known as a "magneto type", and the similarity to those employed on magnetos for the same purpose will be noted in Fig. 16. A characteristic of this type of interrupter is that its contacts normally remain closed so that if the ignition switch is left on, the battery will be run down. To prevent this in the Connecticut system, an automatic switch acting on the thermoelectric principle is employed. The interrupter con-

Fig. 17. Connecticut Igniter Complete Except for Switch
Courtesy of Connecticut Telephone and Electric Company, Meriden, Connecticut

sists of a semicircular arm of sheet steel to make it light. This is pivoted at one end, carries a roller at its center and the movable contact at the other end. It is insulated from its pivot and the roller is of fibre. The vertical binding post is electrically connected with the stationary contact and the second one, at an angle, connects with the movable con-

tact. While an interrupter of this type has practically no lag, means of advancing the moment of ignition are provided (lever extension at left), as the spark must occur earlier at high engine speeds to per-

Fig. 18. Connecticut Automatic Switch

mit of propagating the flame throughout the charge in the extremely short time available in the modern high-speed engine. As the contacts are opened only momentarily, the interrupter is in circuit most of the time and accordingly is not economical of current, so that it is designed only for use with the battery and generator of the lighting and starting system.

Fig. 17 shows the complete Connecticut system (minus the switch) as designed for mounting on a magneto bed plate. The distributor is mounted over the interrupter, while the coil is at the

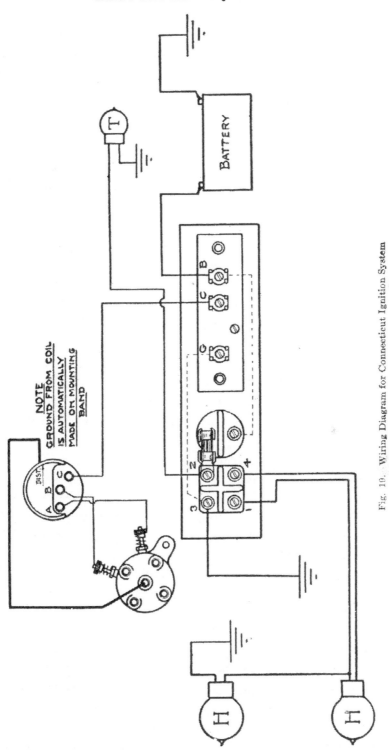

Fig. 19. Wiring Diagram for Connecticut Ignition System

right. The primary of the coil is not grounded, insulated leads being connected to the two binding posts of the interrupter, as shown. The grounding of the secondary winding of the coil is effected through the metal holding band and the bolts fastened to the bed plate. A glass tube is employed to house the safety gap which is mounted under the cover of the coil.

Automatic Switch. The purpose of the automatic switch, Fig. 18, is to open the circuit in case the switch button has been left on with the car stopped. The current passing with the contacts closed, when the engine is idle, is much greater than when it is constantly being interrupted by the rapid-fire action of the cam, but, unlike a circuit-breaker, the device is not designed to act instantly upon the passing of an overload current as this would prevent cranking the motor.

The device consists of a thermostatic arm regulated by the adjustment screw at the top of the figure, an electromagnetic vibrator the armature of which carries a hammer, and the necessary connections. Current enters at either the right- or left-hand screw at the bottom, according to whether the switch is closed at the end of the sectors at the right or left of the figure (*M* or *B* on the switch cover plate), and flows through the heater tape on the arm of the thermostat to the screw at the upper right in the figure. This heater tape is a resistance that becomes warm upon the passage of a certain amount of current for a short time and, with an increase in temperature, causes the arm of the thermostat to bend until it makes contact with the upper thermostatic arm. This puts the windings of the magnet in circuit through the post just below the magnet coils and sets the vibrator in motion, causing the hammer on the armature to strike the switch button and open it.

Fig. 19 shows a typical wiring diagram in connection with the lighting system, the automatic switch being combined with the lighting switch.

The automatic switch prevents the heating of the windings of the coil, which would melt the insulation inside and mean the purchase of a new coil. It prevents damage to the contact points and also prevents the discharge of the battery. If the device fails to operate, a close inspection should be made of the unit for loose terminals and also for a burnt-out resistance unit or heater tape.

INDUCTION COILS

Coils and Vibrators. *Function of the Coil.* Mention has already been made of the function of the induction coil or transformer in stepping up the voltage of the current in order that it may bridge the gap in the spark plug. A coil is also employed in connection with a low-tension system, but it is simply a single winding on an iron core which intensifies the current by what is known as self-induction. Though it raises the voltage by what may be termed the accumulation and sudden release of electrical energy acting in conjunction with a magnetized core, due to the sudden making and breaking of the circuit, it is not an induction coil as that term is ordinarily employed.

The coil, Fig. 20, has two distinct windings, one of a few turns of comparatively coarse wire and the other of many thousand feet

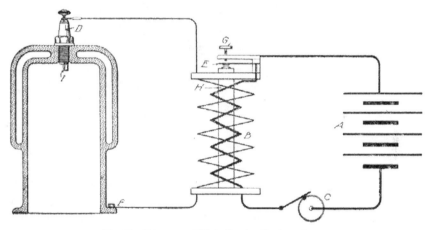

Fig. 20. Diagram of High-Tension Ignition System

of exceedingly fine wire, with high-grade silk insulation. After completing the coil, consisting of two superimposed windings and an iron-wire core passing through their center, it is placed in a wood box which is filled with melted paraffine wax which, upon solidifying, greatly enhances the resisting power of the insulation to breakdown, due to the great difference in potential between various parts of the secondary winding. To set up an induced current in the secondary winding, the primary circuit must be quickly opened and closed.

Necessity for Vibrator. The breaking of the primary circuit is accomplished by the use of a vibrator, a typical form of which is illustrated at *E, G,* and *H,* Fig. 20. This consists simply of the thin blade of spring steel at *E,* provided with an armature at the free end to intensify the attraction of the coil *H,* and adjacent to the adjusting screw at *G,* by which the distances between the contact points can be accurately set. In addition to these elements it is usual to provide a screw adjustment for increasing or reducing the tension of the vibrator blades.

Contacts in the best vibrators are made of platinum, or, better still, of platinum-iridium alloys, which are very hard as well as extremely resistant to the very high, though brief and localized, temperatures of the small arcs that form across the terminals each time

Fig. 21. Pittsfield Multi-Vibrator Coil
Courtesy of Pittsfield Spark Coil Company,
Dalton, Massachusetts

the contacts are separated. In cheaper coils, German silver, silver, and other metals often are much used for contact points, but the only advantage of these over platinum or platinum alloys is their lower price.

Complication of Multi-Vibrator. A vibrator coil is necessary for each cylinder, each coil being energized as the timer passes over the contact corresponding to it, thus putting it in connection with the battery at the moment that particular cylinder is to fire. Fig. 21 shows a four-unit coil, i.e., for a four-cylinder motor. However, the coil cannot act before its core becomes "saturated," that is, thoroughly magnetized, and it must then pull its armature down against the tension of its spring, so that there is both an electrical and a mechanical lag, or, in other words, an appreciable amount of time elapses between the moment the circuit is closed by the timer and that at which it is again broken by the vibrator to cause the spark in the cylinder. A delicate adjustment is most sensitive and minimizes the lag besides economizing on current, but it is difficult to maintain. A stiff adjustment, on the other hand, will remain operative for a longer time, but its greater inertia makes the motor sluggish in action while the current consumption is increased several times over. Despite the use of platinum contact points, the heat of the spark is such that the latter burn away rapidly, necessitating frequent adjustment. As it is next to impossible to adjust four or six vibrators so that they will operate uniformly, it will be apparent why the vibrator coil was given up as soon as the magneto demonstrated that it was not a mystery beyond the understanding of the average motorist. The vibrator coil is accordingly obsolete and but for the fact that its existence has been extended by the Ford, it would probably be unknown to the majority of present-day motorists.

Master Vibrator. To overcome the shortcomings of the four-unit vibrator coil, it is necessary to add a fifth coil. The latter is fitted with an especially sensitive and well-made vibrator which takes the place of the four vibrators on the original coils, so that the extra coil is termed a *master vibrator.* In operation, all four of the original vibrators are screwed down hard so as to make a permanent connection, and the fifth coil is connected in the primary circuit so that the action of its vibrator breaks the circuit in the primary of each one of the coils in turn. It is accordingly only necessary to adjust a single vibrator, and regardless of whether this adjustment be good or bad, it is uniform for all four cylinders so that they fire with the same timing. But at the best, the arrangement is only a makeshift as the vibrator coil long ago ceased to have any legitimate excuse of existence on the automobile.

Non-Vibrator Coil. As the term indicates, this is simply an induction coil minus the vibrator. But instead of using four coils, as with the vibrator type, a single coil is employed, and a distributor is inserted in the secondary or high-tension circuit. The essentials of such a system are shown by Fig. 22, a battery being indicated as the source of current. The timer C is driven by the camshaft of the motor so that the battery circuit is successively closed and opened in the usual firing order of the cylinders, four contacts being made for each two revolutions of a four-cylinder four-cycle motor.

The contact is of sufficient duration to permit the coil to "build up", i.e., to have its soft iron core become thoroughly magnetized, and is then quickly broken. At the instant that the latter occurs, the finger *J* of the distributor is passing the contact of the cylinder *F* to be fired. The timer and distributor must accordingly be driven synchronously, so that the contacts in both occur simultaneously.

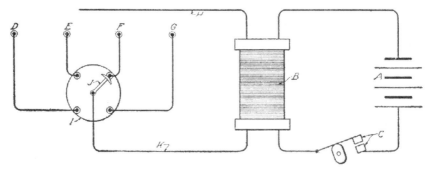

Fig. 22. Wiring Diagram of Non-Vibrator High-Tension System

This is accomplished by combining them in a single unit, as shown in Fig. 23, illustrating the Atwater-Kent "Unisparker", or as in the various types of magnetos illustrated further along.

Fig. 23. Atwater-Kent
Distributor

Fig. 24. Remy Single Non-Vibrator Coil
Showing Method of Installation

Limitations of current supply having been overcome by the adoption of the magneto or the storage battery kept charged by the lighting dynamo, non-vibrator coils are usually wound to a higher resistance than the old vibrator coils, so as to produce a current of higher tension in the secondary. As this type of coil requires no adjustment, it is generally installed horizontally with its face flush with the dash, and on this face is mounted the switch giving three control points, i.e., neutral, battery (for starting), and magneto. The Remy dash coil, Fig. 24, is a typical example.

In repair work it is often necessary to install new coils. Care must be taken in the selection of coils for the different circuits because an open-circuit coil will not operate on a closed-circuit system, neither will a closed-circuit coil operate on an open-circuit system.

The difference in the coils for the two systems is in their windings. The open-circuit coil must build up quickly and become strongly magnetic for the contact points are together only for a very short time. The open-circuit coil has less primary winding on the core and, consequently, will build up faster than a larger number of coils. The closed-circuit has more time to build up therefore a larger number of coils are used in the primary winding. If a closed-circuit coil is used on an open-circuit type, a very weak spark will be given because the coil does not build up to full strength; while if an open-circuit coil is used on a closed-circuit type, the coil will build up so rapidly that the windings will heat and very likely burn, melting the insulating compound inside the coil.

Resistance Unit. The resistance unit is a protective unit as well as a unit for keeping the spark uniform at all engine speeds, for it regulates the amount of current flowing in the primary.

Timer with Resistance Unit. Mention has been made of the fact that the contacts of the interrupter in the battery system of ignition are normally closed, just as they are in the magneto interrupter, only the circuit being opened at this point at the time of ignition. Owing to the rapidity of their action and the extremely short interval between contacts in the interrupter of a high-speed engine, this calls for a very small current consumption. Should the ignition switch be left closed when leaving the car, however, the timer cam is just as likely to stop in the closed position as in the open, and this small, steady discharge will result in exhausting the storage battery. To prevent this waste of current and possible damage to the contacts and coil, a later type of timer has been provided with a resistance unit. This is shown on the left-hand terminal of the timer, Fig. 25, which illustrates the type used on the Cole, among others. The unit consists of a small open coil of high-resistance wire wound upon a porcelain spool mounted on the head of the terminal.

All the current passing through the timer must first pass through this resistance winding, but, owing to the extremely short period it continues between interruptions due to the opening of the contact points, the resistance wire remains cool. When the switch has been left on with the engine idle, however, the current is then continuous and of greater value, and it brings the resistance wire to a red heat in a comparatively short time. At this temperature, its resistance increases so greatly that it permits very little current to pass. It will also be noted that the condenser is mounted on the timer in this case.

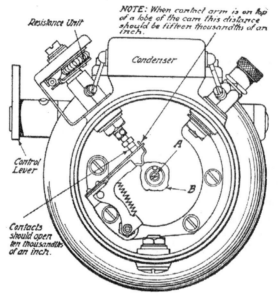

Fig. 25.   Delco Timer with Resistance Unit

The resistance unit is in the primary circuit, and is found either in the timer unit or inside the coil housing. The primary current must pass through this unit. If the current is allowed to keep on flowing, the unit will eventually burn out thus preventing damage to both coil and contact points. It is difficult to inspect the unit wherever it is placed to see if the wire is broken. Consequently it must be detected in some other way. Rotate the engine until the points are together then open them quickly with your finger. If the unit is whole and in good condition, a spark is given. This shows that the primary current is getting to the contact points or, in other words, that the wire is not broken.

ELECTRICAL EQUIPMENT

If the resistance unit should burn out, the unit built for that particular system should be used in replacing it for other units may not be of the correct resistance. A piece of thin iron wire can be used for temporary repair but it should be replaced with the correct unit as soon as possible. These units can usually be bought wound on a porcelain spool ready for installation. When the unit is inside the coil it is a good policy to return the coil to the maker for repairs or replacement because the average garage is not equipped to do repair work on electrical equipment.

SPARK CONTROL DEVICES

The methods used for timing the spark have been many and varied and numerous improvements have been made to keep up with the rapid development of different types of ignition apparatus. The make-and-break system as used with the low-tension magneto was the first practical method. The roller was the next style of contact to be used and is used on the Ford today with the trembler or vibrator coil. Then came the present-day type of contact point used with battery and high-tension magneto with its different applications, such as the Atwater-Kent open-circuit type.

Changes in Ignition Methods. Up to a few years ago, it was generally considered that the magneto practically represented the ultimate type of ignition current generator and that batteries would never play anything but a secondary rôle. Small direct-current dynamos had been tried in a number of instances, chiefly prior to the advent of the magneto, but they were not then sufficiently developed for this form of service and proved quite as unreliable as the dry cell. The magneto was entirely dependable, made possible much greater speeds, and had few shortcomings, none of which were of a serious nature, so that its position was deemed impregnable. This was prior to the successful development of electric-lighting dynamos on the automobile, and more particularly the combined lighting and starting systems which are now in such general use. The latter, in conjunction with improved forms of contact makers, has been responsible for bringing about a reversion to former practice with improved equipment.

Contact Makers or Timers. *Roller Contact Timer*. It was largely due to the crudity of the timing device that so much difficulty was experienced with early ignition systems. As the term indicates, the timer closed the circuit through the coil at exactly the moment necessary to produce the spark in the cylinder ready to fire. But the long wiping or rolling contact usually employed was so wasteful of current that it quickly exhausted even a storage battery. Fig. 26 shows a roller contact timer. The coil vibrators were another serious source of loss. The Delco Dual Type Timer is shown in Fig. 27.

Atwater-Kent Interrupter. The difficulties with roller contact led to the adoption of a totally different principle embodied in the Atwater-Kent interrupter, Fig. 28. This affords an exceedingly

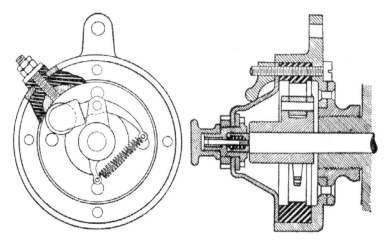

Fig. 26. Roller Contact Timer (*Horseless Age*)

brief contact with an abruptness of the making and breaking of the circuit that is not secured with any other device. The effect is to produce a strong current surge and a heavy spark, but of the briefest possible duration.

The advantage of the brief duration is that great current economy is realized. The fact that only one spark is required for each ignition is an important contributing element to this economy.

With the Atwater-Kent interrupter, embodied in a distributor termed the "Unisparker", it is possible to run a car much further on a set of dry cells than could formerly be done with a storage battery, two to three thousand miles on four or five dry cells being nothing uncommon. This has led to the development of other devices along similar lines, and, with the unfailing source of current now provided by the lighting dynamo and the storage battery which forms part of the system, battery ignition has been raised to a level where it is now almost the equal of the magneto.

Interrupter for High-Speed Engines. For the extremely high-speed engines now coming into general use a special interrupter having two sets of contact points and a three-part cam is employed (for six-cylinder motors). Each set of contacts is connected to a

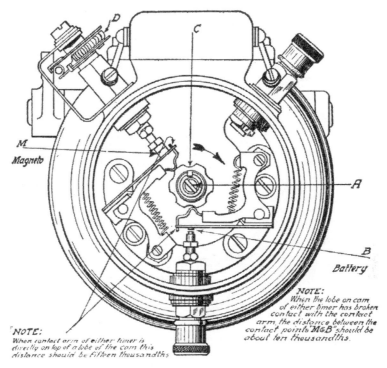

Fig. 27. Delco Dual Type Timer with Two Sets of Contacts

relay so that the circuit is closed through the two relays alternately, thus giving each magnetic interrupter more time in which to open and close the circuit.

Two sets of contacts are used on a multiple-cylinder engine because the space of time between the explosions is so short that one set of contact points would be unable to do the work satisfactorily. The use of two sets of contacts reduces the amount of burning at the contacts; reduces the amount of metal carried across from one contact point to the other; and allows the coil to build up faster owing to the fact that more current will flow through two sets of points than through one during the length of time that they are in contact, thus reducing the amount of work the points have to do. When adjusting two sets of contact points such as are installed on Cadillac "8-cylinder" and Packard "Twin-Six" cars, it is absolutely necessary to see that both points open at the same time and the same amount. In making this adjustment, place a piece of thin paper between the two sets of points and have an assistant crank the engine. Pull lightly on the pieces of paper and you can tell at

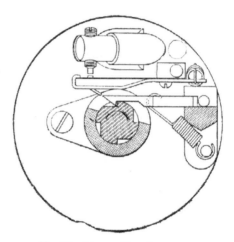

Fig. 28. Atwater-Kent Interrupter
Atwater-Kent Manufacturing Works,
Philadelphia, Pennsylvania

once which point opens first because the strip in that point will be free.

Ignition Failures: Causes, Effect, and Cure. It would be well to consider some of the causes of ignition failure because without good ignition, engine operation will be poor. If the engine will not start after a few turns of the starter, and there is plenty of gasoline, the trouble must be looked for at once. Ignition failure may be caused by several things:

(1) *Dirty contact points:* caused by excessive oil in the ignition unit getting on the contact points and preventing the flow of the primary current. Clean the points with a fine file or remove and dress them on an oilstone.

(2) *Worn contacts:* caused by wearing or burning. If worn, dress them and readjust the gap to about .015 inch. See that the contacts are square and level. Worn contact points will not allow the coil to build up to full strength because the points are not together long enough. If the points are badly burned, they must be renewed and the condenser tested. (See page 5.)

(3) *Contact points set incorrectly:* If *too far apart*, the points would not be together long enough to build the coil to full strength and would cause missing at high speed. If *too close*, the points would hardly break long enough to collapse the primary in order to induce a strong secondary and would cause missing at low speed. They should be adjusted to .015 inch.

(4) *No primary current:* caused by (a) weak battery; (b) by disconnected battery; or (c) by burnt-out resistance. (a) Test the battery with hydrometer and voltmeter. The cure for (b) and (c) are self-evident—connect the battery or install a new resistance unit as the case may be. They would, of course, be found upon inspection. If there is no primary current there will be, naturally, no secondary current. The test for a primary current is to rotate the engine until the contact points come together and then separate them with the finger. If a faint spark is given at the points as they separate, the primary is getting through to the points.

(5) *No secondary current:* caused by any of the foregoing troubles and also by a weak or broken-down condenser. (The test for the latter is found on page 5.) There may be a good secondary as far as the distributor but, if this part is cracked, there is likely to be a leakage of current to the ground or to other segments in the distributor which will cause missing if not a complete failure of the ignition. No repair work can be made in this case and a new distributor must be installed. These troubles will also apply to magneto ignition.

The test for secondary current is to disconnect one spark-plug lead and hold it a short way from the cylinder. Have an assistant turn the crank and, if a spark jumps to the cylinder, there is a secondary current. The current may be weak and not of sufficient strength to jump the spark-plug gap under compression. A good spark will jump a gap of one-fourth inch to three-eighths inch in the open air.

(6) *Pitted contact points:* the metal has been carried across from one contact point to the other causing an insufficient contact to carry the primary current. This will necessitate removing the contact points and dressing them on the oilstone. This trouble also gives the points a tendency to stick and delay the separating of the points, thereby keeping the engine from making the required speed.

(7) *Collection of carbon dust inside the distributor head:* causes a missing in the engine which cannot be traced to any one spark plug. The current will follow the carbon path and cause an intermittent miss in all cylinders. Cleaning the distributor will cure the trouble.

(8) *A punctured coil-winding:* which does not give out all at once but starts with a slight missing and hard starting before the final failure. The coil must be renewed.

(9) *Uneven wearing of the breaker cams:* causing a weaker spark on one side than on the other. This is a frequent cause of trouble, especially, in a magneto that has had a lot of service. This can be tested by measuring the distance between the contact points, when they are open, with a gage. If this trouble is found to exist, it can be overcome by putting thin pieces of paper behind the cam until both sides break alike.

(10) *Sometimes one point on a breaker-cam will wear more than the others:* causing similar trouble in battery ignition systems as in the case of the magneto. The cam must be replaced.

(11) *A loose cam on a shaft:* causing an engine to fire out of time. Tighten cam and inspect taper in shaft for wear. If worn badly, a new shaft must be put in. A worn breaker-arm fiber will alter the gaps at the points and should be inspected after a period of service. This can be overcome by the adjustment of contact points.

(12) *Accumulation on the Ford magneto brush:* preventing the collection of the current from the magneto. Lint and dirt from the brake and transmission bands will collect around the brush. Take out the brush, clean, and replace.

(13) *The magneto magnets may become weak:* the magneto will not generate a good primary current after a period of service, especially if the engine has been overheated at some time. The magnets will need re-magnetizing.

ELECTRICAL EQUIPMENT

(14) *Segments in timer of Ford car become corrugated:* causing the roller to jump and miss contact. When the car stops suddenly and cannot be started again, it is often found that the spring on the roller is broken, which allows the roller to make only one contact. A new roller-spring must be put on the roller.

Most ignition failures can be avoided if a periodical inspection is given to all ignition units. Keep the contact points clean by drawing a piece of emery cloth between them occasionally. Do not lubricate the units too much but keep a little vaseline on the cam and the distributor. Be certain that the battery is always well charged and that all terminals are clean and tight.

DELCO IGNITION GENERATOR
Courtesy of Dayton Engineering Laboratories Company, Dayton, Ohio

IGNITION OPERATIONS

SPARK TIMING

Effect of Irregular Sparking. Like a steam engine, an internal combustion motor depends for its power output on the mean effective pressure developed in the cylinder, usually referred to as its m.e.p. This is affected directly by three factors: *first*, the initial compression of the charge, that is, the pressure to which the piston compresses the gaseous mixture on its upward or compression stroke just before firing; *second*, the time at which the charge is ignited; and *third*, the length of the stroke. It is with the second factor alone that this phase of the ignition problem is concerned. In contrast with the steam engine in which the steam as admitted is at a comparatively low pressure and expands gradually throughout the stroke, the pressure developed in the internal combustion motor at the moment of ignition is tremendous, but it falls off very rapidly. The impulse given the piston is more in the form of a sharp blow than a steady push, as with steam. The mean effective pressure developed depends very largely upon the pressure reached at the moment of explosion and this in turn depends upon the time ignition occurs with relation to the stroke. As the speed of an automobile motor varies over a wide range, it will be apparent that means must be employed for varying the time of explosion. To be most efficient it must occur at the point of maximum compression, i.e., when the piston is exactly at the upper dead center on the compression stroke. As both a mechanical and an electrical lag, or delay, must be compensated for, the setting which will give maximum efficiency at 500 r.p.m. will be much too slow at 1500 r.p.m. and the spark would then not take place until after the piston had started down again and the pressure had dropped considerably, causing a great loss in power. On the other hand, an attempt to run the motor slowly with a spark timing that would give the best results at high speed would often result in causing the explosion to take place against the rising piston. This is evidenced by a hammering sound and a great falling off in the power.

ELECTRICAL EQUIPMENT

Advance and Retard. Means are accordingly provided in the majority of ignition systems for causing the spark to occur earlier or later in the cylinders. This is termed advancing and retarding the spark, the nomenclature being taken from the French, with whom it originated. The explanation given in the preceding paragraph for the necessity of this will make plain the car maker's often repeated injunction to the novice—never to drive *with the spark retarded*. Another and equally important reason is that when operated this way, the combustion is incomplete, the gas continues to burn throughout the stroke, and a greatly increased percentage of its heat has to be absorbed by the water jackets, causing the motor to overheat badly.

Adjusting for Time Factor of Coil. Every induction coil has a certain time constant, which represents the period necessary to completely charge the coil, that is, the time required for the current in the primary winding to attain its maximum value. This time constant depends very largely upon the amount of magnetic energy which can be stored up in the coil. There must be added to this the time required to overcome the inertia of moving parts, such as the timer and the vibrators of a high-tension battery system, or the contact breaker and the distributor in a magneto high-tension system. As these parts are very small and light this would be practically negligible for any other purpose, but when figuring in hundredths of a second, as in the case of the ignition timing of high-speed multi-cylinder motors, it becomes of importance. The object sought, as already mentioned, is to have the spark always occur at the point of maximum compression. To accomplish this with the motor running at high speed, the ignition devices must act while the piston is still an appreciable distance below upper dead center. The timer in the case of a battery system, or the contact breaker of a magneto, is accordingly mounted so that it can be turned through part of a revolution with relation to its driving shaft, or more particularly the cam carried by the latter. For starting the motor by hand, the spark must occur either at or after upper dead center is reached, never before. In the latter case, the piston would be driven backward and the familiar "back kick" result. Hence the manufacturer's admonition—always retard the spark fully before attempting to crank the motor.

ELECTRICAL EQUIPMENT

The meaning of advance and retard spark has been explained and the following pages show the methods used to get the different positions of spark timing in relation to piston position.

Magneto Timing. Timing is usually 30 to 40 degrees, which means that the spark occurrence can be advanced or retarded half that distance from a neutral line representing the upper dead center position of the piston. As shown by Fig. 1, the allowance is 34 degrees in the Splitdorf magneto, "left" and "right" in this connection having

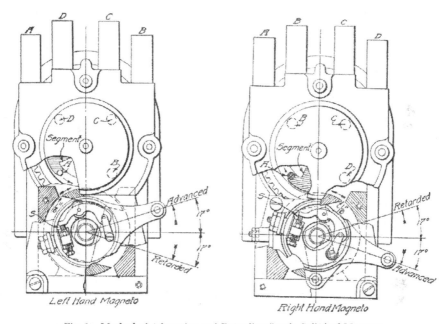

Fig. 1. Method of Advancing and Retarding Spark, Splitdorf Magneto

reference to the direction in which the magneto armature is driven. The necessity of providing this allowance, however, introduces a complicating factor in magneto design.

As the timing of the spark is accomplished by opening the contact points of the interrupter earlier or later, it will be apparent that as the magnetic field remains stationary in the ordinary magneto, the relative positions of the armature and field vary. This is illustrated by the sketch, Figs. 2 and 3. Fig. 2 shows the position of the armature with *advanced spark*. This is the point at which the current and voltage are at their maximum, so that the most efficient spark is produced at the plugs. With the spark retarded, the armature has already had time to turn practically one-eighth of a revolution and the point of maximum intensity has been passed. While this is a factor of which much is usually made in sales literature, it is not so important as the theory of the matter would make it appear, since the spark is seldom retarded except for starting. With the modern high-speed engine there is rarely sufficient

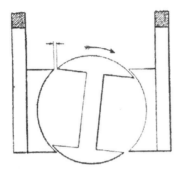

Fig. 2.   Position of Magneto Armature for "Advanced" Ignition

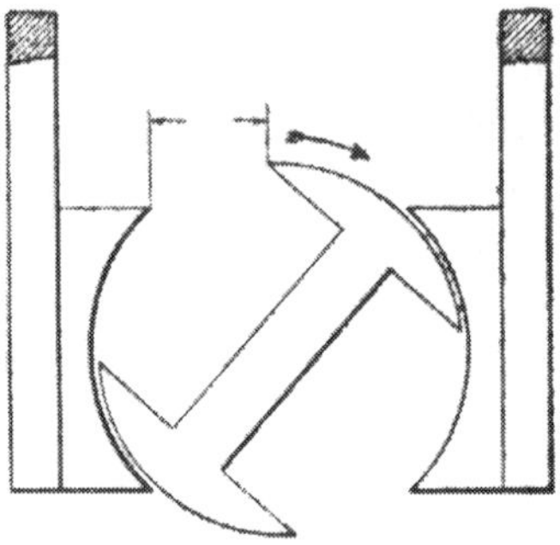

Fig. 3.   Position of Magneto Armature for "Retarded" Ignition

slowing down in hill-climbing to make it necessary to retard the spark, while gear-changing at the proper time further makes this unnecessary, so that practically all the time it is in service the magneto is operating under the most efficient conditions. The great

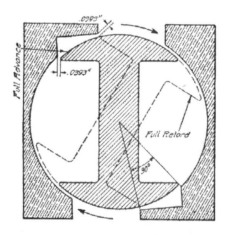

Fig. 4.   Section Simms Magneto Armature and Pole Pieces

difference in the positions of the magneto armature between the advanced and the retarded points of the spark timing shows why it is difficult to crank a motor by hand with the spark retarded, when relying upon the magneto for ignition.

ELECTRICAL EQUIPMENT

As already mentioned, most magnetos are fitted with bipolar armatures, i. e., there are two extensions, or pole pieces, between which the winding is placed. This will be clear upon reference to Fig. 4, which shows the armature core of a Simms magneto. The phases are accordingly 180 degrees apart, that is, the current in the armature winding only reaches its maximum value twice per revolution, and as these maxima are really "peaks", as shown on certain test diagrams, there is not much leeway for variation one way or the other, if the greatest current value is to be utilized.

The Mea and Dixie magnetos make an interesting comparison in regard to the method used for advancing the spark. In the Dixie, Fig. 5, it will be seen that the coils are moved to get the advance

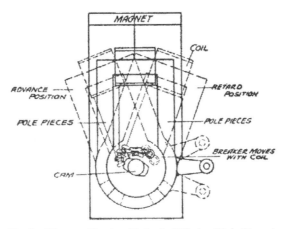

Fig. 5. Diagram Showing Method of Timing Dixie Magneto
Courtesy of Splitdorf Electrical Company, Newark, N. J.

position and the breaker is moved at the same time. The magnets with the breaker mechanism are moved in the Mea while the armature windings, which are on the shuttle, revolve in the usual way, Fig. 6. The bell-shaped magnets of the Mea magneto are shown in Fig. 7.

The difference between the Dixie and the Mea shuttle-type magneto is that in the Dixie the flow of the magnetic flux is changed to give the impulse; while in the Mea, the armature changes polarity. In the shuttle-type magneto the impulse is given at the point of maximum current at either full advance or full retard but it cannot be given in both places. Although different methods are used on these two magnetos for obtaining the full current at all positions the result is the same. Whether the position be full advance or full retard the impulse is given at its maximum current value because the rotor in the Dixie and the armature in the Mea are in exactly the same position with relation to the gaps in the magnets, Figs. 5 and 8.

Power Strokes per Crankshaft Revolution. In the four-stroke cycle engine there is a power stroke for every four piston strokes. In engines of this type all cylinders must be fired in two revolutions

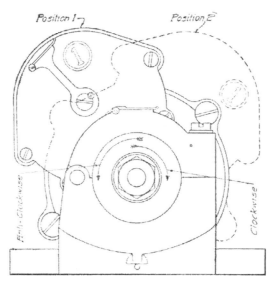

Fig. 6. Spark Advance with Mea Magneto. With Clockwise Instruments, Position 1 Supplies Advanced Spark, Position 2 Retarded Spark

of the crankshaft so that there must be a definite number of sparks given by the magneto for each engine revolution.

Sparks per Armature Revolution. In the shuttle-type magneto there are two sparks or impulses given for every revolution of the armature; while in the Dixie there are four impulses or sparks given for every revolution of the rotor. The flux flow is changed four times and the breaker-cam has four lobes on it, so that a Dixie need only be revolved half as fast as the shuttle-type.

Sometimes a mechanic has to fit or install a magneto on a car that does not have one as a standard equipment or a customer desires to have a magneto simply for ignition purposes. The mechanic may be at a loss to know how fast to run the armature. To find the number of power strokes per crankshaft revolution **divide** the number of power strokes by the number of magneto armature impulses and that will give the speed in relation to the crankshaft revolutions. For example: if we are asked to fit a Dixie magneto on a four-cylinder engine, we must find out how fast the armature of the magneto must run in relation to the speed of the crankshaft.

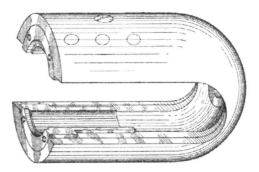

Fig. 7. Bell-Shaped Magnets of Mea Magneto

Following the rule just given, dividing four (the number of cylinders) by two gives two as the number of power strokes. Since we need only two sparks per crankshaft revolution to fire this engine, and the Dixie magneto gives four sparks per revolution of its armature, the

Fig. 8. Relative Position of Armature and Magnets at Moment of Sparking, in Mea Magneto

armature therefore will be required to run at half the speed of the crankshaft to give the two required sparks.

Magneto Speeds. As the revolution of the armature of the magneto always bears a definitely fixed relation to that of the crankshaft of the engine, it will be apparent that the speed at which the magneto is driven will depend upon the number of cylinders to be fired, as well as upon the relation of the cylinders to one another, i.e., firing 180 degrees or 360 degrees apart, as measured on the crankshaft. The following are the various magneto speeds required for engines of the four-cycle type having from one to twelve cylinders:

1-cylinder: Either crankshaft or camshaft speed

2-cylinder: (Impulses 360° apart, as in 2-cylinder opposed motor) camshaft speed; also 2-cylinder twin horizontal engine with cranks in same plane

2-cylinder: (Impulses alternately at 180°, with 540° intervals, as in the 2-cylinder V-type motor) camshaft speed; also 2-cylinder twin horizontal with 180° crankshaft

4-cylinder: Crankshaft speed

6-cylinder: One and one-half times crankshaft speed

8-cylinder: Twice crankshaft speed

12-cylinder: Three times crankshaft speed

Owing to the extremely high speeds necessary, the modern battery type of ignition is favored to a great extent on eight- and twelve-cylinder motors, though magnetos are built even for the latter.

The magneto speeds necessary on two-cycle motors are twice those given above for the corresponding four-cycle types, with the exception that, on the 2-cylinder 180-degree or V-type motor, crankshaft speed would be correct.

Ignition=System Fixed Timing Point. It has become more or less general practice with French builders to provide an ignition system having a fixed timing point, i.e., one that cannot be controlled by the driver through the usual spark-advance lever as found on practically all American pleasure cars. This is particularly the case with taxicabs. While "fixed" in the sense that they are not variable while running, such systems have two firing points—one of maximum advance, which is always employed when the motor is in operation, and the other of maximum retard to enable the driver to crank the motor without danger of injury. So-called fixed-spark ignition systems have come into very general use abroad, more especially on the Continent, but have found very little favor here.

Automatically=Timed Systems. Automatically-timed ignition systems are a distinct advantage with regard to personal safety and equipment. The present-day equipment on automobiles includes a starting motor and while there is not the danger of personal injury there is still the chance of breaking the starting-motor drive. If the spark is not retarded and the motor "kicks back," there is a great possibility of breaking the Bendix drive, if that type is used, or stripping the teeth either in the starting-motor gear or in the flywheel gear, which may mean a new flywheel or a ring gear, or both. Men who drive trucks often forget to retard the spark and

Fig. 9. Eisemann G-A 4 High-Tension Magneto Showing Spark Advance Governor

are badly injured as a result of this carelessness. A system in which the spark is automatically timed does away with this danger. These systems have their disadvantages in that if the mechanism is not kept lubricated they are likely to stick and cause the engine to overheat. However, the advantages offset the disadvantages.

The stress laid by automobile manufacturers on their instructions, "always retard the spark before cranking the motor" and "always run with the spark advanced as far as possible, except when necessary to retard it owing to the motor slowing down on hills and causing a hammering noise in the cylinders," make it evident that there is a considerable amount of discretion left in the driver's hands where this important point is concerned. It is not desirable that this should be exercised by unskilled drivers, particularly those in charge of large and costly commercial vehicles, and automatically timed systems have accordingly been developed.

Eisemann Centrifugal-Governor Type. To advance the spark timing automatically, a centrifugal governor has been mounted on the armature shaft in the Eisemann magneto of this type, as shown in Fig. 9. Normally, the weights are contracted by the spring and the contact breaker is held at the fully retarded position, so that it is always safe to crank the motor without the necessity of taking any precautions. With an increase in speed, these weights tend to fly apart and in doing so they draw a sleeve and with it the armature along the shaft with them toward the left-hand end. As there are **two** helicoidal ridges on the shaft, however, and splines on the inner

Fig. 10. Eisemann G-A 4 Automatic Spark Advance Magneto

diameter of the sleeve engaging them, the sleeve is forced to make a partial revolution as it moves along the shaft, thus automatically advancing the ignition timing in accordance with the speed. The contact breaker is in fixed relation to the armature. An Eisemann magneto fitted with the automatic timing device is shown in Fig. 10. The manufacturers of the Eisemann magnetos make the claim that their late-model magnetos are constructed with water-tight dust-proof joints, so that rain, water leaks, etc., will not interfere with their operation.

Herz Ball-Governor Type. Another method of accomplishing the same end is the Herz automatic coupling, shown in Figs. 11 and 12.

This consists of two juxtaposed disks, each of which is provided with five grooves running in a direction opposite to those of the other

Fig. 11. Herz Automatic
Spark Advance
Coupling

Fig. 12. Herz Automatic
Coupling (Side View)

disk. Five steel balls are held in these grooves and act like the weights of a governor, being forced outward in direct proportion to

Fig. 13. Herz Magneto

the speed of the motor, thus imparting a twisting movement to the magneto armature with relation to its shaft. The device is supplied either as an integral part of the magneto or as an independent coupling. The range of movement is 40 degrees, the adjustment being varied by altering the curve of the grooves. Fig. 13 shows the Herz magneto. In the Eisemann, spindles having grooved slots of several different pitches are supplied, giving from 19 to 60 degrees of advance. The Atwater-Kent, Connecticut, and Westinghouse ignition systems may also be had with automatic advance operated by a centrifugal governor.

Delco System. A magneto-type interrupter, substantially similar to that of the Connecticut system except that it is provided with an automatic-spark advance, is used, Fig. 14. The arm B carries the movable contact D and a fiber-striking lug which bears against the four-part cam and is lifted by its revolution against the tension of the leaf spring held against the inner wall of the casing. The stationary contact, which is at C, is adjusted by means of the screw and locked in place by the nut N. These contacts should be so adjusted that, when the fiber-block on B is on top of one of the

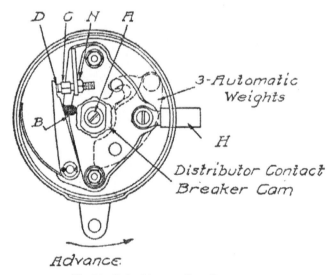

Fig. 14. Delco Magneto Type Interrupter

lobes of the cam, the contacts will be open sufficiently to allow the gage provided with the system to close the gap. The contacts normally remain closed, as in the Connecticut interrupter, being opened momentarily by the cam which has as many projections as there are cylinders to be fired.

ELECTRICAL EQUIPMENT

As the engine gains speed the weights are thrown out and, being attached to the distributor housing by lever, they advance the ignition in relation to the speed of the engine and reduce the knocking which is caused by the spark being too far advanced when the engine is running at low speed. A spring is used to bring the ignition back to the retard position. This automatic advance has another advantage in that it prevents the heating of the engine because of retarded spark when running at normal speed.

In four-, six-, and most V-type cylinder engines the crankshaft travel between firing points is equal. There are one or two engines of the V-type, such as the Lincoln and Liberty engines, in which the cylinders are not spaced so that the firing points are an equal distance apart. Most of the eight-cylinder engines have the cylinders 90 degrees apart, and in the twelve-cylinder engines they are spaced at 60 degrees. In other words, the cylinders form an angle of the above degree. In the eight-cylinder with a 90-degree setting, the crankshaft moves that number of degrees between each cylinder firing; while in the twelve-cylinder with a 60-degree setting, the shaft moves that number of degrees between firings.

The Liberty engine cylinders have a 45-degree setting which gives an uneven firing. Suppose that the first cylinder to fire is the first one on the right block as you stand back of the engine. This moves the crankshaft 45 degrees, the next to fire will move the crankshaft 75 degrees, and so on through the entire cycle. The Lincoln engine has a 60-degree setting so that the distance between firing points is 60 and 120 degrees. If the cam should be removed for any reason, care should be taken to see that the cam is put back correctly because there is a long and short lobe on the cam. The contact points should open at 30 and 60 degrees exactly; this is very important. This corresponds to the 60 and 120 on the flywheel or crankshaft travel.

The method used to set the points on this type of engine (which applies to the Wills St. Claire as well as to the Lincoln) is as follows: The contact points should first be set to .020 inch and then the position of the breaker mounting plate should be moved slightly until the points open exactly at the 30- and 60-degree point. The plate can be moved within small limits after the three small screws which hold it to the housing have been loosened.

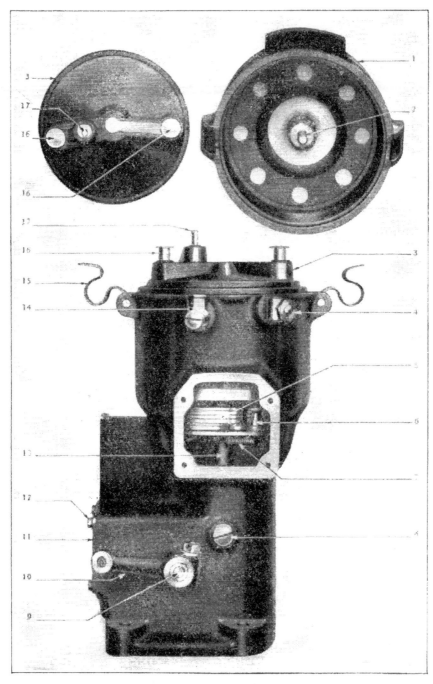

Fig. 15.   Lincoln Distributor
1—Distributor head cover; 3—High-tension rotor;
16—High-tension contact.

ELECTRICAL EQUIPMENT

The following method can be used to accurately time the 30- and 60-degree intervals. Small marks should be made on the distributor housing opposite a previously made mark at any point of the rotor indicating the actual points between the opening of the two sets of contact points. The straight-line measurement between the marks should be $2\frac{1}{32}$ inches for the 60-degree interval and $1\frac{1}{16}$ inches for the 30-degree interval. If the setting of the plate is not correct, the position of the plate should be altered until it is so. If

Fig. 16. Lincoln Contact Points

1—Left block low tension terminal; 2—Left block breaker arm; 3—Distributor cam set screw; 4—Distributor cam; 5—Distributor cam bearing oiler; 6—Spark advance lever; 7—Spark gap adjusting screw; 8—Spark gap adjusting screw lock nut; 9—Spark gap; 10—Right block low tension terminal; 11—Condenser to lower tension wire—right; 12—Right block breaker arm.

this alters the point-opening distance, they should be reset to the .020 inch again and the setting checked. There is a coil and set of contacts for each set of cylinders in the Lincoln system. Fig. 15 shows the distributor and rotor assembly with the rotor in position and Fig. 16 shows the contact point and cam position.

ELECTRICAL EQUIPMENT

In the even-firing engine the usual method of timing is used as explained on page 18. This method can be used in all other systems with the exception of the Atwater-Kent. In this system the actual point opening cannot be seen, but the click of the ratchet can be heard so that the setting can be done as follows: retard the spark lever and rotate the engine until the ratchet is heard to click. The distance between the top of the piston and cylinder should be measured. If the piston is not at the top or does not start to move down as soon as the crank is moved, the ignition must be reset.

Ignition Setting Point. It will be apparent that as provision is made for advancing the time of ignition beyond a certain point as well as retarding it so as to occur before that point, there must be what may be termed a neutral position. This is usually referred to as the ignition setting point. In the majority of instances, this is the upper dead center, particularly where a magneto is employed. For the reason that it is possible to start the motor by handcranking on the magneto with the time of ignition advanced very much farther than would be safe with a battery, as explained in another section, it is seldom necessary to provide for retarding the ignition timing of a magneto past upper dead center. Consequently, the ignition setting point for the majority of systems is upper dead center when the spark-advance lever on the quadrant is at the point of maximum retard. It is not necessary to provide for what is termed a *late* spark, i.e., one occurring after the piston has actually started down on the power stroke, nor is it necessary to provide as great a range of advance in the case of the magneto as where a battery is employed, since the magneto, to a certain extent, automatically advances the moment of ignition as the speed increases.

Where a battery is employed, however, it is customary to allow a greater range of timing in both directions with a *late* spark to insure safety in starting, particularly by handcranking. The relation of the ignition distributor of a battery system to the crankshaft is shown in Fig. 17, which illustrates the ignition diagram of the four-cylinder Regal Motor. The firing order in this case is 1- 2- 4- 3, and it will be noted that the ignition setting point is upper dead center. Both the ignition and the valve timing of practically all motors built in recent years may be checked by marks on the flywheel. A corresponding mark or pointer on the crankcase is used as a checking point.

ELECTRICAL EQUIPMENT

Fig. 17 shows that when piston No. 1 is exactly at upper dead center, contact No. 1 of the distributor is under the brush leading to the spark plug of that cylinder, and, as shown by the center line, this is the ignition setting point for that motor. As the distributor turns in a clockwise direction, rotating it toward the right, as shown in the diagram, retards the time of ignition, while turning it to the

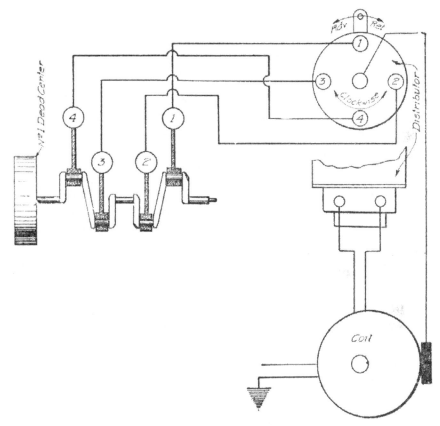

Fig. 17. Relation of Ignition Distributor to Engine Crankshaft
Courtesy of Regal Motor Car Company, Detroit, Michigan

left advances it. The interrupter is just below the distributor and while its battery, ground, and distributor cables are shown, the contacts themselves are not illustrated.

Upper Dead Center. In many cases it is no longer possible to check the ignition timing or the position of the pistons by the flywheel, as the latter is entirely enclosed. To find the upper dead center of the piston of the first cylinder it is accordingly customary to take out a spark plug and use a long knitting needle or similar piece of straight wire. While an assistant turns the motor over slowly by hand, watch the valves of cylinder No. 1. When the inlet valve of this cylinder has closed, the piston is traveling upward on the compression stroke and the needle will rise. It must be borne in mind, however, that the piston is not actually at upper dead center for ignition purposes when the needle ceases rising. In other words, a certain part of the revolution of the crank is not represented by a corresponding movement of the piston, and the proportion that this bears to the whole revolution naturally increases with the length of the stroke.

The starting crank should accordingly be turned until the needle actually starts downward again on the firing stroke, and then the motor turned backward again slightly until it ceases to rise. This may be done by putting the gear lever in *high*, engaging the clutch, jacking up one rear wheel and turning it backward. This will give the proper ignition setting point for any system in which this point is given as "upper dead center with the spark at the point of maximum retard." But unless the precaution in question is taken, the spark timing will have a slight amount of advance and, in a long-stroke motor using a battery system of ignition, this may be sufficient to cause the motor to "kick back" when cranked slowly by hand.

In some cases, where the flywheel rim is not accessible, the ignition setting point is marked on the distributor itself.

FIRING ORDER

Typical Firing Orders. It is naturally quite as important that the sparks occur in the different cylinders of a multi-cylinder motor in the proper order as that each individual spark should take place at just the right moment. Regardless of the number of cylinders, the crankshaft throws are always in pairs. Hence, the pistons rise and fall in pairs, and the cylinders of these pairs (which have no relation whatever to the method of casting the cylinders themselves) naturally cannot follow each other in firing, the firing order alternating from one pair to the other. For example, 1- 3- 4- 2- as in the upper diagram of Fig. 18, or 1- 2- 4- 3- as in the diagram just below it, the motors in both these instances running "clockwise," i.e., with the crankshaft turning from left to right. A similar variation is

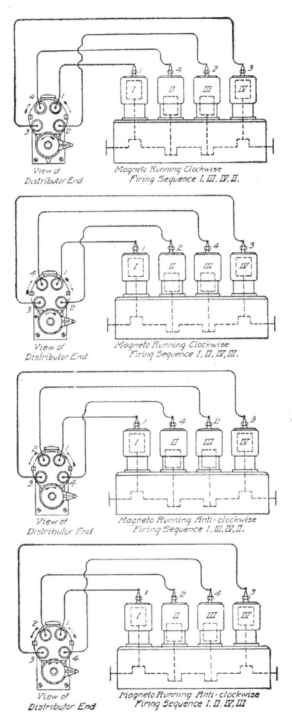

Fig. 18. Firing Order of Four-Cylinder Motors
(*Bosch Magneto Company*)

possible with the motor turning "anti-clockwise," or from right to left, as shown in the two lower diagrams, which show firing orders of 1- 3- 4- 2- and 1- 2- 4- 3-, the changes being made by shifting the distributor connections to the spark plugs of the various cylinders. In the case of a high-tension battery system using unit coils, the timer connections are varied in the same manner. In six-cylinder motors the crank throws are 120 degrees apart, but as the pistons are attached in pairs to cranks in the same plane, the method of distributing the firing order among them is similar to that already given. The Bosch

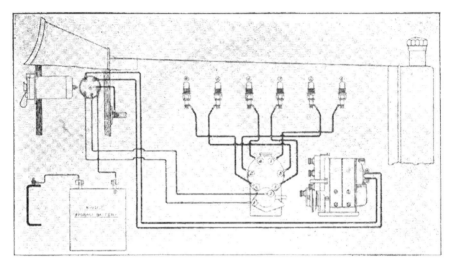

Fig. 19. Firing Order of Six-Cylinder Winton Motor

dual ignition system, as installed on the six-cylinder Winton, is a typical firing order for a six. As shown by Fig. 19, this runs 1- 5- 3- 6- 2- 4.

Possible Combinations. There are so many possible firing orders in the six-cylinder motor and likewise in the more recent eight-cylinder and twelve-cylinder motors that one of the most puzzling questions arising in the repair shop frequently has been to determine just which one has been adopted by the manufacturer for his particular motor. So much uncertainty exists that many makers have solved this for the repair man by attaching a plate to the motor or to the dash, giving the firing order. There are eight firing orders possible for the six or eight. With the six these are:

(a)	1	2	3	6	5	4	(e)	1	4	5	6	3	2
(b)	1	2	4	6	5	3	(f)	1	5	4	6	2	3
(c)	1	3	2	6	4	5	(g)	1	4	2	6	3	5
(d)	1	3	5	6	4	2	(h)	1	5	3	6	2	4

While any of these firing orders will give an equally good impulse balance, the question of proper distribution of the incoming charge and the free escape of the exhaust also have an important bearing on the matter, so that the last two orders given are in most general use. The Winton Six, Fig. 19, shows the employment of order (h).

For the V-type eight-cylinder motor, the possible firing orders are as follows:

(i)	1R 1L 2R 2L 4R 4L 3R 3L		(m)	1R 1L 3R 2L 4R 4L 2R 3L
(j)	1R 1L 3R 3L 4R 4L 2R 2L		(n)	1R 1L 2R 3L 4R 4L 3R 2L
(k)	1R 4L 2R 3L 4R 1L 3R 2L		(o)	1R 4L 2R 3L 4R 1L 3R 2L
(l)	1R 4L 3R 2L 4R 1L 2R 3L		(p)	1R 4L 2R 3L 4R 1L 2R 2L

As the last four mentioned involve different firing orders in each set of four cylinders, they need not be considered. With the rocker-arm type of valve lifters using only eight cams, as in the De Dion (French, and the first to use an eight-cylinder motor) and the King engines, it is only possible to use the orders k and l, while, as a matter of fact, all three employ the order given in l, which is shown diagrammatically in Fig. 20. The other possible order for an eight (k) may be read from the same diagram by turning it around and changing the numbers from 4L to 1R, 3L to 2R, and so on. A curious fact is that in each of these orders the sum of the numbers of two cylinders which fire in succession is always 5. By starting always with a right-hand cylinder, the firing order can readily be determined by noting whether the firing order in one of the groups of four cylinders is 1-3-4-2 or 1-2-4-3.

Just as the eight-cylinder V-type motor is simply a combination of two groups of four cylinders, each of which considered alone would have the standard firing order of a four, so the twelve-cylinder V-motor is simply the bringing together on one crankshaft of two six-cylinder motors. The firing order adopted is accordingly one of the two preferred for the six-cylinder motor (g and h), alternating from the right-hand to the left-hand group in the same manner as shown for the eight-cylinder motor.

Although it is a good plan to remember the usual firing orders used in the present-day cars, a mechanic need never be at a loss to find the firing order of a strange engine, even if all the wires are disconnected, if he will remember the following rule. The order in which the intake valves open will be the firing order. To the list of firing orders which the average mechanic remembers should be added the Packard Straight-Eight and the new Cadillac Twin-Four. For

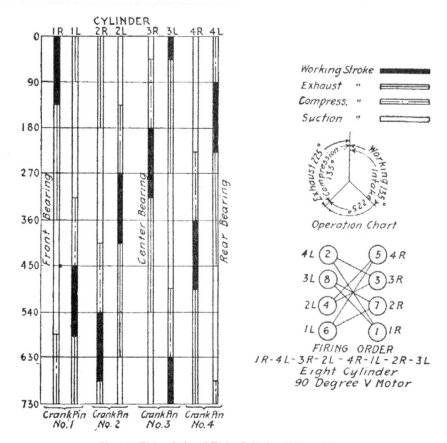

Fig. 20. Firing Order of Eight-Cylinder, V-Type Motor
Courtesy of "Automobile Topics", New York City

the Packard they are 1-3-2-5-8-6-7-4; and for the Cadillac 1L-4R-4L-2L-3R-3L-2R-1R.

Indications and Causes of Late Spark. For no apparent reason whatever an engine will start to overheat and lose its speed; does not pick up quick enough; and will be sluggish in operation. In engines where chains are used to drive the timing gears, the chain will sometimes jump a tooth and cause the engine to be out of time. If the breaker cam gets loose on its shaft, it will cause the spark timing to be late. The following test can be made in both cases: put the ignition lever in full retard position and open the throttle so that the engine runs a little faster and then advance the lever—if the timing is all right, the engine should increase its speed; if there is no noticeable increase, the timing is retarded and should be checked. There are other reasons for an engine overheating which are not relative to the ignition and need not be mentioned here.

AUBURN, MODEL 8-88, BROUGHAM

MOTORS

STARTING PRINCIPLES

Magnetism, in addition to its uses in generation and induction, is also used in converting electrical energy to mechanical energy. Several methods have been tried and devices have been used to do away with hand cranking in starting the engine of an automobile. Compressed air was one of the first things to be tried. The air had to be contained in cylinders, which added to the weight of the car, and often the supply in the cylinders gave out when most needed. Another system was one in which a coiled spring was attached to the front of the crankshaft, but any dirt that worked into the case put the device out of gear and operation. One of the earliest electrical devices was an equipment consisting of a combination starting-motor and generator which took the place of the flywheel. This unit was very heavy and it was inaccessible for making repairs and small adjustments. This unit was the U.S.L. such as was fitted to the old Rambler car.

It will be noticed as the different units are studied that great improvements have been made in this class of equipment in regard to size and efficiency. Some of the more recent installations are of the 12-volt starting and 6-volt generator type, which cause some confusion when considering replacements or repairs. The manufacturers are practically all standardizing on the 6-volt system.

Theory of Operation. A machine that is designed to convert mechanical into electrical energy or the reverse is known as a *dynamo-electric machine*. When its armature is rotated by an external source of power, such as a steam engine, hydraulic turbine, or gasoline engine, it is a *generator*. By sending a current through it from another generator or a battery it converts electrical into mechanical energy and is a *motor*. It is evident, then, that a generator and a motor are fundamentally one and the same thing, and that by a reversal of the conditions one unit may be made to serve both purposes. It will naturally depend upon how closely these purposes approach each other so far as their operating conditions are concerned, whether it will be practical to employ the same machine for both. In practice, operating conditions rarely approximate and so before the advent of the single-unit starting-and-lighting system on automobiles the use of the same machine for both generating current and converting it into mechanical energy was practically unknown. Space considerations were the chief factor which led to the development of the single system, as the demands on the machine for charging the battery and starting the engine are radically different.

How Rotation Is Produced. The operation of an electric motor will be clear if the essentials of a dynamo-electric machine and their relations are kept in mind. There is, first, the magnetic field and its poles—two or any multiple thereof, though for space reasons more than four poles are seldom used in starting motors; then the armature, which must also have an even number of poles corresponding to the number of segments in the commutator. Each separate coil in the armature winding magnetizes that section of the armature core on which it is wound, when the current passes through it, as its terminals, connected to different segments on the commutator, come under the brushes. In an electric motor having either two or four field poles, and eight, twelve, or sixteen armature poles, it is apparent that every few degrees in the revolution of the armature an oppositely disposed set of its poles is either just approaching or just leaving the magnetic field of two of the field poles. Bearing in mind that like poles repel one another and that unlike poles attract, and that the polarity of the armature coils is constantly being alternated by the commutator, we see that each section of the armature is constantly being attracted toward and repelled from the field poles.

The fundamental law just stated can be easily illustrated by taking two common horseshoe magnets, such as can be bought for a few cents. Placing their north and south poles together it will be found that they have no attraction for each other and cannot be made to adhere in this relation. If they had sufficient force they would actually move apart when placed on a smooth surface in this position. But if one of the magnets is turned around so as to bring the north and south poles of the two opposite each other, the magnets will be immediately attracted and will hold together to the full extent of their force.

What may be called one cycle of the operation of an electric motor may be described as follows: the motor turns clockwise; it is of the bipolar type, that is, it has two field poles; and there are eight coils on the armature. At the moment assumed, the left field pole is the north, and the right south; consequently, the section of the armature just entering the field is of opposite polarity, presenting a south pole to the north pole of the field and a north pole to the south pole of the latter. The armature is therefore strongly attracted. This attraction is maintained by the current in the windings continuing in the same direction until the magnetic attraction reaches a maximum, at which point the stationary and moving poles are practically opposite each other. Unless a change occurred just at that point the armature would be held stationary and could be turned from it only by the expenditure of considerable force, that is, assuming that the field did not lose its exciting current. (This may be observed on a small scale by attempting to revolve the armature of a magneto by turning its shaft by hand.) But either at that point, or just before it is reached, the revolution of the armature brings a different set of commutator bars under the brushes and the direction of the current is reversed in that particular winding and with it the polarity of the armature poles. Instead of being mutually attracted the armature and field poles become mutually repellent. In brief, the armature is first pulled and then pushed around in the same direction by reason of the force exerted both by the field magnets and by its own magnets. The passing of one section of the armature through this change as it enters and leaves the zone of influence of a pair of pole pieces may be said to constitute a cycle of its operation, by analogy with alternating-current generation. The cycles are repeated as many times per revolution as there are coils on the armature and the number of coils miltiplied by the speed will give the number of changes per minute. For example, in a motor assumed to have eight armature coils, as in the present instance, there would be, at a speed of 1,000 r.p.m., 16,000 changes per minute, which makes clear the reason for the very smooth pull or torque that an electric motor exerts.

Counter E.M.F. Though being rotated by means of current obtained from an external source of power, it is apparent that the motor armature in revolving its coils in the magnetic field is fulfilling the conditions previously mentioned as necessary for the generation of an e.m.f. Experiment shows that the voltage and current thus generated are in an opposite direction to that which is operating the motor. It is accordingly termed a counter e.m.f. as it opposes the operating current. This, together with the fact that the resistance of copper increases with its temperature and that the armature becomes warmer as it runs, explains why the resistance of a motor is apparently so much greater when running than when standing idle. The counter e.m.f. approaches in value that of the line e.m.f.. or voltage at which current is being supplied to the motor. It can, of course, never quite equal the latter for in that case no current would flow. The two opposing e.m.f.'s would equalize each other; there would be no difference of potential.

Types of Motors. Being the counterparts of electric generators, electric motors differ in type according to their windings in the same manner as already explained for generators. The plain series-wound motor is nothing more or less than the simple series-wound generator to which reference has already been made; the shunt and compound motors likewise correspond to the shunt and compound generators. But while the series-wound generator was of extremely limited application and has long since become obsolete, the series-wound motor possesses certain characteristics which make it very generally used. It is practically the only type employed for starting service on the automobile, and it is also in almost universal use for railway service. The reasons for this are its very heavy starting torque which increases as the speed of the motor decreases, the quick drop in the current required as the motor attains speed, and its liberal overload capacity. It is essentially a variable speed motor, and, just as the plain series-wound generator delivers a current varying with the speed at which it is driven, so the speed of the motor changes in proportion to the load. These are characteristics which make it valuable for use both as a starting motor for the gasoline engine, and for a driving motor on the electric automobile, though in the latter case it is seldom a simple series-wound type. As its speed is inversely proportional to the load, however, it tends to race when the load is light; in other words, it will "run away" if the load is suddenly removed, as in declutching from the automobile engine after starting the latter, unless the current is instantly shut off or very much reduced. This is provided for, as will be explained in detail later in connection with the various systems.

Shunt motors and compound-wound motors are the same as their counterparts, the generators of the same types, but as they are not used in this connection, no further reference need be made to them here.

Dynamotors. As the term suggests, this is a combination of the generator or dynamo and the electric motor, and it is a hybrid

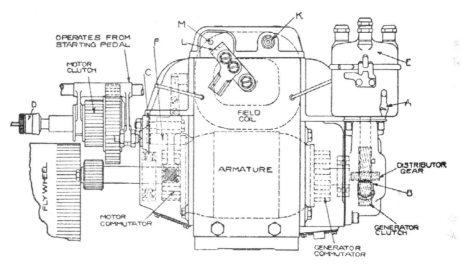

Fig. 1. Dynamotor (Single Unit) of the Delco System

for which the automobile starting system has been responsible. It is frequently mistermed a "motor-generator" and while its assumption of the two rôles may justify the name, the use of the term is misleading as it becomes confused with the motor-generators employed for converting alternating into direct current. The latter consist of an a-c. motor on one end of a shaft and a d-c. generator on the other end of the same shaft. The two units are distinct except for their connection, whereas a dynamotor is a single unit comprising both generator and motor, and it can perform only one of these functions at one time. A motor-generator, such as is used in garages for transforming alternating into direct current for charging storage batteries, must carry on both functions at the same time in order to operate, that is, the a.c. motor must run as a motor in order to drive the d.c. generator and cause it to generate a direct current. Hence, the term "motor-generator" as applied to the single-unit type of electric-starting system for an automobile is not in accordance with the accepted meaning of the words and is likely to cause confusion.

A typical example of the dynamotor is to be found in the Delco single-unit system, Fig. 1. This is composed of the windings of two different machines, a shunt-wound generator and a series-wound motor, placed on the same armature core and field poles. The terminals of the two sets of windings on the armature are brought out in different directions and two commutators are used; that at the right hand having the generator windings and that at the left the motor windings. There are no electrical connections between these two windings or between the series and shunt-field coil windings. There are practically four distinct operations used when using this unit for starting purposes. When the ignition switch is turned on, current flows through the generator windings, motoring the generator and causing the armature to revolve slowly so that the gears can be easily meshed. The first part of the pedal movement draws the starter gears into mesh with the flywheel and further pressure breaks the battery and generator circuit and thus prevents the windings from opposing each other. The last part of the pedal movement brings the starting-motor brushes into contact with the motor-commutator, thus completing the circuit between the motor windings and the battery.

Referring to Fig. 1, the detail at the left shows the gearing and the starting connections for coupling the starter gears with the flywheel of the engine; that at the right shows an ignition distributor for the high-tension current. In the later type Delco units the armature has the two commutators on one end of the shaft, such as found in the Buick.

STARTING MOTORS

Speaking broadly, there are three classes of starting devices worthy of mention: the mechanical or spring-actuated devices; the compressed fluid devices; and the electrical starters. While still employed to some extent abroad, compressed air and similar devices are now only of historical interest here as they have been displaced almost entirely by the electric starter.

Modern Electric Starting System Anticipated Sixteen Years. Although it has only come into general use within the last few years, the possibilities of the electric starter on the automobile were foreseen at an early day. Those to whom it has appeared as a novel development of very recent adoption will doubtless be surprised to learn that a car embodying many of the features of present-day electrical systems was built in 1896. Indeed, the following description of it might well apply to the present U.S.L. system, which employs the flywheel type of dynamotor. The machine in question was a Diehl specially wound Gramme-ring type designed to operate at 12 volts. The armature, which weighed 111 pounds, served as the flywheel of a two-cylinder horizontal opposed 6- by 7-inch motor. The system was described as follows:

"The flywheel is constructed as a dynamo, which by rotary motion charges a storage battery carried in the vehicle. At the time of starting the carriage, the motorman turns a switch which discharges the storage battery through the dynamo, converting it for a few seconds into a motor, which, being upon the main crankshaft, gives rotation and does away with the necessity of starting the flywheel by hand. After the motor gives the crankshaft a few turns, the cylinders take up their work and the battery is disconnected from the dynamo, which then acts as a flywheel.

"The flywheel dynamo furnishes the current for the induction coil of the sparking mechanism as well as for the electric lamps at night, thus doing away with the necessity of going to a charging station. Attached to the crankshaft is a device for changing the point of ignition of the spark in the combustion chamber, perfectly controlling the point of ignition, acting as a 'lead' and allowing the motors to be operated at a variable speed, according to the work done."

From this it will be seen that as early as the spring of 1896, the present complete electrical equipment of the automobile, including ignition with automatic spark advance, electric lighting and starting, was fully worked out and applied to an actual machine. It was not until sixteen years later that what had been anticipated at such an early day in the history of the automobile became accepted practice in all the essential points mentioned. In addition, the machine in question was provided with a magnetic clutch which automatically connected and disconnected the engine every time the gear-shifting lever was moved, thus anticipating the present-day electromagnetically operated gearbox.

Requirements in Design. The conditions in applying an electric starting motor to the gasoline engine bear no relation whatever to those of the lighting dynamo, so that the problem is not, as might be supposed, merely a question of reversing the functions of a single unit of the same characteristics. Practically the only requirements of the dynamo that differ from standard practice in other fields are that it shall commence to generate at a comparatively low (car) speed and that its output shall not exceed a safe limit no matter how high the speed at which it is turned over. The problem of the starting motor, on the other hand, involves conditions which have not had to be met in the application of electric motors to other forms of service. For example, a very high torque must be developed to overcome the inertia of the load, and the latter takes the form of intermittent rather than of steady resistance to the driving effort, owing to the alternate compression and expansion in the motor cylinders. The trolley car might be cited as a parallel to the heavy starting torque required, but the intermittent load, as well as the highly important limitations of weight, restricted current supply, voltage, and space considerations, are entirely lacking.

In the last analysis, the electric starter is nothing more nor less than a storage-battery starter, since most of its limitations are centered in that most important essential. The matters of driving mechanism, starting speed, and other equally important details can all be based on what is either accepted practice of long standing in other fields, or on the knowledge of starting requirements gained in the years of experience in applying manual effort to that end, but the storage battery will always constitute the chief limiting factor. This should be borne in mind in considering the forms that various solutions of the problem have taken, and, above all, it must be given first consideration in the successful maintenance of any electric starting system, as the majority of troubles met with have their origin in the neglect of the battery.

ELECTRICAL EQUIPMENT

Wide Variation in Starting Speeds. In view of the long experience in hand-cranking the motor, it would seem that a definite basis for the starting speed would be an easy thing to establish, but this has not been the case. If "motor" briefly summed up in one word all of the varying characteristics to be found in the great variety of engine designs to which starters must be applied, this might have been easier of accomplishment. What suffices to start one make is, however, frequently found to be totally inadequate for others of apparently identical characteristics, so that in the different makes of starters this essential is found to range all the way from 25 r.p.m. to 200 r.p.m. or over. The necessary speed is largely influenced by the carburetion, as with the stand-by battery ignition almost universally provided, dependence need not be placed on the magneto to start; but to draw a mixture from the carbureter of a cold engine calls for speeds in excess of the lower limit of the range given. The most severe service demanded of the starter and the time when it is most needed are coincident, i.e., in winter use, and the equipment must naturally be designed to meet successfully the most unfavorable conditions. Even with starting speeds of 100 r.p.m. or over, it has been found impossible to start some motors without resort to priming. Some idea of the great variation in the speeds adopted will be evident from the fact that the North East starter, as originally built, was designed to turn the Marmon six-cylinder motor over at only 25 r.p.m.; the Hartford on a similar motor at 70 r.p.m.; the Westinghouse, 80 r.p.m.; Delco, 150 to 175, and the U.S.L. at 200 or over. These speeds are not invariable by any means, as in every case the starting equipment is designed particularly for the motor to which it is to be applied, and will run at different speeds in accordance with the requirements of the engine on which it is installed.

Practice Becoming Standardized. So far as practice may be said to have become standardized at the present writing, speeds of 80 to 100 r.p.m. represent a close approach to the average. One of the reasons for making the speed so much higher than could be effected by hand-cranking is the slowing down of the motor as the pistons reach the maximum compression point in the cylinders, while another is the necessity for drawing a charge of fuel from the carbureter under the most adverse conditions so that starting shall always be accomplished without resort to priming.

ELECTRICAL EQUIPMENT

Voltage. When an engine has been standing idle for some time at a temperature well below the freezing point, the lubricating oil becomes extremely viscous and the current required for starting at a low voltage is very high. The 6-volt standard inherited from dry-cell-ignition days accordingly appeared to be entirely too low at the outset, and several systems employing 12- and 24-volt batteries were developed. The higher efficiency of the latter in starting is opposed by certain disadvantages inherent in this type of installation. Experience has shown, however, that with proper installation and maintenance the 6-volt system affords advantages which more than offset any increase of efficiency derived from the use of a higher voltage, and the majority of well-known starting systems are now designed to operate on a potential of 6 volts.

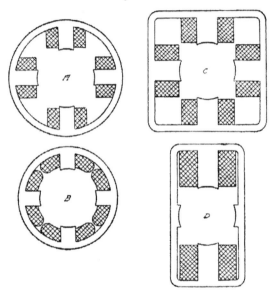

Fig. 2. Cross-Sections Typical Electric Starting Motor
Courtesy The Automobile, New York City

Motor Windings and Poles. The necessity for developing a powerful torque at low speeds naturally calls for a series-wound motor, such as is employed in street-railway and electric-automobile service, and all starting motors are of this type. Motors built to operate at such a low voltage being new to the electrical designer there is more variation in the form and size of starting motors than exists in power units running on current at commercial voltages.

Standard Designs. Briefly stated, the electrical requirements demand a concentrated and correctly proportioned mass of iron and copper in the minimum space. The cross-sections, Fig. 2, show how these requirements have been met in various instances. As the motor is only required to operate for very short periods, both the conductors and insulation can be kept down in size as compared with a motor designed to run constantly under heavy load.

ELECTRICAL EQUIPMENT

Commercial Forms. The problem is to provide for a certain number of ampere turns around the poles and a magnetic circuit through the latter, as well as steel housing or frame of sufficient cross-section to carry the required degree of magnetization with the

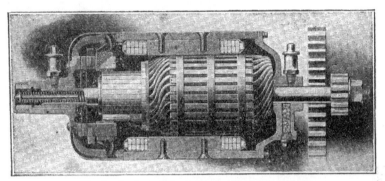
Fig. 3. Section of Bosch-Rushmore Starting Motor

shortest magnetic circuit. Consequently, shallow windings with long flat pole pieces are more efficient than the reverse of this form, particularly as air space in the magnetic field lessens its intensity and calls for a heavier winding to magnetize the extra weight of metal to the same degree. Hence, the type represented by *B*, Fig. 2, is the most efficient, in theory at least, of the four forms illustrated.

Whether the windings be placed on two poles or on four poles is something that each designer decides according to his own preference in the matter. The Bosch-Rushmore starting motor, Fig. 3,

Fig. 4. Westinghouse Starting Motor

exemplifies type *B* referred to above, except that it is bipolar. Windings and pole pieces of the same type are shown in the Westinghouse starting motor, Fig. 4, this being patterned after form *D* in Fig. 2, though it is of somewhat broader section. The auxiliary unwound pole pieces at the sides do not show very clearly in the illustration; they are of substantially the same form, though con-

Fig. 5. Bipolar Type Westinghouse Starting Motor

siderably wider than those illustrated in the section in question. For a more restricted space a straight rectangular bipolar type is made, Fig. 5. From the standpoint of both electrical efficiency and space considerations, practice favors the cylindrical rather than the rectangular form.

TRANSMISSION AND REGULATION DEVICES

Installation. As the driving requirements of starting with such a small power unit as space and weight limitations make necessary

Fig. 6. Double-Reducing Gear Type Installation, Wagner Starting Motor

call for a high-speed motor and a high gear ratio to effect the necessary speed reduction, the mounting of the starting motor is totally different from that of the lighting dynamo. The electric motor runs at 1800 to 3000 r.p.m. or over, according to its design, while, as already mentioned, the engine starting speeds usually average 80 to 100 r.p.m. The great speed reduction required is effected in the majority of instances by utilizing the flywheel as the driven gear, a gear being bolted to it, as shown in Fig. 6, which illustrates the application of a Wagner starter to the Moline-Knight 50-horsepower four-cylinder motor. Or the gear teeth may be cut directly in the periphery of the flywheel itself. This style is used on the double-unit

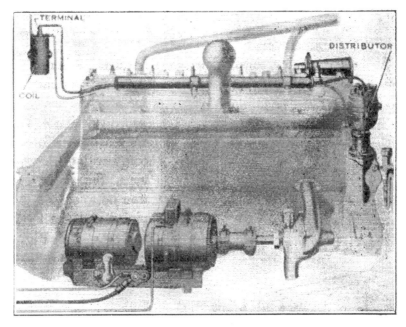

Fig. 7. Double-Unit System

system mounted on the Hudson Six, 1923, Fig. 7. In either case, this does not afford sufficient reduction in the speed, and an intermediate set of gears is necessary in installations such as those illustrated. This gearing may be mounted as an attachment to the engine or combined with the starting motor, as shown in Fig. 8, showing a Ward-Leonard starting motor with enclosed gearing. In some instances, a planetary type of gear is employed, an example of which is found in one type of the Westinghouse starting motors, Fig. 9, the gearbox being incorporated in the motor housing and the pinion driving direct. In view of the large reduction available in a planetary gear, a starting motor of this type may be employed to drive through a camshaft or similar location. Planetary gears are also utilized on some of the single-unit systems, such as the Northeast, the gear ratio used being something like 40 to 1 when the dynamotor is used for starting and 1 to $1\frac{1}{2}$ or 2 when running as a generator, Fig. 10. Silent chains are made

Fig. 8. Reducing Gearing Attached to Ward-Leonard Starting Motor

use of in some cases, but this is done more frequently where a starting and lighting system is applied to an old car rather than to one

Fig. 9. Westinghouse Starting Motor with Planetary Reduction Gear

for which it has been especially designed. Where the starting motor is of a comparatively low-speed type, the single reduction between the motor pinion and the flywheel suffices. In Fig. 11 is shown a starting

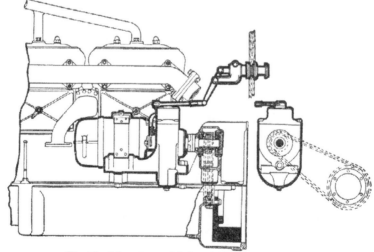

Fig. 10. Mounting and Drive of Northeast Dynamotor

motor designed for direct engagement with the flywheel gear. The purpose of the spring shown on the end of the shaft is to take up the shock when the power is applied to the starter.

Driving Connections. Except in the case of the single-unit type, which is in a permanent driving relation with the engine, it is necessary to provide some form of driving connection with the

Fig. 11. Starting Motor for Direct Engagement

engine in order that the electric motor may turn it over to start, and release it the moment the engine fires. This is made clear in Fig. 12, which shows an Overland four-cylinder starting motor. In some types the starting pedal serves both to connect

Fig. 12. Starting Motor on Overland Engine

the motor with the battery and to engage the driving pinion with the toothed ring of the flywheel. The switch is usually located directly beneath the footboards just back of the dash. Depressing the pedal part way makes preliminary contact through a resistance, turning the electric motor over very slowly, and at the same time draws the starter pinion toward the flywheel gear, its slow turning insuring easy engagement. As the pedal is depressed further, it breaks the first contact and closes the main switch, sending the entire battery current through the starting motor and turning the engine over rapidly. Releasing the pedal automatically opens the switch contacts and disengages the starting motor from the flywheel. It is also frequently made in the form of a pedal and placed on the slope of the footboards under the cowl of the dash, the location in any case must be out of the way of the other controls.

Automatic Engagement. *Auto-Lite Type.* In Fig. 13 is illustrated a starter which eliminates the necessity of mechanically engaging the starting pinion with the flywheel gear. The armature shaft is extended and a sleeve having spiral-cut threads on its outer surface is placed over this armature shaft. One end of a coil

spring is fastened to this sleeve and the other end of this spring is fastened to the armature shaft. The driving pinion has a counterweight on one side and spiral threads inside to fit the sleeve. When the starting button is depressed, a direct circuit, having no resistance inserted, is completed, causing the armature to revolve at a high rate of speed. As

Fig. 13. Automatic Engagement and Release of Starting Motor, Overland Engine

the driving pinion is counterweighted, it turns but little and is threaded into mesh with the teeth on the flywheel. When this pinion is in full mesh with the flywheel gear, the turning torque is transmitted through the spring, sleeve, and pinion to the flywheel. When the engine starts under its own power, the increased speed of the flywheel threads the pinion out of mesh with the flywheel gear. This is known as the Bendix drive and is now used by over 95 per cent of the manufacturers.

Bosch-Rushmore Type. Another form of automatic engagement, which is electrically operated in this instance, is that of the Bosch-Rushmore starter. By referring back to Fig. 3, which shows a section of this starting motor, it will be noted that there is a heavy spring on the left-hand end of the armature shaft and that the armature itself is normally held out of its usual running position by this spring. In other words, it is not centered in the armature tunnel but is two inches or more to the right of the center of the magnetic field. This is just sufficient to keep the pinion out of mesh when the motor is installed, as shown in Fig. 14. The first contact of the starting switch sends sufficient current for the field poles to exert enough magnetic drag on the armature to draw it back into its normal centered position, at the same time turning it over slowly, so that engagement is quickly effected automatically. The moment the current is shut off, the spring pushes the armature back and disengages the pinion. Exceptions to the practice reflected by the foregoing examples are to be found on cars like the Reo, in

Fig. 14. Mounting of Bosch-Rushmore Starting Motor

which the Remy starting motor is mounted on the transmission housing and drives to one of its shafts through a worm and worm wheel. The latter lowers the speed sufficiently through a single reduction, and the revolution of the armature in starting picks up a clutch which automatically releases as soon as the engine starts.

Clutches. *Necessity for Disengaging Device.* To prevent the gasoline engine from driving the starting motor when the former takes up its cycle, some form of over-running clutch must be provided unless the starter is geared directly to the crankshaft or has a mechanical disengaging device, such as the Bendix or electrical, as the Bosch-Rushmore and Westinghouse. To take care of the speed reduction, assume that this gear ratio is 30 to 1 and that the throttle is half open when the engine is being cranked. As soon as the explosions begin to take place, the engine will shortly speed up to about 500 r.p.m. Before the gasoline engine is started, however, the electric motor will be running pretty near its maximum rate, say 3000 r.p.m. An electric motor of this type will run as high as 5000 r.p.m. safely, but speeds in excess of this are liable to damage it. If the throttle of the engine should happen to be three-quarters of the way open when started and it should speed up to 1000 r.p.m. before the starting motor was disengaged, the armature shaft of the latter would attain a speed of 15,000 r.p.m., which is far beyond the safety limit. This makes it necessary to provide some device which, while permitting the starting motor

to drive the engine, will prevent the latter from driving the starting motor as soon as the former takes up its regular cycle.

A number of different devices are employed for this purpose, such as the jaw clutch similar to that employed on all handcranks, roller clutch, friction clutch, pawl and ratchet, inertia clutch, worm and worm wheel, and others. A description

Fig. 15. U.S.L. Dynamo on Sheffield Simplex (British) Engine

of one or two types will suffice to make clear the principle on which most of the mechanical devices are based. The roller clutch and the over-running jaw clutch are most frequently used. With starters of the design of the U.S.L., shown on a Sheffield-Simplex (British) six-cylinder motor in Fig. 15, it is obviously unnecessary to provide any form of flexible coupling, as the armature is mounted directly on the crankshaft and consequently cannot exceed the speed of the latter.

Where the crankshaft is driven direct through a train of gears or a combination of gears and a silent chain, the clutch is usually placed between the last gear of the train and the crankshaft. None of the gears is then in operation except when starting. On the flywheel-gear type of installation used in connection with a second-gear reduction by means of a countershaft, the clutch is placed on the countershaft. Otherwise, it is mounted on the armature shaft. In the case of a worm and worm-wheel drive, it is incorporated in the worm wheel.

Roller Type. The roller type is the most commonly used and, as the various forms in which it is made differ but little, a description of one will suffice to make clear the principle employed. It consists of an inner driving member and an outer driven member, connected by a number of rollers when the driving member is rotated in one direction and disconnected when it is rotated in the opposite direction, i.e., when the driven member tends to run faster than the driver. Fig. 16 shows the double-roller over-running clutch employed on the North East dynamotor. A double clutch is employed in this case to permit the dynamotor to be driven at one speed when operating as a dynamo and at another when starting the engine. Fig. 17, which shows the Leece-Neville starter on a Haynes six-cylinder motor, is an example of the use of a roller clutch and chain in place of the gear and pinion connection previously described.

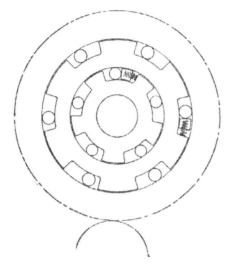

Fig. 16. North East Double Roller Over-Running Clutch (*Horseless Age*)

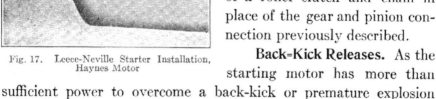

Fig. 17. Leece-Neville Starter Installation, Haynes Motor

Back=Kick Releases. As the starting motor has more than sufficient power to overcome a back-kick or premature explosion (with the spark-timing lever too far advanced) of the engine, and is only slowed down by it, only a few instances of the employment of a back-kick release are found in practice. One of these on the Northeast starter is in the form of a friction clutch held in contact by springs. This clutch will slip under such circumstances. A friction disc clamped between two steel discs, similar to a shock absorber, is employed on the Hartford starter, this being required because of the irreversible worm and worm-wheel drive used, as the teeth of the latter would be injured in case the engine "back-kicked". Another device employs a brake band on the starting gears so designed that it holds in one direction only.

Switches. Two types of switches are employed in connection with starting and lighting systems—those designed to control the lighting circuits to the various lamps, and those employed to connect the battery with the starting motor. As the first type seldom carries more than 5 amperes at 6 volts and proportionately less at higher voltage, it does not differ from the standard forms of switches employed for house lighting, except that it is made much smaller in size. The starting switch,

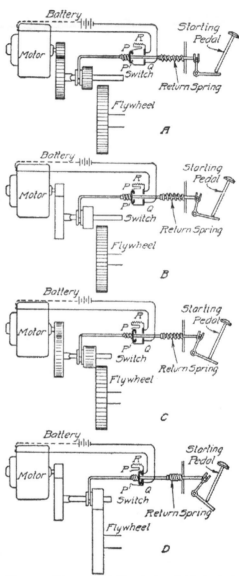

Fig. 18. Diagrams of Electrical and Mechanical Connections of Motor and Switch for Flywheel Drive with Double-Gear Reduction (*Westinghouse*)

on the other hand, has to carry currents ranging from 50 to 250 amperes or more at voltages varying from 6 to 24, so that such a switch must be well built mechanically and have liberal contact

ELECTRICAL EQUIPMENT

areas. On account of the heavy currents handled by these switches there is a tendency to destructive arcing at the contact points unless provision is made to prevent it.

Westinghouse Starting Switch. For starting use, two forms of switches are employed according to the method by which the motor starts the engine. Where the motor is connected directly to the battery terminals by the switch, as in the case of single-unit systems such as the Delco, only a single set of contacts is necessary; but in case gears must be engaged before the starting motor can take the full battery current, two progressively operated sets of contacts are used. The first set completes the circuit through a heavy resistance to turn the starting motor over very slowly, and the second set cuts out this resistance, the driving gears then being engaged. The operation of a switch of this type is graphically illustrated by a series of sketches,

Fig. 19. Details of Westinghouse Switch

Fig. 18, showing a Westinghouse starter installation. In sketch *A*, both contacts are open, the return spring holding them apart. When the starting pedal is partly depressed, as in sketch *B*, the first set of contacts *P* come together and current from the battery passes to the starting motor through the resistance *R*. This connection continues through the spring fingers *P* and *Pl* until the sliding member is almost in contact with the main-switch points *Q*, when it is broken and the circuit is directly closed with the battery by a butt contact. The operation only requires a fraction of the time necessary to describe it. The moment the foot is removed from the starting pedal, the return spring automatically breaks the circuit. The construction of this switch is shown in Fig. 19. Switches of this type are usually mounted directly under the footboards, a slight movement being sufficient to close the contacts. The starting plug may be removed by

145

the driver when leaving the car to prevent tampering, a pin across the tube making it impossible to insert a pencil or stick. The resistance mentioned is in the form of a ribbon and is incorporated in the switch.

Miscellaneous Starting Switches. The type of switch used in connection with the Remy system is shown in Fig. 20. Both this and the Westinghouse switch described are known as butt-contact switches. The knife type of switch is also employed in several systems, Fig. 21 showing the Dean switch of this class. A somewhat unique form of contact is shown in the Gray and Davis switch, Fig. 22. There being no starting gears to mesh, it is only necessary to turn the current directly from the battery into the

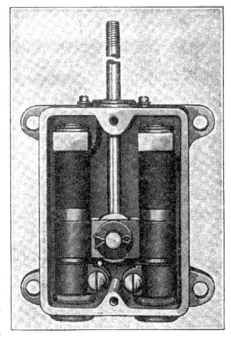

Fig. 20. Remy Starting Switch

motor to start. *P* is the foot button of the starter, *F* the floorboard of the car, and *T* and *M* the terminals of the switch from which cables are led to one side of the battery and to one of the motor brushes, the others being grounded, as this is a single-wire system. Into the cast

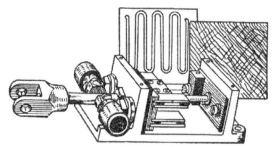

Fig. 21. Dean Knife Starting Switch

receptacle of the switch is fitted an insulating disc carrying the contacts *C* and *O* and also serving to insulate the terminals. These contacts are circular in form, and their free ends are turned away from each other so as to slip down over the knives *R* and *S* set in the insulated disc. The contacts are pressed downward by P, which is returned by the spring G pressing against the spindle P. The terminals T and M are fastened to the semicircular knives R and S, respectively, so that bringing down the contacts C and O upon these knives

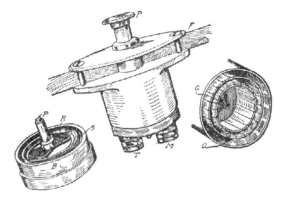

Fig. 22. Gray and Davis Button Starting Switch

completes the circuit from T to M. Several other forms of foot-operated switches are also employed, the Gray and Davis laminated contact switch, Fig. 23, for flywheel-gear installations, and the Ward-Leonard "harpoon" type, Fig. 24; these are seldom used today.

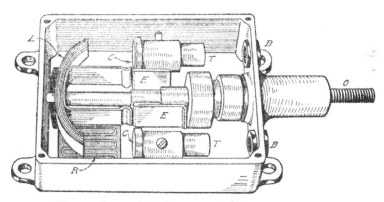

Fig. 23. Gray and Davis Laminated Type of Starting Switch
Courtesy of The Horseless Age

Electrically Operated Switches. In this type a conventional push-button switch, either on the dash or mounted on the steering column, as shown in Fig. 25, which illustrates the Packard control, takes the place of the foot button. This push-button switch, however, only handles a shunt current of low value, which, on contact energizes a solenoid to close the contacts of the main switch and also to engage the gears where this is necessary. The Westinghouse magnetically operated switch is explained in detail in connection with the description of that system. This form of control is employed on electric-railway trains and on electric automobiles.

In addition to housing the push-button switch of the starting system, the two steering column control units mentioned also incorporate all the switches necessary to control the entire electrical equipment of the car, as will be noted by the indications alongside the various buttons on the Overland controller. The electrical control of the Packard car, which is shown in Fig. 25, is no longer standard, but is given because there are many cars still in use which have this control.

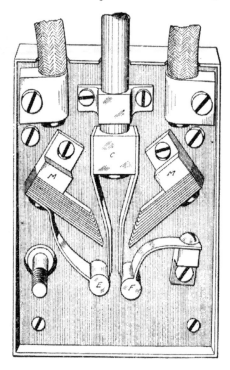

Fig. 24. Ward-Leonard "Harpoon" Starting Switch

Where a higher potential than the usual 6-volt standard is employed, the switch has another function, that of changing the battery

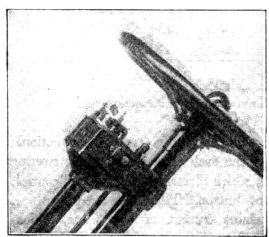

Fig. 25. Packard Electrical Control

connections from the multiple arrangement, which is used for lighting, to the series connection, which is necessary to send the full voltage and current of the battery through the starting motor. This is the case with the U.S.L. system, which is made in either 12—6-volt or 24—12-volt forms.

ELECTRICAL EQUIPMENT

Starting=Motor Troubles; Causes and Cures. The chief causes of the starting motor failing to operate are as follows:

(1) *Weak or discharged battery:* generator not charging at high enough rate or starter is used too often and engine not run long enough to recharge the battery. To cure this, advance the third brush to increase the generator output or remove the battery and recharge.

(2) *Dirty commutator:* caused by excessive lubrication and carbon accumulation. Remove the unit and clean thoroughly.

(3) *Worn brushes or weak brush springs:* caused by too soft brushes, natural wear, or too heavy spring pressure. Renew the brushes and check up on the brush-spring pressure.

(4) *Loose terminals, either at the battery or in the circuit:* caused by poor installation, broken terminals, or battery straps.

(5) *Corroded terminals:* same causes as for loose terminals. They need constant attention and should be kept clean.

(6) *Short-circuit, open-circuit, or ground in the windings of the armature or the field coils:* caused by poor insulation or overheating of the unit windings or field coils. The starter must be removed and the windings tested thoroughly and the armature rewound.

(7) *Starter out-of-line:* the bolts that hold the starter in place have become loose or were not installed correctly. It will be necessary to adjust the starter until the gears mesh correctly.

(8) *A sticky or gummed-up thread, in the case of a Bendix drive, on the shaft which will not allow the pinion to thread into mesh:* Clean the thread with a little gasoline or kerosene and lubricate with a light-grade oil.

(9) *Insufficient lubrication:* in the case of the over-running clutch-type, this will cause the clutch to stick. Holding the pedal down too long will also cause this trouble which, in turn, will cause harm to the windings.

(10) *The starter will sometimes fail to motorize in the Delco single-unit type and prevent the gears from meshing:* caused by poor brush contact or dirty commutator. The brushes may have to be "sanded in" or new brushes installed and the spring pressure regulated. The commutator should be cleaned. The brushes in all units should slide freely in their holders but not so much as to twist or cock in the holder.

ELECTRICAL EQUIPMENT

A great deal of trouble could be avoided if the starting-motor unit was given a periodical inspection.

We have seen in the Delco unit a generator and a starting motor combined. Fig. 26 shows such a unit installed on a Buick engine.

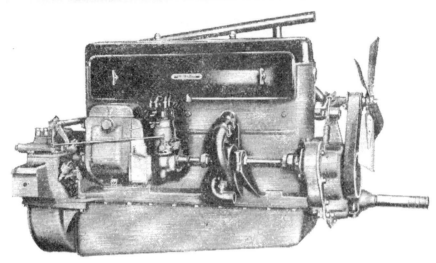

Fig. 26. Buick Single Unit
Courtesy of Buick Motor Car Company

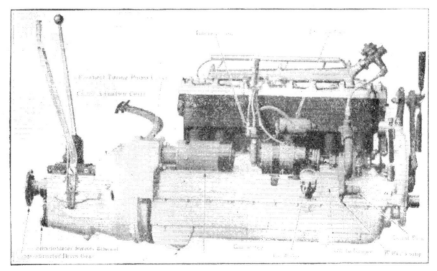

Fig. 27. Two-Unit Installation
Courtesy of Haynes Motor Company

As opposed to this installation there is the double unit as installed on the Haynes car, Fig. 27.

ELECTRICAL EQUIPMENT

TYPES OF WIRING SYSTEMS

There are two systems of wiring used on the automobile today, known as the single- and double-wire systems. The double-wire system is being discarded rapidly because it is more expensive to install as standard equipment than the single-wire system, and also it is more complicated, making it difficult to locate trouble. The majority of cars have a double-unit single-wire system, while the rest have a single-unit single-wire system or a double-wire system with both types of unit installation.

Single-Wire System. The single-wire system consists of one wire which carries the current supply to all units of the equipment while the frame is used for the return. A single-unit single-wire

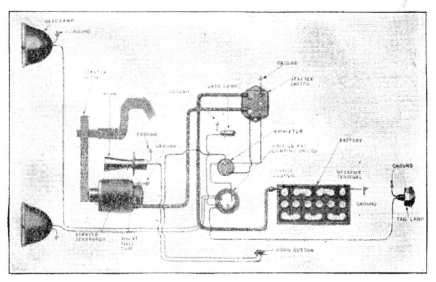

Fig. 28.   North East Single-Unit Single-Wire System

system is shown in Fig. 28, which shows the North East equipment as installed in the Dodge car. A double-unit single-wire system, as installed on the Packard Straight-Eight car, is shown in Fig. 29. One terminal of the wire is grounded in the single-wire system. In the Packard system the positive terminal is grounded while in the Dodge system the negative terminal is grounded. This is simply a matter of design or preference of the engineers and makes no difference in the operation of the units. However, the battery

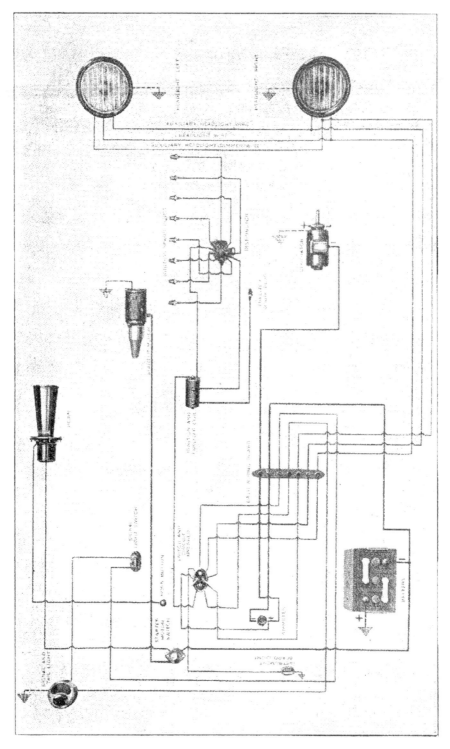

Fig. 29. Two-Unit Single-Wire System

must be connected correctly when a replacement is made. There is no standard connection for battery-ground terminals and this causes considerable confusion where general repair work is done. The following is a good test to see whether the battery is connected correctly: after the battery is connected turn on the lights and if the connection is correct the ammeter needle will move over to discharge, but if incorrect the needle will move to charge. The

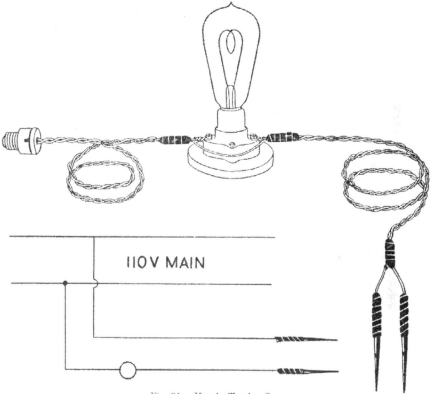

110V MAIN

Fig. 31.   Handy Testing Set

advantages of the single-wire system are simplicity, the low expense of installation, and ease of locating or "shooting" trouble. The great disadvantage is the risk of fire, but this chance becomes less as better methods of installation are used.

Double-Wire System. The double-wire system has a wire to carry the current supply to the units and a wire to return the current to its source. A double-wire system, as installed on the early-type Packard, is shown in Fig. 30. A comparison of the two systems will clearly show the complications in the double-wire system. The

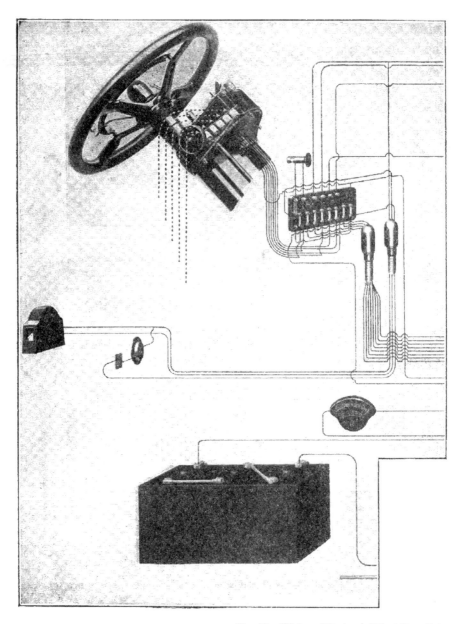

Fig. 30.   Wiring of Packard (Bijur) Two-Unit.
Courtesy of Packard Motor Car

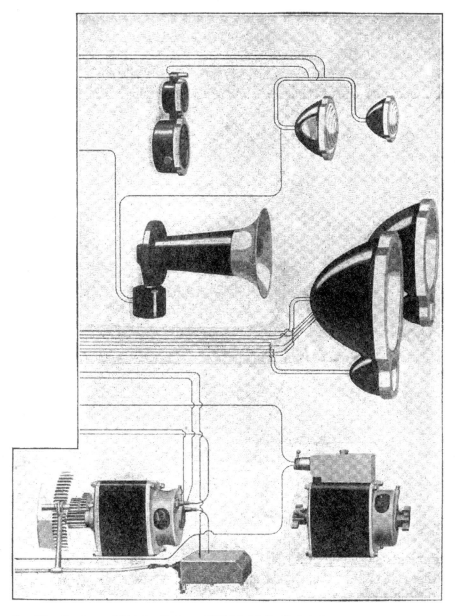

Two-Wire Starting and Lighting System   (1916 Model, Six-Cylinder)
Company, Detroit, Michigan

same care should be taken in the connection of the battery in this system as in the single-wire system.

A good test set to hunt for grounds in a single-wire system, is shown in Fig. 31. It can also be used to locate grounds in a double-wire system. Fig. 32 shows a diagram of a ground in a circuit. The test set is made of a porcelain-base socket attached to a wooden base. Connect one side of the lamp socket to a screw plug. Make two brass

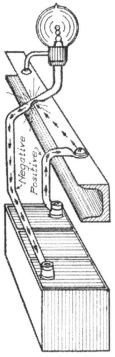

Fig. 32. Diagram of Ground or Short Circuit

Courtesy of Gray and Davis Company

terminals as shown and point them. Connect one test-point to the other side of the lamp socket and connect the other test-point to the other side of the screw-plug. All joints on the test wires should be soldered to make perfect joints. A carbon-filament lamp is used in the set because it is the most durable. The danger of damage to the automobile because of the lamp is reduced since the latter consumes but a small amount of the current. The points on the test set should be pressed on places where no current passes. If a headlight will not burn, the probable cause of the trouble is in the circuit. In testing, disconnect the ground terminal at the battery. Place one test point on the frame and disconnect the wire at the headlight and place the other test point on that terminal. If the lamp burns, it indicates a ground. Each circuit can be tested in the same way and the ground located. If outside current is not to be had, a test set can be made in the same style, using the car battery and a six- or a twelve-volt lamp, according to the system used on the car.

TYPICAL BOSCH RUSHMORE STARTING MOTOR
Courtesy of American Bosch Magneto Corporation, Springfield, Massachusetts

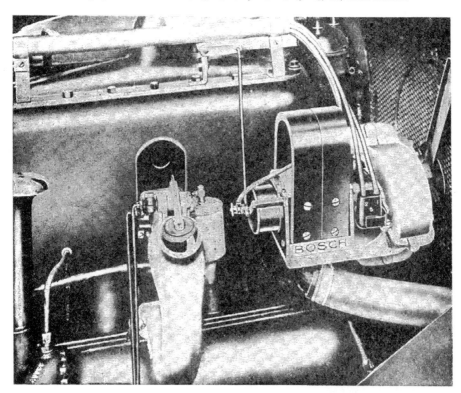

TYPICAL BOSCH MAGNETO INSTALLATION
Courtesy of American Bosch Magneto Corporation, Springfield, Massachusetts

GENERATORS

GENERATOR PRINCIPLES

Applied to the Automobile. The difference between the generator and the starting motor is chiefly in the windings. The starting motor is usually a series-wound machine with windings of heavy strip copper. A generator can be run with the same windings as a motor, however. A series-wound motor has a strong pull at low speeds. A series-wound generator will rotate in the opposite direction when run as a motor. A shunt-wound generator will run in the same direction when run as a motor. The shunt-wound generator is the type used on the automobile. The generator consists of an armature shaft—having suitable windings on it—with a laminated core around which the wire coils are wound. The field coils, which are made up of many coils of fine wire, are arranged as a shunt. This allows only a small part of the total current generated to flow through the coils to magnetize the pole pieces. It is a good example of an electromagnet. The commutator, brushes, bearings, and frame make up the complete machine. Some of these generators are driven by gear or chain, connected by some means to the crankshaft through other gears at the front end of the engine and in mesh with the timing gears. Some generators are driven by a belt—either the fan belt or an independent one. When adjusting the output of a belt-driven machine, see that the belt does not slip for this is often the cause of a low generator output and an incorrect adjustment will be made.

The generator is an important unit in the automobile equipment and should be given close and careful attention. The ignition unit and the battery are both dependent upon its output. The cost of repairing the generator is not a small matter, especially if the armature becomes damaged and has to be rewound. The output should be so adjusted that with the lights on and the engine running there will be enough surplus to charge the battery, and the battery will float on the line.

ELECTRICAL EQUIPMENT

METHODS OF REGULATION

Necessity for Control of Generator Output. The speed with which the armature coils cut the lines of force of the magnetic field is the chief factor determining the e.m.f. and, in consequence, the current output of the generator. This, in connection with the heating effect of the current due to the resistance of the conductor, limits the amperage that the latter will carry safely. Beyond this point the insulation will take fire and, with a further increase in the temperature due to excessive current, the conductors themselves will fuse. With the extreme variation in speed presented by the operation of the automobile engine, the necessity for regulating the output of the generator will be apparent. There are almost as many methods of regulation as there are systems in use.

The magneto is an electric generator that requires no current-controlling device, as the magnetic excitation of its fields is permanent. That is, barring gradual exhaustion through age, heat, and vibration, its magnetic field is constant, thus enabling it to generate a current at very low speeds; but the limitations of this type of field are such that electromagnetic fields are employed as in large direct-current generators. These fields depend for their excitation upon the current derived from the armature of the machine itself, and, as the amount developed by the latter increases in direct proportion to its speed, the fields become stronger as the speed increases and correspondingly more current is generated by the armature. As an automobile motor is driven at a great range of speeds, varying from 200 or 300 r.p.m. up to 2000 to 2500 r.p.m., or even higher, and the generator is usually geared in the ratio $1:1\frac{1}{2}$ so as to develop its rated output at the normal speed of the engine—its windings would be quickly burned out unless some provision were made to control its output.

Constant=Current Generator. Generators of the so-called constant-current type are frequently regulated by the winding alone. They are usually compound-wound, the series coil being so connected as to oppose the shunt. Assuming the coils to be in equally advantageous positions on the core, the limiting current then is one which gives the same number of ampere turns to the series coil as to the shunt field. Thus, assuming 500 shunt turns in the winding and a shunt current of one ampere, there are 500 ampere turns in

ELECTRICAL EQUIPMENT

the shunt winding. If there are 25 turns in the series winding, the limiting current will be 20 amperes, 500 being the product of 20 by 25. With this winding 20 amperes will be the absolute limit of the current regardless of speed. As a matter of fact, it will be considerably lower than this in practice, owing to the armature reaction.

Methods of Regulating the Output of the Generator. The peculiar demands on the automobile generator make it necessary to control the voltage within certain limits, also to keep the amount of current at a fairly constant value over a very wide range of speed. Owing to mechanical

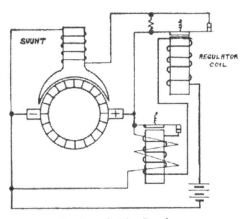

Fig. 1. Vibrating Regulator

difficulties it is impractical to drive the generator armature at a constant speed regardless of the car or engine speed. It is, therefore, necessary to provide some means of keeping this output at a constant value. If the voltage increases above a predetermined value, the head lamps will burn out and damage will also be caused to the ignition system.

There are on the market at the present time two popular methods of regulating the output of a generator. These are the third-brush method and the vibrating regulator method. A number of other forms have been used in the past but as most of these are now obsolete they will not be taken up at this time.

A typical example of a vibrating type of regulation is shown in Fig. 1. In this system the amount of current generated by the armature is governed by the strength of the shunt field. However, this principle is true of all forms of regulation. The current that magnetizes the field flows from the positive main brush and passes through the regulator points, which are normally closed, through the shunt field returning to the negative main brush. As the charging circuit which passes through the regulator coil becomes of sufficient strength to overcome the spring tension that is holding the regulator points together, the points will open and cause the shunt current to flow through the shunt resistance before going through the shunt field. This cuts down the value of the current flowing through the shunt field and thereby decreases the amount of current generated at the positive main brush.

It must be remembered that the amount of current induced in any generator is dependent upon the number of magnetic lines of force cut per second, and the number of magnetic lines of force in a field are mainly determined by the strength of the current flowing around that field. When the shunt field is reduced in strength, the corresponding reduction in the charging rate causes the regulator core to become demagnetized and the regulator points to close. The points open and close so fast that it is hardly visible, and this process causes the output of the generator to remain at a fairly constant value.

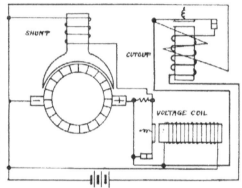

Fig. 2.   Regulator Coil in Parallel with Battery

The vibrating regulation resistance type is divided into two classes. The method of connecting the regulator coil determines their classification. A vibrating regulator whose regulator coil is connected in parallel with the battery is shown in Fig. 2. This method of regulation is known as the constant-potential type. In other words, this system is regulated by means of constant voltage. The regulator coil is wound with a large number of turns of fine wire and the amount of current flowing through this coil is determined by the voltage of the battery and the voltage of the generator. There will be more current flowing through this coil with a fully charged battery, as a battery in this condition offers more resistance.

This type of regulator has been used for some time by Bijur people. Its main advantage is that the output of the generator is controlled to a great extent by the condition of the charge of the battery. A heavy charging current will be produced when the battery charge is low, but as the battery becomes fully charged the output of the generator tapers off gradually. This is due to the less amount of current flowing through the regulator coil when the charge of the battery is low. The battery in this system can be removed from the car and the lights will operate quite satisfactorily as the regulator will insert sufficient resistance into the circuit to prevent the output from increasing beyond the amount of current that the lights use.

The method of regulating the output by means of constant current is shown in Fig. 3. If Figs. 2 and 3 are compared, it will be noted that they are similar except that the regulator coil in Fig. 3 is connected in series with the charging circuit, while in Fig. 2 it is connected in parallel with the charging circuit. The regulator coil of the current-regulation type consists of a few turns of heavy wire while the regulator coil of the voltage type consists of a number of turns of fine wire.

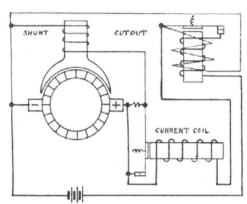

Fig. 3. Regulator Coil in Series with Battery

Referring again to Fig. 3, the current is collected at the positive brush of the generator. As the output increases, the magnetism of the regulator coil becomes of sufficient strength to overcome the spring tension on the regulator points causing them to open and insert a shunt resistance in the shunt circuit. The shunt current will then flow from the positive brush of the generator through the shunt resistance, through the shunt fields and back to the negative brush of the generator; but when the points are closed the current will flow through the points instead of through the shunt resistance. These points, like the ones in the constant voltage regulator, operate at a very rapid rate and on account of this rapidity cause the output of the generator to be held within certain limits. This form of regulation is typical of that used on the Remy and other systems for several years. Most Remy systems, however, at the present time are of the third-brush regulation.

In order to increase the output of the current type of regulator, it is necessary to increase the spring tension on the regulator points. This will prevent them from opening until a higher value of current is obtained from the generator. In order to regulate the output of the voltage regulator, no attention should be paid to the amperes generated as this will depend entirely upon the condition of the battery. The regulator spring must be adjusted so that the voltage will not exceed 8 volts in the case of a 6-volt system.

There is, however, a certain disadvantage in the vibrating type of regulation, and manufacturers have been constantly experimenting with forms of regulation so that a method of control much simpler in operation and less expensive to manufacture could be produced. The result of this experimenting is the third-brush method of regulation. Generators having this type of control have an extra brush called the third brush, located between the two main brushes. In case it is a four-pole four-brush machine the "third brush" would be the "fifth brush."

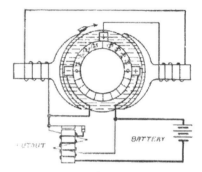

Fig. 4-a. Third-Brush Generator Running Slow

Referring to Fig. 4-a, the magnetic lines of force pass from the north field pole through the armature coils and into the south field pole. In this illustration the armature is revolving at a slow rate of speed. The magnetic lines of force pass in straight parallel lines. The figures on the commutator bars represent the voltage drop between each bar. The sum of these voltage drops when one-half of the commutator is considered will equal the voltage between the main brushes. In Fig. 4-a, the generator is producing 8 volts. Attention is called to the fact that these figures are not absolutely accurate figures but have merely been selected as relative values for the sake of illustrating the principle of third-brush regulation. The third brush in Fig. 4-a is a positive brush; in other words, the current collected at the third brush has a voltage equivalent to the figures between the third brush and the negative main brush which, in this case, is 4 volts. Let us assume that the shunt field has a resistance of 1 ohm. We will then have a current flow of 4 amperes through the shunt winding.

It is very evident that if water in a bucket is stirred with a stick, the water will have a tendency to follow the stick around, and as we increase the speed of stirring, the movement of the water will also be increased. This is also true of magnetic lines of force. As the speed of the armature increases, there is a greater tendency for the magnetic lines of force to be twisted out of shape and to follow the movement of the armature than to pass straight across from the north to the south pole. Fig. 4-b shows the field when the armature is turning at a high rate of speed. At this time the magnetic lines of force are not distributed evenly at all points of the field but have a tendency to pile up at points A and B. Bearing

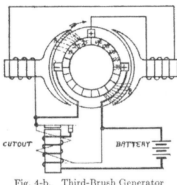

CUTOUT   BATTERY

Fig. 4-b.   Third-Brush Generator Running Fast

in mind that the greater the number of magnetic lines of force cut per second, the greater will be the output of the generator, it is at once noticed that the output of the armature in Fig. 4-b would be much less than that shown in Fig. 4-a. The third brush is now bearing on a segment which has the same relative position but the voltage drop between the commutator bars from the negative brush to the third brush is now only 1 volt because the number of magnetic lines of force being cut under the third brush are less. As the resistance of our shunt field is 1 ohm there will be a current of 1 ampere flowing through the shunt field instead of 4. This naturally decreases the field strength, and the number of lines of force traveling from the north to the south field is greatly reduced. As the armature is traveling at a higher rate of speed, it will still be cutting the same number of lines of force per second and the output of the generator will be practically the same as in Fig. 4-a. As these magnetic lines of force are twisted out of shape, the drop between the coils varies considerably.

Increasing the charging rate of a third-brush generator is very easily accomplished. Referring to Fig. 4-b, it will be noted that if the positive third brush is moved in the direction of rotation there will be a greater voltage between this brush and the negative main brush. As this voltage is increased, the strength of the shunt field will be increased and the output of the generator also increased. If the output is to be reduced, moving the third brush in the opposite

165

direction of rotation will reduce the current in the shunt field and the output accordingly.

A rather novel combination of regulation has recently been placed in the market by the Delco people, one of the typical installations being on the Pierce-Arrow cars. This regulation consists of a combination third-brush generator and a vibrating regulator.

The connections for this system as used on the Pierce-Arrow car are shown in Fig. 4-c. The regulator coil of this system is wound with sufficient resistance to prevent the regulator points from being opened when the battery is discharged. The points then remain closed constantly and the generator acts as a simple third-brush machine, the output being controlled only by the third brush. As the battery becomes charged and approaches a specific gravity of approximately 1250, the resistance of the battery increases and more current will then be forced through the voltage coil of the regulator.

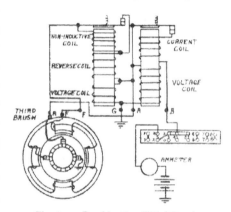

Fig. 4-c. Combination Third-Brush and Voltage Regulation

The regulator points then begin to vibrate, throwing the resistance in the shunt circuit and cutting down the output.

Referring to Fig. 4-c, the voltage coil consists mainly of an electromagnet having three windings and a set of contacts which are normally closed. The voltage coil consists of a large number of turns of fine copper wire connected directly across the main generator circuit, that is, in parallel. Another coil, a reversed winding, consists of a large number of turns of fine wire wound around the core in the opposite direction to the voltage winding. The last winding is a noninductive coil, having half the turns wound in each direction around the core. The reverse and noninductive windings are in parallel with the contacts and add resistance to the field circuit when the contacts are open. This prevents the generator output from becoming too great at high car speeds. The noninductive winding is also used to prevent arcing at the contact or regulator points.

There is another type of control which is used in conjunction with the third brush. It is automatic in its operation and uses a thermostatic arm. This installation is a part of the Remy lighting equipment. More current is needed in cold weather than in warm because the lights are burned longer and it is more difficult to start the engine. If the generator is set to give the greatest amount of current in the winter time, in warm weather the battery would be in a constant state of over-charge and would soon be ruined. The thermostatic arm* takes care of this automatically. It consists of a thermal member, or a blade of two different metals riveted together at their ends, Fig. 5. It is held fast at one end and at the other end it carries a contact point designed to complete the circuit by touching a stationary contact. One of these metals expands more than the other upon an increase in temperature and springs the blade away from the stationary contact. Fig. 5 shows the unit with

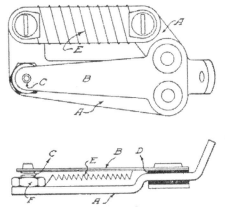

Fig. 5. Details of Remy Thermostatic Switch

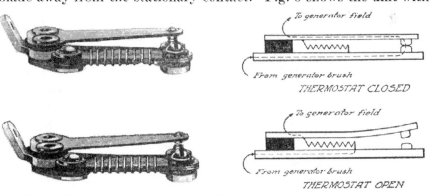

Fig. 6. Photographic Reproductions and Diagrams of Action of Thermostatic Switch When Closed and Opened

Courtesy of Remy Electric Company, Anderson, Indiana

the points together while Fig. 6 shows the blades apart. The generated current must flow through the resistance when the blades

---

* To gain a clear idea of the action of this device one must recall the heating effect of a current when passing through a resistance unit and the fact that some metals expand more than others when they are heated

are separated. This reduces the current supplied by the third brush
and the generator output is reduced. Brass and nickel steel are
used in the blade. The unit is placed close to the commutator, the
hottest part of the machine. The movable blade is warped upward

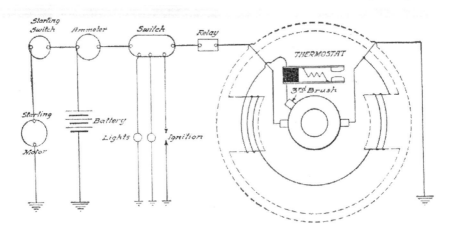

Fig. 7. Wiring Diagram of Switch Connections

when the temperature gets above 150° F., thus bringing about th
resistance. When the temperature falls below this point, the quicke
contraction of the brass pulls the blade down, cutting down th
resistance and increasing the output of the generator. Fig. 7 show
the position of the unit as installed in the system.

PROTECTIVE DEVICES

Various Forms. When fully charged, the storage battery hold
in chemical form the equivalent of two or more horsepower, i.e
40 to 160 amperes at 6, 12, or 24 volts, according to the syster
employed and the capacity of the battery furnished. To guar
against damage from short circuits, various forms of protectiv
devices are employed, and the different systems vary as much i
this respect as they do in others. In some instances, a circu
breaker is depended upon to take care of all the circuits. In other
protection is afforded by the employment of fuses.

Automatic Battery Cut=Out. It will be evident that, if th
storage battery were at all times in direct connection with th
generator, it would immediately discharge through the latter as soc
as the driving speed fell to a point where the dynamo was no long

producing sufficient voltage to charge the battery. If the generator were free to run instead of being positively connected to the engine, it would become "motorized" and operate as an electric motor on the battery current. As it is so connected, the battery current would simply burn out its windings, owing to the low resistance of the latter at low speeds. Consequently it is necessary to insert an automatic switch in the circuit in order to connect the battery with the generator when the speed of the latter reaches a certain point, and to disconnect it as soon as it falls below that value. Such switches are termed automatic cut-outs or "reverse-current relays."

Fig. 8. Ward-Leonard Current Controller and
Automatic Cut-out

In single-unit systems, such as the Dyneto, no battery cut-out is employed. A single hand-operated switch controls both the ignition and the generator battery circuits, so that this switch is left closed as long as the engine is running. Should the engine stall, the battery current automatically "motorizes" the generator and re-starts the engine. With such systems the engine must not idle slowly and the starting switch must not be left closed after the engine has stopped.

Ward=Leonard Type. The Ward-Leonard is typical in that it clearly illustrates the principles upon which most of these devices are based, though their construction varies widely, as will be noted by Fig. 8. The switch mechanism is shown at the left. In this device A is the coil, B the magnet core, C the movable arm, and D and D' the contacts. The generator with this equipment generates sufficient voltage at a car speed of about 7 miles per hour to attract C and hold it, closing the battery circuit through D and D'. The cut-out is not always incorporated with the current controller or voltage regulator. A separate unit is shown in Fig. 9 in the form of a reverse current relay. It will be found in practically all cases where cut-outs are used in the automobile generator circuits that the cut-out points are set too close at a car speed of about 7 miles per hour. If this point is remembered when adjusting this device, the adjustment will not be far wrong. A generator should never be operated when the cut-out is not working correctly because the windings might be burned out. Should the ammeter needle come

Fig. 9.   Remy Reverse-Current Relay

back to neutral or zero with the car running below 30 miles per hour under ordinary conditions, the car should be stopped and the cause ascertained. (The testing of this unit is taken up under "Electrical Repairs"). It should always be remembered that the cut-out is in the generator and battery circuit. The two windings of this device are the current coil and the voltage coil. The current flows through the voltage coil and energizes the magnet, pulling the points together, and the full current flows through the current coil and holds the points firmly together, putting the battery on charge.

Generator Troubles. The following are some troubles that are usually found in generators and their effect on the operation of the unit, causing low output or no current at all:

ELECTRICAL EQUIPMENT

(1) *Mechanical*

Broken bearings, loose pinions, loose pole pieces, commutator burst and bent shaft are all mechanical. They will cause a noise and, if the armature has been rubbing against the pole pieces, the laminations must be straightened before putting the unit into service again. It may mean a renewal of the armature.

(2) *Electrical*

(a) Open circuit caused by loose connections, brush stuck in the brush holder, brush worn so that it is not in good contact with the commutator, brush spring broken, and a dirty commutator.

(b) Open circuit in the armature and in the field coils.

(c) Grounds or short-circuits in either the armature or field windings, main terminal connections, main brush connections, and brush holders. Grounds or short-circuits in the armature will cause the windings on the shaft to heat and burn the insulation, causing a low-power output. The field coils and the commutator will heat under the same conditions.

(d) A third-brush setting that is incorrect will either give a high or a low output according to its position. With an output that is not constant at high speed, either the brush is not correctly fitted to the commutator or the spring pressure is not correct.

(e) If a generator heats, a close inspection should be made of the cut-out. If the points remain open, it will cause the windings to get very hot and burn the insulation with a consequent renewal of the armature. If the cut-out remains closed, it will cause the battery to discharge through the generator and the ammeter will show a discharge of 20 amperes when the engine is not running.

(f) If the ammeter shows a steady output at low-engine speed and the needle vibrates at higher speeds, an uneven commutator or high mica will be found to be the trouble. Loose connections in the circuit will also cause a needle to vibrate.

(g) General heating: battery connections should be free of corrosion because the added resistance will cause the units to heat.

The generator should never be operated when the battery has been removed because the windings in the generator will be burned out. Some units have a fuse in the generator windings which melts and prevents damage. (Grounds and short- and open-circuits can only be found by proper testing tools and will be taken up under

"Electrical Repair"). A periodical inspection of the generator should be made and the commutator kept clean and smooth. If a squeaking noise is heard in the generator, it either indicates that the commutator is rough or that the brushes need "sanding in." The unit should be taken off to fit the brush correctly but the commutator can be smoothed or polished by holding a piece of fine sandpaper against it while it is revolving. Emery cloth should not be used for this purpose because it is metallic and the substance will get between the bars and cause a short-circuit. The black substance between the bars is mica. Mica will stand above the bars in time for it is harder than copper and will not wear down as quickly. The mica

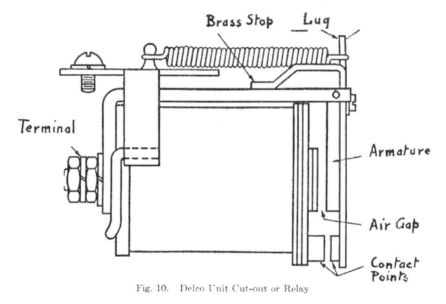

Fig. 10.   Delco Unit Cut-out or Relay

should be below the copper bars at all times. The mica must be cut down evenly and squarely so that there is no thin strip against the side of the bars and it is necessary to take the commutator out to do this. High mica will cause the brushes to jump and will cause sparking at the brushes as well as burning at the bars, which is indicated by the commutator bars being black and dirty. This condition also indicates short-circuit in the armature.

The bearings in a generator should not be lubricated too often because the oil will get onto the commutator and cause poor generation. If the generator is taken off for repairs, it is a good plan to pack the bearings with good vaseline before replacement.

ELECTRICAL EQUIPMENT

Relay Adjustments. When the relay gets out of adjustment the following method is used to adjust the cutting-in and the cutting-out points. Take the Delco unit, Fig. 10, as an example of the cut-out used on the average car. The first thing is to check the gap between the contact points, which should be about .025″. Make this adjustment by bending the brass stop with a pair of pliers. This increases or decreases the air-gap, a particular adjustment, because it governs the cut-in point. The contacts should meet squarely and be parallel to the armature. The points should be clean. A piece of fine sandpaper should be drawn between the points to clean and square them while they are lightly held together. To check the cut-out operation use a voltmeter that will indicate at least 10 to 15 volts. Connect one terminal of the voltmeter to the contact points and the other to the relay base or generator frame. If the voltmeter moves in the wrong direction, change the connections. Slowly speed the generator and notice when the contacts close, which should occur when the voltmeter shows about 8 volts. If the cut-in point voltage needs raising, increase the spring tension. Decreasing the spring tension lowers the cut-in voltage. The cut-out points should open when the discharge through the relay is about 3 amperes. The terminal is the point through which the generated current passes to the cut-out and on through the windings to the battery. This test can be used on any cut-out after the cut-out to generator terminal has been found. The ideal adjustment is to have the air-gap as small as the limits will allow so that there is no appreciable spring tension.

Relay Troubles. (1) An oily generator commutator will prevent the generator from building sufficient voltage to close the cut-out points even though the relay is in perfect condition. The commutator should be thoroughly cleaned and freed of all oil and dirt and may have to be trued up on a lathe to make it perfectly smooth and round. (2) Incorrect point settings. (3) Dirty or burnt points. (4) Battery points being loose or corroded will tend to heat up the windings and cause trouble in time.

Circuit Breaker. While the cut-out and circuit are very much alike they should not be confused. The circuit breaker is a protective device and designed to operate when a current in excess of what it is intended to carry passes through its windings. All current for lights, ignition, and horn pass through it. If there is a ground or other trouble in the circuit, the rush of current will start the circuit breaker vibrating and in this way indicate that there is something wrong in the system. The device takes about 25 amperes to start it vibrating but only about 5 amperes to keep it going. The circuit breaker takes the place of the fuse in the circuit but, of course, the fuse must be renewed when it blows out. If the trouble is not found at once, several fuses may be destroyed in trying to find it, but the circuit breaker will continue to vibrate until the trouble is found and corrected.

Circuit=Breaker Adjustments. It has been stated that the circuit breaker should not operate on less than 25 amperes. An ammeter should be used to test this and should be connected in series with the

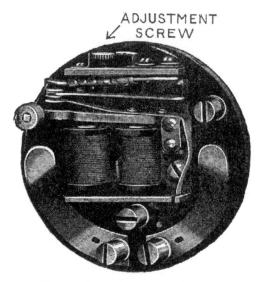

Fig. 11. Connecticut Automatic Switch

coil and then the points, which are lightly held together, should be allowed to open and a reading quickly taken. If the unit operates on less than 25 amperes, the spring tension should be increased.

Automatic Switches. There are protective units in the ignition circuit which use the principle of the expansion of metals also to operate the device. An example is shown in Fig. 11, which shows the Connecticut automatic switch. The object of this device is to open the switch if the engine should stop and the switch left on, preventing damage to both coils and breaker points. Although there is a great deal of current flowing through the points when the engine is running slowly, or idle, the device is not made to operate instantly upon the passing of an overload as is the circuit breaker. The unit consists of a thermostatic arm, regulated by an adjustment screw at the top, Fig. 11, and an electromagnetic vibrator the armature of which carries a hammer and the necessary connections. Current enters at the right- or left-hand screw at the bottom according to whether the switch is at the end of the sectors at the right or left of the figure and flows through the heater tape on the arm of the thermostat to the screw at the upper right in the figure. The heater is a resistance unit that becomes warm when current passes through it. With the continual flowing of the current it becomes so hot that it causes the arm to bend until it makes contact with the upper arm. This puts the windings of the magnet in circuit and sets the vibrator in motion, causing the hammer to strike the button and open the switch. There are several devices which operate in a similar manner. The switch will often open too quickly in these units when the engine is running slowly. This can be corrected by bending the arm so that there is a greater distance between the two arms. The heater tapes may burn out, making it necessary to renew the entire assembly.

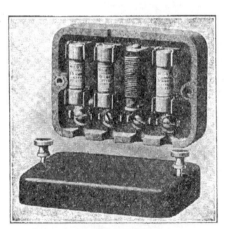

Fig. 12. Type of Fuse Employed on Lighting Circuits

Fuses. There is a protective device in the shape of a fuse which is made of a certain metal. This fuse melts very quickly when a current passes through it which is stronger than that which the fuse is made to carry. When there is trouble in the circuit, this small piece of wire melts and no current will flow through the circuit in which it is located until the fuse is renewed. The trouble should be found and corrected before replacing the fuse. These fuses are made to stand a certain amount of current and care should be taken to see that a fuse of the right amperage is used as a replacement. The fuse, Fig. 12, is made of wire inclosed inside a glass tube which has metal clips on the end. The strength of fuse is stamped on the end and is usually 10 amperes

DETROIT ELECTRIC AUTOMOBILE

STORAGE BATTERIES

PART I

STARTING AND LIGHTING

Importance of the Battery in Starting and Lighting. In the last analysis, every electric lighting and starting system on the automobile is necessarily a battery system. An electric starter is, first and last, a battery starter, since no system can be any more powerful than its source of energy. In other words, the storage battery is the business end of every electrical starting and lighting system. Just as the most elaborate and reliable ignition apparatus is of doubtful value with poor spark plugs, so the finest generators, motors, and auxiliaries become useless if the battery is not in proper working order. The battery is one of the most abused units on the automobile, especially with regard to attention paid in keeping it in good condition, and too much blame is laid to it when there is a failure in the electrical system. With average care and attention, the battery on a car should last a long time without repair.

Storage Battery Requires Careful Attention. A little experience in the maintenance of electric starting and lighting systems will demonstrate very forcibly that the relative importance of the storage battery is totally disproportionate to that of all the remaining elements of the system put together. The latter essentials have been perfected to a point where they will operate efficiently without attention for long periods. The battery, on the other hand, requires a certain amount of attention at regular and comparatively short intervals. Usually, this attention is not forthcoming, or it may be applied at irregular intervals and with but scant knowledge of the underlying reasons that make it necessary. Consequently, the battery suffers. It is abused more than any other single part of the entire system and, not being so constituted that it can withstand the effects of this abuse and still operate efficiently, it suffers correspondingly. Then the entire system is condemned.

ELECTRICAL EQUIPMENT

Other things being equal, the successful operation of any starting and lighting system centers almost wholly in the proper maintenance of the storage battery. Not all the defections that this part of the electrical equipment of the car suffers are caused by the battery, but unless properly cared for, it will be responsible for such a large proportion that the shortcomings of the rest of the system will be entirely forgotten. To make it even stronger, it may well be said that unless the storage battery is kept in good condition, the rest of the system will not have an opportunity to run long enough to suffer from wear. In a great many cases that come to the repair man's attention, the battery is ruined in the first six months' service, usually through neglect. For this reason, considerable attention is devoted to the battery and its care in this connection, despite the fact that it is very fully covered in the volume on Electric Vehicles. The conditions of operation, however, are totally unlike in the two cases. In one instance, the energy of the battery is called for only at a rate of discharge which is moderate by comparison with the ampere-hour capacity, while the battery itself is constantly under the care of a skilled attendant. In the other instance, the demand for current is not alone excessive but wholly disproportionate to the total capacity of the battery when it is used for starting, and intelligent care is usually conspicuous by its absence.

PRINCIPLES AND CONSTRUCTION

Function of Storage Battery. In the sense in which it is commonly understood, a battery does not actually store a charge of electricity. The process is entirely one of chemical action and reaction. A battery is divided into units termed *cells*. Each cell is complete in itself and is uniform with every other cell in the battery, and one of the chief objects of the care outlined subsequently is to maintain this uniformity. Each cell consists of certain elements which, when a current of electricity of a given value is sent through them in one direction for a certain length of time, will produce a current of electricity in the opposite direction if the terminals of the battery are connected to a motor, lamps, or other resistance. The cell will, of course, also produce a current if its terminals are simply brought together without any outside resistance. This, however, would represent a *dead short-circuit* and would permit the battery to discharge itself so rapidly as to ruin its elements. This is one of the things that must be carefully guarded against. When attending a battery, see that its terminals are not left exposed where tools may accidentally drop on them. When the current is being sent into the battery, as mentioned above, it is said to be charging; when it is connected to an outside resistance, it is discharging.

Parts of Cell. *Elements.* These are known as the positive and negative plates and correspond to the positive and negative electrodes of a primary battery. They consist of a foundation composed of a casting of metallic lead in the form of a grid, the outer edges and the connecting lug being of solid lead, while the remainder of the grid is like two sections of lattice work so placed that the openings do not correspond. Every manufacturer has different patterns of grids, but this description will apply equally well to all of them. Fig. 1 illustrates the grid of the Philadelphia battery. The object in giving them this form is to make the active material of the plates most accessible to the electrolyte, or solution, of

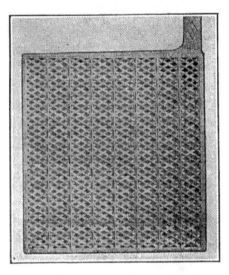

Fig. 1. Lead Grid Ready for Active Material
Courtesy of Philadelphia Storage Battery Company, Philadelphia, Pennsylvania

the battery, and at the same time to insure retaining this active material between the sides of the grid.

This active material consists of peroxide of lead (red lead) in the positive plate and litharge, or spongy metallic lead, in the negative plate. The plates are said to be pasted, to distinguish them from the old-style plates which were "formed" by a number of charges and discharges. The active material is forced into the interstices of the grid under heavy pressure, so that when completed the plate is as hard and smooth as a piece of planed oak plank. The positive plate may be distinguished by its reddish color, while the negative is a dark gray. Each positive plate faces a negative in the cell, and as the capacity of the cell is determined by the area of the positive plates, there is always one more negative plate than positive plates in a cell. The lead connectors of each of the plates is burned to its neighbor of the same kind, thus forming the positive and negative groups which constitute the elements of the cell.

Separators. As the elements must not be allowed to come in contact with each other in the cell because to do so would cause an internal short-circuit to which reference is made later, and as the maximum capacity must be obtained in the minimum space, the plates are placed very close together with wood and perforated hard rubber separators between them. These are designed to fit very snugly, so that the combined group of positive and negative plates is a very compact unit. When reassembling a cell, it is important that these separators be properly cared for in accordance with the directions given later.

Electrolyte. To complete the cell, the grouped elements with their separators are immersed in a jar holding the electrolyte. This is a solution consisting of water and sulphuric acid in certain proportions, both the acid and the water being chemically pure to a certain standard. This is the grade of acid sold by manufacturers as battery acid and in drug stores as C.P. (chemically pure), while the water should be either distilled, be cleanly caught rain water, or melted artificial ice. In this connection, the expression "chemically pure" acid is sometimes erroneously used simply to indicate acid of full strength, i.e., undiluted, or before adding water to make the electrolyte. It will be apparent that whether at its original strength or diluted with distilled water, it is still chemically pure. In mixing electrolyte, a glass, porcelain, or earthenware vessel must be used and *the acid must always be poured into the water.* Never attempt to pour the water into the acid, but always add the acid, a little at a time, to the water. The addition of the acid to the water does not make simply a mechanical mixture of the two but creates a solution in the formation of which a considerable amount of heat is liberated. Consequently, if the acid be poured into the water too fast, the containing vessel may be broken by the heat. For the same reason, if the water be poured into the acid, the chemical reaction will be very violent, and the acid itself will be spattered about. Sulphuric acid is highly corrosive; it will cause painful burns whenever it comes in contact (even in dilute solution) with the skin and will quickly destroy any fabric or metal on which it falls. It will also attack wood, for which reason nothing but glass, earthenware, or hard rubber containers should be employed.

Specific Gravity. The weight of a liquid as compared with distilled water is known as its specific gravity. Distilled water at 60° F. is 1, or unity. Liquids heavier than distilled water have a specific gravity greater than unity; lighter liquids, such as gasoline, have a specific gravity less than that of distilled water. Concentrated sulphuric acid (battery acid, as received from the manufacturer) is a heavy oily liquid having a specific gravity of about 1.835. A battery will not operate properly on acid of full strength, and it is therefore diluted with sufficient water to bring it down to 1.275. This, however, is the specific gravity of the electrolyte only when the battery is fully charged. The specific gravity of the electrolyte affords the most certain indication of the condition of the battery at any time, and its importance in this connection is outlined at considerable length under the head of Hydrometer Tests. The desired specific gravity can be easily secured by adding concentrated sulphuric acid to the water. Never add the water to the acid as it will cause undue heat.

Action of Cell on Charge. When the elements described are immersed in a jar of electrolyte of the proper specific gravity, and terminals are provided for connecting to the outside circuit, the cell is complete. As the lead-plate storage battery produces current at a potential of but two volts per cell, however, a single cell is rarely used. The lowest number of cells in practical use is the three-cell unit of the 6-volt battery used for starting and lighting on the automobile. The different cells of the battery are usually permanently connected together by heavy lead straps, while detachable terminals are provided for connecting the battery to an outside circuit. When the charging current is sent through the cell, the action is as follows: The original storage-battery cell of Planté consisted simply of two plates of lead; when the current was sent through such a cell on charge, peroxide of lead was deposited on the positive plate and spongy metallic lead on the negative. This was termed "forming" the plate. By modern methods of manufacture, this active material is formed into a paste with dilute sulphuric acid, and is pressed into the grids. On being charged, this acid is forced out of the plates into the electrolyte, thus raising the specific gravity of the electrolyte. When practically all of this acid has been transferred from the active material of the plates to the solution, or electrolyte, the cell is said to be fully charged and should then show a specific gravity reading of 1.275 to 1.300. The foregoing refers of course to the initial charge. After the cell has once been discharged, the active material of both groups of plates has been converted into lead sulphate. The action on charge then consists of driving the acid out of the plates and at the same time reconverting the lead sulphate into peroxide of lead in the positive plates and into spongy metallic lead in the negative plates.

Action of Cell on Discharge. The action of the cell on discharge consists of a reversal of the process just described. The acid which has been forced out of the plates into the electrolyte by the charging current again combines with the active material of the plates, when the cell is connected for discharge to produce a current. When the sulphuric acid in the electrolyte combines with the lead of the active material, a new compound, lead sulphate, is formed at both plates. This lead sulphate is formed in the same way that sulphuric acid, dropped on the copper-wire terminals, forms copper sulphate, or dropped on the iron work of the car, forms iron sulphate. In cases of this kind, it will always be noted that the amount of sulphate formed is all out of proportion to the quantity of metal eaten away. In the same manner, when the sulphuric acid of the electrolyte combines with the lead in the plates to form lead sulphate, the volume is such as to completely fill the pores of the active material when the cell is entirely discharged. This makes it difficult for the charging current to reach all parts of the active material and accounts for the manufacturers' instructions, never to discharge the battery below a certain point.

As the discharge progresses, the electrolyte becomes weaker by the amount of acid that is absorbed by the active material of the plates in the formation of lead sulphate, which is a compound of acid and lead. This lead sulphate continues to increase in bulk, filling the pores of the plates, and as these pores are stopped up by the sulphate, the free circulation of the acid is retarded. Since the acid cannot reach the active material of the plates fast enough to maintain the normal action, the battery becomes less active, which is indicated by a rapid falling off in the voltage. **Starting** at slightly over 2 volts per cell when fully charged, this voltage will be maintained at normal discharge rates with but a slight drop, until the lead sulphate begins to fill the plates. As this occurs, the voltage gradually drops to 1.8 volts per cell and from that point on will drop very rapidly. A voltage of 1.7 volts per cell indicates practically complete discharge, or that the plates of the cell are filled with lead sulphate and that the battery should be placed on charge immediately.

During the normal discharge, the amount of acid used from the electrolyte will cause the specific gravity of the solution to drop 100 to 150 points, so that if the hydrometer showed a reading of 1.280 when the cell was fully charged, it will indicate but 1.130 to 1.180 when it is exhausted, or completely discharged. The electrolyte is then very weak; in fact, it is little more than pure water. Practically all of the available acid has been combined with the active material of the plates. While the acid and the lead combine with each other in definite proportions in producing the current on discharge, it is naturally not possible to provide them in such quantities that both are wholly exhausted when the cell is fully discharged. Toward the end of the discharge, the electrolyte becomes so weak that it is no longer capable of producing current at a rate sufficient for any practical purpose. For this reason, an amount of acid in excess of that actually used in the plates during discharge is provided. This is likewise true of the active material.

Capacity of a Battery. The amount of current that a cell will produce on discharge is known as its capacity and is measured in ampere hours. It is impossible to discharge from the cell as much current as was needed to charge it, the efficiency of the average cell of modern type when in good condition being 80 to 85 per cent, or possibly a little higher when at its best, i.e., after five or six discharges. In other words, if 100 ampere hours are required to charge a battery, only 80 to 85 ampere hours can be discharged from it. This ampere-hour capacity of the cell depends upon the type of plate used, the area of the plate, and the number of plates in the cell, i.e., total positive-plate area opposed to total negative-plate area. To accomplish this, both outside plates in a cell are made negative. The ampere-hour capacity of a battery, all the cells of which are connected up as a single series, is the same as that of any single cell in the series; as in connecting up dry cells in series, the current output is always that of a single cell, while the voltage of the current increases $1\frac{1}{2}$ volts for each cell added to the series. In the case of the storage battery, it increases two volts for each cell.

The capacity of the cell as thus expressed in ampere hours is based on its normal discharge rate or on a lower rate. For example, take a 100-ampere-hour battery. Such a battery will produce current at the rate of 1 ampere for practically 100 hours, 2 amperes for 50 hours, or 5 amperes for 20 hours; but as the discharge rate is increased beyond a certain point, the capacity of the battery falls off. The battery in question would not produce 50 amperes of current for 2 hours. This is because of the fact that the heavy discharge produces lead sulphate so rapidly and in such large quantities that it quickly fills the pores of the active material and prevents further access of the acid to it. Thus, while it will not produce 50 amperes of current for 2 hours on continuous discharge, it will be capable of a discharge as great or greater than this by considerable, if allowed periods of rest between. When on open circuit, the storage battery recuperates very rapidly. It is for this reason that when trying to start the switch should never be kept closed for more than a few seconds at a time. Ten trials of 10 seconds each with a half-minute interval between them will exhaust the battery less than will spinning the motor steadily for a minute and forty seconds.

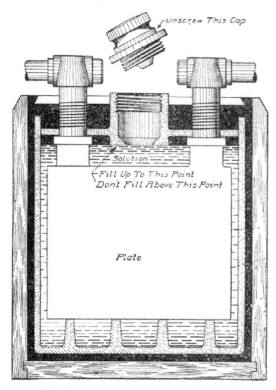

Fig. 2. Section of Willard Starting Battery, Showing Mud Space

ELECTRICAL EQUIPMENT

Construction Details. For automobile starting and lighting service, the elements of the cells are placed in insulating supports in the bottom of the hard rubber jars and sealed in place. These supports hold the plates off the bottom of the jar several inches in the later types of starting batteries. Figs. 2 and 3 show sections of the Willard starter battery and another standard type This is known as the mud space and is designed to receive the accumulation of sediment consisting of the active material which is shaken off the plates in service. This active material is naturally a good electrical conductor, and if it were allowed to come in contact with the bottoms of the groups of plates, it would short-circuit the cell. Sufficient space is usually allowed under the plates to accommodate practically all of the active material that can be shed by the plates during the active life of the cell. In a battery having cells of this type, it is never necessary to wash the cells, as the elements themselves would require renewal before the sediment could reach the bottom of the plates.

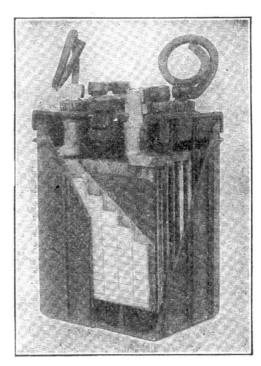

Fig. 3. Typical Starting Battery with Plates Cut Down, Showing Assembly

In sealing the elements into the jar, a small opening is left for the purpose of adding distilled water as well as to permit the escape of the gas when the battery is charging. Except when being used for refilling the jars, this opening is closed by a soft rubber stopper which has a small perforation through which the hydrogen passes out of the cell when the latter is gassing, as explained later. The different cells of a battery are electrically connected by heavy lead straps, these strips being usually burned onto the plates by the lead-burning process.

185

Edison Cell Not Available. It will be noted that the foregoing description has been confined entirely to the lead-plate type of storage battery and that no mention has been made of the Edison cell. The latter is not available for starting service on the automobile, because its internal resistance is too high to permit the extremely heavy discharge rate that is necessary. In extremely cold weather or where the engine is unusually stiff for other reasons, this may be as high as 300 amperes momentarily, while, under ordinary conditions, it will reach 150 to 200 amperes at the moment of closing the switch. The efficiency of the Edison cell also drops off very markedly in cold weather, though this is also true to a lesser extent of the lead-plate type.

CARE OF THE BATTERY

The following instructions are given about in the order in which it is necessary to apply them in the care of a storage battery.

Adding Distilled Water. In order to function properly, the plates in the cells must be covered by the electrolyte at

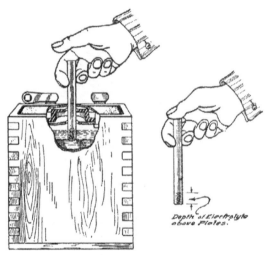

Fig. 4. Diagram Showing Method of Measuring Height of Electrolyte over Plates
Courtesy of U. S. Light and Heat Corporation, Niagara Falls, New York

all times to a depth of half an inch. Fig. 4 shows a handy method of determining this definitely. A small piece of glass tube, open at both ends, is inserted in the vent hole of the battery until it rests on the tops of the plates. A finger is then pressed tightly on top of the upper end of the tube, and the tube is withdrawn. It will bring with it at its lower end an amount of acid equivalent to the depth over the plates. This should always be returned to the same cell from which it was taken. The electrolyte consists of sulphuric acid and water. The acid does not evaporate, but the water does. The rapidity with which the water evaporates will depend upon the conditions of charging. For example, if a car is constantly driven on long day runs and gets very little night use, the storage battery is likely to be continually overcharged and may need the addition of water to the electrolyte as often as every three days, whereas, in ordinary service, once a week would be sufficient. Even with intermittent use, the battery should not be allowed to run more than two weeks without an inspection of the level of the electrolyte and the addition of distilled water, if necessary. Distilled water is always specified, since the presence of impurities in the water would be harmful to the battery, this being particularly the case where they take the form of iron salts. Where it is not convenient to procure distilled or rain water in sufficient quantities, samples of the local water supply may be submitted to any battery manufacturer for analysis.

While it is necessary to maintain the electrolyte one-half inch over the plates, care must be taken not to exceed this, for, if filled above this level, the battery will flood when charged, owing to the expansion with the increasing temperature. The best time for adding water is just before the car is to be taken out for several hours of use. It may be done most conveniently with a glass and rubber syringe of the type used with the hydrometer. Care should be taken when washing the car to see that no water is allowed to enter the battery box, as it is likely to short-circuit the cells across their lead connectors and to carry impurities into the cells themselves.

Adding Acid. When the level of the electrolyte in the cell becomes low, it is, under normal conditions, caused by the evaporation of the water, and this loss should be replaced with water only. *There being no loss of acid, it should never be necessary to add acid to the electrolyte during the entire life of the battery.* When a jar leaks or is accidentally upset, and some of the solution lost, the loss should be replaced with electrolyte of the same specific gravity as that remaining in the cell, and not with full strength acid nor with water alone. The former would make the solution too heavy, while the latter would make it too weak. Consequently, unless acid is actually known to have escaped from the cell, none should ever be added to it. Under the sections on the Hydrometer and Specific Gravity, further reasons are given why no acid or electrolyte should be added to the cell under normal conditions, and the causes which would seem to make the addition of acid necessary are explained.

Hydrometer. Next to the regular addition of distilled water to the cells, the garage man will be called upon most frequently to test the condition of the cells with the hydrometer. This is termed taking the specific gravity and is one of the most important tests in connection with the care of the battery. The specific gravity of a liquid is determined by means of an instrument consisting of a weighted glass tube having a scale marked on it. This instrument is the hydrometer, and in distilled water at 60 degrees it should sink until the scale comes to rest at the surface of the liquid at the division 1.000. The lighter the liquid, the further the instrument will sink in it; the heavier the liquid, the higher the instrument will float. For constant use in connection with the care of lighting and starting batteries, the hydrometer shown in Fig. 5 will be found the most convenient. Where the battery is located on the running board of the car, the test may be made without removing the syringe from the cell, but care must be taken to hold it vertical to prevent the hydrometer from sticking to the sides of the glass barrel. Wherever possible, the reading should be made without removing the syringe from the vent hole of the cell, so that the electrolyte thus withdrawn may always be *returned to the same cell.* Where the battery is located in a position difficult of access, as under the floor boards, the syringe may be drawn full of electrolyte and then lifted out; as the soft rubber plug in the bottom of the glass barrel is in the form of a trap, when the instrument is held vertical, the solution will not run out while the reading is being taken.

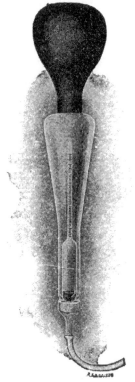

Fig. 5. Syringe Hydrometer Set

Failure to replace the electrolyte in the same cell from which it was taken will result in destroying the uniformity of the cells. For example, if electrolyte has been withdrawn from cell No. 1 of the battery and, after taking the reading, it is put into cell No. 2, the amount taken from No. 1 must later be made up by adding water, and the solution will be that much weaker, while the **electrolyte of No. 2 will be correspondingly stronger.**

ELECTRICAL EQUIPMENT

Hydrometer Tests. In taking a hydrometer reading, first see that the instrument is not held by the sides of the glass syringe barrel; then note the level of the instrument in the liquid by looking at it from below, i.e., hold it up above the level of the eye. Reading the hydrometer in this way is found to give more accurate results than looking down upon it. While the hydrometer affords the best single indication of the condition of the battery—the cells should test 1.250 to 1.300 when fully charged and 1.150 when fully discharged, below which point they should never be allowed to go—there are conditions under which the instrument may be entirely misleading. For example, when fresh distilled water is added to a cell to bring the solution up to the proper level, the additional water does not actually combine with the electrolyte until the cell has been on charge for some time. Consequently, if a hydrometer reading were taken of that particular cell just after the water had been added, the test would be misleading, as it would apparently show the cell to be nearer the fully discharged state than it actually was, owing to the low specific gravity of the electrolyte. If, on the other hand, fresh electrolyte or pure acid has been added to a cell just prior to taking readings, and without the knowledge, of the tester the reading would apparently show the battery to be fully charged, whereas the reverse might be the case. In this instance, the specific gravity would be higher than it should be. To determine accurately the condition of the cells in such circumstances, the hydrometer readings would have to be checked by making tests with the voltmeter, as described later.

Under average conditions, however, the hydrometer alone will closely indicate the state of charge, and its use should always be resorted to whenever there is any question as to the condition of a battery. For instance, an irate owner will sometimes condemn the battery for failure of the starting motor to operate and will be absolutely positive that the battery has been fully charged, since he has been driving in daylight for hours. The hydrometer reading will show at once whether the battery is charged or not. If it is not, it will indicate either that the generator, its regulator, or the battery cut-out are not working properly, or that there is a short-circuit or a ground somewhere in the lighting or ignition circuits which permits the battery to discharge itself. Another more or less common complaint, the cause of which may be definitely assigned one way or the other by the aid of the hydrometer is that "the battery is not holding its charge". Except where it is allowed to stand for long periods without use, as where a car is laid up for a month or more, there is no substantial decrease in the capacity simply through standing, unless the battery is allowed to stand in a discharged condition.

Consequently, the owner's impression that the charge of the battery is mysteriously leaking away overnight through some shortcoming of the cells themselves is not correct. If there is a fault, it is probably in the wiring; or a switch may have been left on inadvertently; or, as is very often the case, the car is not driven long enough in daylight to permit the generator to charge the battery sufficiently. When driving at night with all lights on, as is commonly the custom, the generator supplies very little current in excess of that required by the lamps. As a result, the battery receives but a fraction of its normal charge, so that one or two attempts to use the starting motor exhaust it. A hydrometer test made just before using the starting motor will show that there is only a small fraction of a charge in the cells, so that they are not capable of supplying sufficient current to turn the engine over longer than a few seconds. The hydrometer is equally valuable in indicating when a battery is being overcharged, though this is a condition which carries its own indication, known as gassing, which is described in detail under that head.

Variations in Readings. Specific-gravity readings between 1.275 and 1.300 indicate that the battery is fully charged; between 1.200 and 1.225, that the battery is more than half discharged; between 1.150 and 1.200, that the battery is quickly nearing a fully discharged condition and must be recharged very shortly, otherwise injury will result. Below 1.150 the battery is entirely exhausted and must be recharged immediately to prevent the plates from becoming sulphated, as explained in the section covering that condition.

Where the specific gravity in any cell tests more than 25 points lower than the average of the other cells in the battery, it is an indication that this cell is out of order. Dependence should not be placed, however, on a single reading where there is any question as to the specific gravity. Take several readings and average them. Variations in cell readings may be caused by internal short-circuits in the cell; by putting too much water in the cell and causing a loss of electrolyte through flooding or overflowing; or by loss of electrolyte from a cracked or leaky jar. Internal short-circuits may result from a broken separator or from an accumulation of sediment in the mud space of the jars reaching the bottom of the plates.

Quite a substantial percentage of all the troubles experienced with starting batteries, which are only too often neglected until they give out, is caused by letting the electrolyte get too low in the jars. The effect of this is to weaken the battery, causing it to discharge more readily, and frequently resulting in harmful sulphating of the plates and injury to the separators. When such sulphating occurs, it permits the plates to come into contact with each other, and an internal short-circuit results. The importance of always maintaining the electrolyte one-half inch above the tops of the plates will be apparent from this.

One of the most frequent causes of low electrolyte in a single cell is the presence of a cracked or leaky jar. If one of the cells requires more frequent addition of water than the others to maintain the level of its electrolyte, it is an indication that it is leaking. Where all the cells of a battery require the addition of water at unusually short intervals, it is an indication that the battery is being constantly overcharged. (See Gassing.) Unless a leaky jar is replaced immediately, the cell itself will be ruined, and it may cause serious damage to the remainder of the battery. Jars are often broken owing to the hold-down bolts or straps becoming loose, thus allowing the battery to jolt around on the running board, or they may be broken by freezing. The presence of a frozen cell in a battery shows that it has been allowed to stand in an undercharged condition in cold weather, as a fully charged cell will not freeze except at unusually low temperatures.

Frozen Cells. In some cases, the cells may freeze without cracking the jars. This will be indicated by a great falling off in the efficiency of the cells that have suffered this injury, or in a totally discharged condition which cannot be remedied by continuous charging. In other words, the battery is dead and the plates are worthless except as scrap lead. In all cases where cells have been frozen, whether the jar has cracked or not, the plates must be replaced at once. It must always be borne in mind that low temperatures seriously affect the efficiency of the storage battery and that care should be taken to keep it constantly in a charged condition. A variation in the temperature also affects the hydrometer readings themselves. The effect of the temperature on the hydrometer tests is explained under Adjusting the Specific Gravity.

Low Cells. When one cell of the battery tests more than 25 points below the specific gravity of the others, as shown by the average of several readings taken of each, it should be placed on charge separately from an outside source of current. This may be done without removing it from the car or disconnecting it from the other cells, since the charging leads may be clipped to its terminal posts. If no other facilities are available and direct-current service is at hand, use carbon lamps as a resistance in the manner illustrated on another page. As the normal charging rate of the average starting battery is 10 to 15 amperes or more, that many 32-c.p. carbon filament lamps may be used in the circuit. Where only alternating current is available, a small rectifier, as described under Charging from Outside Sources, will be found most convenient in garages not having enough of this work to warrant the installation of a motor-generator. After the low cell has been on charge for an hour or two, note whether or not its specific gravity is rising, by taking a hydrometer reading. If, after several hours of charging, its specific gravity has not risen to that of the other cells, it is an indication that there is something wrong with the cell, and it should be cut out. (See Replacing a Jar and Overhauling the Battery.)

Adjusting the Specific Gravity. Except in such cases as those mentioned under Hydrometer, where water has been added to the electrolyte just before testing, or electrolyte has been added without the knowledge of the tester, specific gravity of the electrolyte is the best indication of the condition of the cell, and the treatment to be given should always be governed by it. As explained in the section on Action on Charge and Discharge, the acid of the electrolyte combines with the active material of the plates to produce the current on discharge. The further the cell is discharged the more acid there will be in the plates, and the less in the solution. Consequently, low-gravity readings practically always mean lack of acid in the solution, and that implies lack of charge. Unless there is something wrong with the cell, charging will restore the acid to the electrolyte and bring the specific-gravity readings up to normal. In case a jar is leaking or has been overturned and lost some of its electrolyte, no amount of charging will bring its specific gravity up to the proper point.

The gravity readings of the cells vary somewhat in summer and winter, and they also decrease with the age of the plates, but the battery will continue to give good service as long as its specific gravity rises to between 1.250 and 1.300 when fully charged. In case it rises above 1.300, there is an indication that excess acid has been added to the electrolyte, and this must be corrected by drawing off some of the electrolyte with the syringe and replacing it with distilled water. A gradually decreasing specific gravity in all the cells of a battery is an indication that sediment is accumulating in the bottom of the jars and that the battery, if of the old type with low mud space, requires washing; if of the later type with high mud space, that its elements require renewal. Before accepting this conclusion, however, make certain that the low reading is not due to insufficient charging. In actual practice, starter batteries seldom remain long enough in service without overhauling ever to need washing.

Many starter batteries are kept in an undercharged condition so constantly, owing to frequent use of the starting motor with but short periods of driving in between, that they should be put on charge from an outside source at regular intervals. In fact, this is the only method of determining definitely whether the battery itself is really at fault or whether it is the unfavorable conditions under which it is operating. Where the cells give a low reading, no attempt should ever be made to raise the specific gravity of the electrolyte by adding acid, until the battery has been subjected to a long slow charge. The maximum specific gravity of the electrolyte is reached when all the acid combined in the active material of the plates has been driven out by the charging current. Adding acid will increase the specific gravity, but it will not increase the condition of charge; it will simply give a false indication of a charged condition. For example, if the electrolyte of a cell tested 1.225, and, without giving it a long charge, acid were added to bring the specific gravity up to 1.275, it would then rise to 1.325 if put on charge, showing that 50 points of acid had remained combined in the plates when the low readings were taken.

The necessity for adjusting the specific gravity of the electrolyte in a cell can only be determined by first bringing it to its true maximum. To do this with a starter battery, it must be put on charge from an outside source at a low rate, say 5 amperes, and kept on charge continuously until tests show that the specific gravity of the electrolyte has ceased to rise. This may take more than twenty-four hours, and readings should be taken every hour or so, toward the end of the charge. Should the battery begin to gas violently while tests show that the specific gravity is still rising, the charging current should be reduced to stop the gassing, or, if necessary, stopped altogether for a short time and then renewed.

If after this prolonged charge, the specific gravity is not more than 25 points below normal, some of the solution may be drawn off with the syringe and replaced with small quantities of 1.300 electrolyte, which should be added very gradually to prevent bringing about an excess. Should the specific gravity be too high at the end of the charge, draw off some of the electrolyte and replace it with distilled water to the usual level of one-half inch over the plates. A charge of this kind is usually referred to as a conditioning charge and, given once a month, will be found very greatly to improve starter batteries that are constantly undercharged in service.

Temperature Corrections. All specific-gravity readings mentioned are based upon a temperature of 70° F. of the electrolyte, and as the electrolyte, like most other substances, expands with the heat and contracts with the cold, its specific gravity is affected by variations of temperature. This, of course, does not affect its strength, but as its strength is judged by its specific gravity, the effect of the temperature must be taken into consideration when making the tests. The temperature in this connection is not that of the surrounding air but that of the electrolyte itself, and as the plates and solution of a battery increase in temperature under charge, the electrolyte may be 70° F. or higher, even though the outside air is close to zero. Consequently, the only method of checking this factor accurately is to insert a battery thermometer in the vent hole of the cell. If, on the other hand, the battery has been standing idle for some time in a cold place, the electrolyte has the same temperature as the surrounding air, and a hydrometer reading taken without a temperature correction would be very misleading.

For example, assume that the car is standing in a barn in which the temperature is 20° F. and that it has not been running for some time so that the electrolyte is as cold as the surrounding air. A hydrometer reading shows the specific gravity of the electrolyte to be 1.265, which would indicate that the battery was approximately fully charged. But the correction for temperature amounts to one point (.001) for each three degrees above or below 70° F., and in this case a difference of 50 degrees would have to be allowed for. This amounts to practically 18 points, and the specific gravity of the cells is 1.265 minus 18, or 1.247. The battery is accordingly three-quarters charged, instead of fully charged as the uncorrected reading would appear to indicate. The electrolyte contracts with the drop in temperature, and its specific gravity becomes correspondingly higher without any actual increase in its strength. The opposite condition will be found when the battery has commenced to gas so violently that the temperature of the electrolyte is raised to 100° to 105° F. At the former figure there would be a difference of 30 degrees, or 10 points, to allow for, in which case a specific gravity reading of 1.265 would actually be 1.275. Hydrometer scales, with a a temperature scale showing at a glance the corresponding correction necessary, simplify the task of correcting the readings; but to do this properly a battery thermometer must be employed, as the temperature of the electrolyte itself is the only factor to be considered.

Gassing. When an electric current is sent through a storage-battery cell, it immediately attacks the lead sulphate into which the active material of both the positive and the negative plates has been converted during the discharge and begins to reconvert it into peroxide of lead at the positive plate and into spongy metallic lead at the negative. As long as there is an ample supply of this lead sulphate on which the current may work, as in a fully discharged battery, the entire amperage being sent through the battery is restricted to carrying on this process. In other words, the current will always do the easiest thing first by following the path of least resistance. When the cell is in a discharged state, the easiest thing to do is to decompose the lead sulphate. As there is a comparatively large amount of this lead sulphate in a fully discharged battery, a correspondingly large amount of current can be used in charging at the start. But as the amount of sulphate progressively decreases with the charge, a point is reached at which there is no longer sufficient sulphate remaining to utilize all the current that is passing through the cell.

The excess current will then begin to do the next easiest thing, which is to decompose the water of the electrolyte and liberate hydrogen gas. This gassing is not owing to any defect in the battery, as some owners seem to think, but is simply the result of over-charging it. In one instance, a car owner condemned the starting battery with which his machine was equipped, for the reason that it was "always boiling". In fact, it "boiled" itself to pieces and had to be replaced by the manufacturer of the car after only a few months of service; while, as a matter of fact, the conditions under which the car was driven were wholly responsible. It was used for long runs in the day time with infrequent stops, and was rarely run at night; therefore, the battery was continually charging but seldom had an opportunity to discharge.

This erroneous impression is also closely interlinked with another that is equally common and equally harmful. This is that one of the functions of the battery cut-out is to break the circuit and prevent the battery from becoming overcharged. It is hardly necessary to add that this is not one of its functions, but that as long as the generator is being driven above a certain speed, the cut-out will keep the battery in circuit, and the generator will continue to charge it. Its only purpose is to prevent the battery from discharging itself through the generator when the speed of the generator falls to a point where its voltage would be overcome by that of the battery unless the battery were automatically disconnected. The cut-out does not protect the battery from being overcharged; only the driver or the garage man can do that by noting the conditions under which the car is operated and taking precautions to prevent the battery from overcharging.

Gassing is simply an indication that too much current is being sent into the battery. Another indication of the same condition is the necessity for refilling the cells with distilled water at very short intervals, as an excess charge raises the temperature of the electrolyte and causes rapid losses by evaporation. That is the reason why it is likely to be so harmful to the battery unless remedied, as if allowed to exceed 110° F., the active material is likely to be forced out of the grids, and the cells to be ruined. While it is essential that the battery be fully charged at intervals and that it be always kept well charged, continuously overcharging it is likely to be as harmful as allowing it to stand undercharged. Where the conditions of service cannot be altered to remedy the trouble, the regulator of the generator should be adjusted to lower the charging rate, or, if nothing else will suffice, additional resistance, controlled by an independent switch, may be inserted in the charging circuit.

Care of Battery in Winter. There is a more or less general impression that special treatment must be given the storage battery

Group Showing Effect of Lack of Filling   Overheated Group Caused by Sulphation

during cold weather. This is probably owing to the fact that lack of attention makes itself apparent much more readily in winter than in summer because of the lower efficiency of the battery re-

Plates from Frozen Battery

sulting from the lower temperature. The care necessary in winter does not vary in any respect from that which should be given in warm weather, except possibly that replacement of the water due to evaporation is not called for so often, but unless it is conscientiously carried out, the battery is apt to suffer to a greater extent.

ELECTRICAL EQUIPMENT

In speaking of low temperatures, it must be borne in mind that this always refers to the temperature of the electrolyte of the battery, and not to that of the surrounding atmosphere. The latter may be considerably below freezing, whereas the liquid in the cells may be approaching 100° F. when the battery is under charge.

Make the usual hydrometer and voltage tests, as described under the headings in question, and see that the battery is constantly kept more fully charged than would be necessary to render satisfactory service in warmer weather. This is important for two reasons: first, because of the greatly increased drain on the battery owing to the difficulty of starting the engine when cold; and second, because of the liability of the electrolyte to freeze if the battery is allowed to stand discharged in very cold weather. There is not the same excess supply of current available for charging the battery in winter as there is in summer, as the lights are in use during a much greater part of the time and not so much driving is likely to be done during the day. As the lamp load consumes almost the entire output of the generator in the average starting and lighting system, there is very little left for the battery when all the lamps are in use. The practice of turning on all the lights on the car—headlights, side lights, spot light, and instrument lights—whether they are necessary or not, should be discouraged in winter, as it is likely to result in exhausting the battery. The instrument lights are usually in series with the tail light, and so cannot be dispensed with, but it is never necessary to have the headlights and side lights going at the same time, and this also applies to the spot light, which consumes almost as much current as one of the headlights and should be restricted to the use for which it is intended, i.e., reading signs by the roadside.

Unless the lamp load is reduced, it may be necessary to increase the charging rate of the generator during the cold months, and this is not beneficial to the battery, as it may cause severe gassing and injury to the plates when continued too long. In case the car is not driven enough to keep the battery properly charged, it may be necessary to charge it from an outside source or, if the latter be not available, to run the engine with the car idle just for this purpose. Care must be taken to prevent any danger of freezing, and the best method of doing this is to keep the battery fully charged, as when in this condition it will freeze only at very low temperatures. The more nearly discharged a battery is, the higher the temperature at which it will freeze, and freezing will ruin the cells, regardless of whether it happens to crack the jars or not.

Higher Charge Needed in Cold Weather. While the regulator of the generator is set by the manufacturer to give the best average results, and some makers warn the user against altering its adjustment, experience has demonstrated that a fixed adjustment of the regulation will not suffice for cars driven under all sorts of service conditions, nor for the same car as used at different seasons of the year. The efficiency of the storage battery is at its lowest in cold weather, which is the time when the demand upon it is greatest. A battery that would be constantly overcharged during the summer may not get more than sufficient current to keep it properly charged in winter, though driven under similar conditions in both seasons.

Undercharged Plate

On the other hand, a battery that is generally undercharged under summer conditions of driving will be practically useless in winter, as it will not have sufficient current to meet the demands upon it.

It may be put down as a simple and definite rule that if the battery of a starting system never reaches the gassing stage, it is constantly undercharged and is rapidly losing its efficiency, as the sulphate remaining on the plates becomes harder with age and prevents the circulation of the electrolyte. Even when in the best condition, the electrolyte cannot reach all of the active material in the plates, so that any reduction means a serious falling off. Likewise, when a battery is constantly gassing, it is in a continuous state of overcharge and is apt to be entirely ruined in a comparatively short time. The danger from undercharging is known as sulphating—the plates become covered with a hard coating of lead sulphate that the electrolyte cannot penetrate—while that from overcharging is due to the electrolyte and the plates reaching a dangerous temperature (105° F. or over) at which the active material is apt to be stripped from the grids. The conditions of service are such that a battery can seldom be kept in good condition for any length of time on the charging current from the generator alone.

The hydrometer should be used frequently to keep track of the condition of the battery. At least once a month the battery should be given a long conditioning, or equalizing, charge. This charge is required because under ordinary conditions a battery seldom receives a complete charge and every time it is discharged without being followed by a charge, which is prolonged until the electrolyte has reached its maximum specific gravity, more lead sulphate accumulates in the plates. The object of the long charge is to convert this lead sulphate into peroxide of lead at the positive plate and into spongy metallic lead at the negative plate.

Syringe Hydrometer in Use
Courtesy of Willard Storage Battery Company

Why Starting Is Harder in Cold Weather. The electric starting and lighting system, or rather the storage battery, which is its mainstay, is much more severely taxed in winter than in summer for the following five reasons:

(1) The efficiency of the storage battery decreases with a decrease in temperature, because the action of the storage battery is chemical, and chemical action is dependent upon heat, and, therefore, always decreases as the temperature decreases.

(2)   The lower the temperature the stiffer the lubricating oil, which gums the moving parts together, adding a very considerable load to the ordinary amount of inertia which the starting motor must overcome and likewise adding to the difficulty of turning the engine past compression. This condition can be helped a great deal if the clutch pedal is pushed down because it eliminates the heavy drag of the transmission grease.

(3)   Gasoline will not vaporize readily at a low temperature, so that it is necessary to turn the engine over a great many revolutions before the cylinders become sufficiently warmed from the friction and the repeated compression to create an explosive mixture. The better the mixture the more readily it will fire, and consequently a greater heat value is required in the spark to ignite it where the mixture is poor or only partly vaporized. Anything that reduces the efficiency of the storage battery likewise reduces the heat value of the ignition spark.

(4)   In the winter the lights are burning for a much longer period and therefore the battery has a greater amount of work to do, although the running periods are shorter. Consequently the amount of current taken out of the battery is more than the amount put into the battery, and there is less current in the battery for starting purposes.

(5)   Low heat value of the spark often makes it difficult to start an engine when cold. This lack of heat in the spark is caused by a partially discharged battery as well as the lower efficiency of the battery caused by the cold weather; also by the necessity for repeated operation of the starting motor, whereby the voltage of the battery is temporarily cut down.

Intermittent use of the starting motor with a brief period between attempts will frequently result in starting a cold engine where continued operation of the starting motor will only result in exhausting the battery to no purpose. The longer the starting motor is operated continuously the lower the voltage of the battery becomes, with a corresponding drop in the heat value of the ignition spark. Cranking intermittently a number of times has practically as great an effect in warming the cylinders and generating an explosive mixture as running for the same period (actual operating time in each case), while the brief periods of rest permit the battery to restore its normal voltage, which increases the heat value of the spark and causes the engine to fire.

Both the storage battery and the remaining essentials of the starting and lighting system are designed to give satisfactory service in cold weather, but as a very low temperature brings about conditions representing the maximum for which the system is designed, more skillful handling is necessary in winter than in summer to obtain equally good results.

Sulphating. At the end of a discharge, both sets of plates are covered with lead sulphate. This conversion of the active material of the plates into lead sulphate, which takes place during the discharge, is a normal reaction and, as such, occasions no damage. But if the cells are allowed to stand for any length of time in a discharged condition, the sulphate not only continues to increase in bulk, but becomes hard. It is also likely to turn white. In this condition, the plates have lost their porosity to a certain extent and it is correspondingly more difficult for the charging current to penetrate the active material. When a battery has stood in a discharged condition, it becomes sulphated. The less current it has in it at the time and the longer it stands, the more likely it is to be seriously damaged.

Where a car is used but little in the daytime, and then only for short runs with more or less frequent stops, the battery never has an opportunity to become fully charged. The demands of the starting motor and the lights are such that the battery is never more than half charged at any time. Consequently, there is always a certain proportion of the lead sulphate that is not reconverted, but which remains constantly in the plates. As already mentioned, this condition does not remain stationary; the sulphate increases in amount and the older portions of it hardens. The sulphate forms a cover over the paste that has not been acted upon by the electrolyte. It becomes practically useless because the acid is unable to enter the plate due to this covering. Active material encased in the sulphation is inactive and the battery capacity is cut down. The formation of the sulphate on each plate and the acid absorbed from the solution causes the voltage of the cell to drop at a constantly increasing rate. This represents a loss of capacity which finally reaches a point where the cells are no longer capable of supplying sufficient current (holding enough of the charge, as the owner usually puts it) to operate the starting motor. A battery that has been operating under conditions of this kind is not prepared for the winter's service, which accounts for the great number of complaints about the poor service rendered by starting systems in the early part of every winter. As long as the weather is warm, the battery continues to supply sufficient current in spite of the abuse to which it is subjected, but when cold weather further reduces its efficiency, it is no longer able to meet the demand.

The only method of preventing this and of remedying it after it has occurred is the equalizing charge mentioned in the previous section. Long continued and persistent charging at a low rate will cure practically any condition of sulphate, the time necessary being proportionate to the degree to which it has been allowed to extend. It is entirely a question of time, and, as a high rate would only produce gassing, which would be a disadvantage, the rate of charge must be low. In case the cells show any signs of gassing, the charge must be further reduced.

Extra Time Necessary for Charging. The additional length of time necessary for charging a battery that has been constantly kept in an undercharged condition is strikingly illustrated by the following test made with an electric vehicle battery: The cells were charged to the maximum, and the specific gravity regulated to exactly 1.275 with the electrolyte just $\frac{1}{2}$ inch above the tops of the plates, this height being carefully marked. The battery was then discharged and recharged to 1.265 at the normal rate in each case. The specific gravity rose from 1.265 to 1.275 during the last hour and a half of the charge. During the following twelve weeks, the battery was charged and discharged daily, each charge being only to 1.265, thus leaving 10 points of acid still in the plates. At the end of the twelve weeks, the charge was continued to determine the time required to regain the 10 points and thus restore the specific gravity to the original 1.275. Eleven hours were needed, as compared with the hour and half needed at first. This test further illustrates why it is necessary to give a battery an occasional overcharge or equalizing charge to prevent it becoming sulphated. Had the battery in question been charged daily to its maximum of 1.275 and discharged to the same extent during the twelve weeks, $9\frac{1}{2}$ hours of the last charge would have been saved. These periods of time, of course, refer to the charging of the electric-vehicle battery, but they indicate in a corresponding manner the loss of efficiency suffered by the starting battery owing to its being continually kept in an undercharged condition.

Restoring Sulphated Battery. There are only three ways in which a battery may become sulphated: The first and most common of these is that it has not been properly charged; second, excess acid has been added to the electrolyte; third, an individual cell may become sulphated through an internal short-circuit or by drying out, as might be caused by failure to replace evaporation with water, or failure to replace promptly a cracked jar. The foregoing only holds good, however, where the sediment has not been allowed to reach the bottom of the plates, and where the level of the electrolyte has been properly maintained by replacing evaporation with distilled water.

To determine whether a battery is sulphated or not—it having been previously ascertained that it does not need cleaning (washing)— it should be removed from the car (the generator should not be run with the battery off the car without complying with the manufacturer's instructions in each case, usually to short-circuit or bridge certain terminals on the generator itself) and given an equalizing charge at its normal rate. The normal rate will usually be found on the name plate of the battery. If the battery begins to gas at this rate, the rate must be reduced to prevent gassing, and lowered further each time the cells gas. Frequent hydrometer readings should be taken, and the charge should be continued as long as the specific gravity continues to increase. A battery is sulphated only when there is acid retained in the plates. When the specific gravity reaches its maximum, it indicates that there is no more sulphate to be acted upon, since, during the charge, the electrolyte receives acid from no other source. With a badly sulphated battery, the charge should be continued until there has been no further rise in the specific gravity of any of the cells for a period of at least twelve hours. Maintain the level of the electrolyte at a constant height by adding pure water after each test with the hydrometer (if water were added just before taking readings, the water would rise to the top of the solution and the reading would be valueless). With a battery on a long charge, the battery thermometer should be used at intervals to check the temperature of the electrolyte, and the hydrometer readings should be corrected in accordance with the temperature.

Specific Gravity too High. Should the specific gravity of any of the cells rise above 1.300, draw off the electrolyte down to the top of the plates and put in as much distilled water as possible without flooding the cell. Continue the charge and, if the specific gravity again exceeds 1.300, this indicates that acid has been added during the previous operation of the battery. The electrolyte should then be emptied out and replaced with distilled water and the charge continued. The battery can only be considered as restored to efficient working condition when there has been no rise in the specific gravity of any of the cells during a period of at least twelve hours of continuous charging.

Upon completion of the treatment, the specific gravity of the electrolyte should be adjusted to its proper value of 1.280, using distilled water or 1.300 acid, as necessary. In cases where one cell has become sulphated while the balance of the battery is in good condition, it is usually an indication that there is a short-circuit or other internal trouble in the cell, though this does not necessarily follow. To determine whether or not it is necessary to dismantle the cell, it may first be subjected to a prolonged charge, as above described. If its specific gravity rises to the usual maximum, the condition may be considered as remedied without taking the cell apart. It is the negative plate which requires the prolonged charge necessary to restore a sulphated battery. When sulphated, the active material is generally of light color and either hard and dense or granular and gritty, being easily disintegrated. Unless actually buckled or stripped of considerable of their active material, the positive plates are unchanged in appearance and can be restored to operative condition, though their life will be shortened by this abuse. Sulphated plates of either type should be handled as little as possible. By keeping close check with the hydrometer on the condition of the starting battery and, where it is not being kept in an overcharged condition constantly, giving it an equalizing charge once a month, the charge being continued until the cells no longer increase in specific gravity after a period of several hours, and the reading of all the cells being within at least 25 points of each other, sulphating may be avoided entirely.

Internal Damage. This trouble is usually caused by a short-circuit, owing either to an accumulation of sediment reaching the plates or to the breaking of a separator, which may be caused by the active material being forced out of the grid, usually termed buckling, which is caused by overheating. It is important to be able to determine whether or not the low efficiency of a certain cell is caused by internal trouble without having to dismantle the cell. The repair man's most important aid for this class of work is the high-grade portable voltmeter mentioned in connection with other tests of the starting and lighting system.

Voltage Tests. Under some conditions, the voltmeter will also indicate whether the battery is practically discharged or not, but, like the hydrometer, it should not be relied upon alone. To insure accuracy, it must be used in conjunction with the hydrometer. Since a variation as low as .1 (one-tenth) volt makes considerable difference in what the reading indicates regarding the condition of the battery, it will be apparent that a cheap and inaccurate voltmeter would be a detriment rather than an aid. The instrument illustrated in connection with tests of other parts of starting and lighting systems (see Delco) is of the type required for this service. Complete instructions for its use will be received with the instrument, and these must be followed very carefully to avoid injuring it. For example, on the three-volt scale, but one cell should be tested; attempting to test the voltage of more than one cell on this scale is apt to burn out the three-volt coil in the meter. The total voltage of the number of cells to be tested must never exceed the reading of the particular scale being used at the time; otherwise, the coil of the scale in question will suffer, and the burning out of one coil will make it necessary to rebuild the entire instrument.

Clean Contacts Necessary. Where the voltage to be tested is so low, a very slight increase in the resistance will affect it considerably and thus destroy the accuracy of the reading. Make certain that the place on the connector selected for the contact point is clean and bright, and press the contact down on it firmly. To insure a clean bright contact point, use a fine file on the lead connector. The contact will be improved by filing the test points fairly sharp.

Even a thin film of dirt or a weak contact will increase the resistance to a point where the test is bound to be misleading. The positive terminal of the voltmeter must be brought into contact with the positive terminal of the battery, and the negative terminal of the voltmeter with the negative of the battery. If the markings of the cell terminals are indistinct, connect the voltmeter across any one cell. In case the pointer butts up against the stop at the left instead of giving a reading, the connections are wrong and should be reversed; if the instrument shows a reading for one cell, the positive terminal of the voltmeter is in contact with the positive of the battery. This test can be made with a voltmeter without any risk of short-circuiting the cell, as the voltmeter is wound to a high resistance and will pass very little current. Connecting an ammeter directly across a cell, however, would short-circuit it and instantly burn out the instrument.

How to Take Readings. It is one of the peculiarities of the storage cell that when on "open circuit", i.e., not connected in circuit with a load of any kind, it will always show approximately two volts, regardless of whether it is almost fully charged or almost the reverse. Consequently, voltage readings taken when the battery is on open circuit, i.e., neither charging nor discharging, are valueless, *except when a cell is out of order*. Therefore, a load should be put on the battery before making these tests. This can be done by switching on all the lamps. With the lights on, connect the voltmeter, as already directed, and test the individual cells. If the battery is in good condition, the voltage readings, after the load has been on for about ten minutes, will be but slightly lower than if the battery were on open circuit. This should amount to about .1 (one-tenth) volt. Should one or more of the cells be completely discharged, the voltage of these cells will drop rapidly when the lamps are first switched on and, when a cell is out of order, will sometimes show a reverse reading. Where the battery is nearly discharged, the voltage of each cell will be considerably lower than if the battery were on open circuit, after the load has been on for five minutes.

Detecting Deranged Cells. To distinguish the difference between cells that are merely discharged and those that are out of order, put the battery on charge, either from an outside source or by starting the engine, which should always be cranked by hand when any battery trouble is suspected. Then test again with the voltmeter. If the voltage of each cell does not rise to approximately two volts after the battery has been on charge for ten minutes or more, it is an indication of internal trouble which can be remedied only by dismantling the cell. (See instructions under that heading.)

Temperature Variations in Voltage Test. When making voltage tests, it must be borne in mind that the voltage of a cold battery rises slightly above normal on charge and falls below normal on discharge. The reverse is true of a warm battery in hot weather, i.e., the voltage will be slightly less than normal on charge and higher than normal on discharge. As explained in connection with hydrometer tests of the electrolyte, the normal temperature of the electrolyte may be regarded as 70° F., but this refers only to the temperature of the liquid itself as shown by the battery thermometer, and not to the temperature of the surrounding air. For the purpose of simple tests for condition, voltage readings on discharge are preferable, as variations in readings on charge mean little except to one experienced in the handling of storage batteries.

Joint Hydrometer and Voltmeter Tests. As already explained above, neither the hydrometer nor the voltmeter reading alone can always be taken as conclusive evidence of the condition of the battery. There are conditions under which one must be supplemented by the other to obtain an accurate indication of the state of the battery. In making any of the joint tests described below, it is important to take into consideration the four points following:

(1) The effect of temperature on both voltage and hydrometer readings.

(2) Voltage readings should be taken only with the battery discharging, as voltage readings on an idle battery in good condition indicate little or nothing.

(3) Never attempt to use the starting motor to supply a discharge load for the battery, because the discharge rate of the battery is so high while the starting motor is being used that even in a fully charged battery it will cause the voltage to drop rapidly.

(4) The voltage of the charging current will cause the voltage of a battery in good condition to rise to normal or above the moment it is placed on charge, so that readings taken under such circumstances are not a good indication of the condition of the battery.

In any battery which is in good condition, the voltage of each cell at a normally low discharge rate, i.e., 5 to 10 amperes for a starter battery of the 6-volt type or slightly less for a higher voltage battery, will remain between 2.1 and 1.9 volts per cell until it begins to approach the discharged condition. A voltage of less than 1.9 volts per cell indicates either that the battery is nearly discharged or is in a bad condition. The same state is also indicated when the voltage drops rapidly after the load has been on for a few minutes. The following joint hydrometer and voltmeter tests issued by the Prest-O-Lite Company of Indianapolis will be found to cover the majority of cases met with in actual practice.

(1) A voltage of 2 to 2.2 volts per cell with a hydrometer reading of 1.275 to 1.300 indicates that the battery is fully charged and in good condition.

(2) A voltage reading of less than 1.9 volts per cell, with a hydrometer reading of 1.200 or less indicates that the battery is almost completely discharged.

(3) A voltage reading of 1.9 volts or less per cell, with a hydrometer reading of 1.220 or more, indicates that excess acid has been added to the cell. Under these conditions, lights will burn dimly, although the hydrometer reading alone would appear to indicate that the battery was more than half charged.

(4) Regardless of voltage—high, low, or normal—any hydrometer reading of over 1.300 indicates that an excessive amount of acid has been added.

(5) Where a low voltage reading is found, as mentioned in cases 2 and 3, to determine whether the battery is in bad order or merely discharged, stop the discharge by switching off the load, and put the battery on charge, cranking the engine by hand, and note whether the voltage of each cell rises promptly to 2 volts or more. If not, the cell is probably short-circuited or otherwise in bad condition.

Battery Troubles and Cures*

Battery loses charge slowly

1. Slight short circuit or accidental ground in external wiring. Wires soaked with oil. *Repair wiring.*

---

*By the courtesy of the Willard Battery Company, Cleveland, Ohio

2. Wood separators starting to break down. *Reinsulate battery*.

3. Battery shorted by sediment. *Clean out sediment*.

Battery suddenly goes "dead"

1. Short in external wiring. *Repair wiring*.

2. Wood separators punctured by buckled plates. *Reinsulate. New plates may be necessary*.

3. Foreign substance may have been put in battery. *Repairs depend upon character of impurity*.

No current in cold weather

1. Battery frozen. *Very difficult to repair. Try long charge at low rate*.

2. Battery discharged. *Recharge*.

Gravity does not come up on charge

1. Plates sulphated. Active material crystallized. *Try long charge at one half finish rate*.

2. Lack of acid. Acid spilled or otherwise lost. *Have gravity balanced by good battery man*.

3. Presence of impurities. *Take battery to battery service station*.

Gravity low. No capacity. Starter will not turn motor

1. Battery undercharged. *Recharge from external source, or use lights and starter sparingly*.

2. Generator not charging. *Have generator regulated by expert*.

Continual low gravity and low level in one cell

1. Wood separators starting to break down. *Have battery reinsulated*.

2. Broken jar or cover. *Have broken part replaced*.

Overheated buckle plates

1. Electrolyte low. *Fill with water*.

2. Charging apparatus out of adjustment. *Regulate generator output or burn lamps*.

Broken down wood separators

1. Adding acid instead of water. *Have gravity balanced by competent battery man*.

2. Continuous charging at normal rate after battery is fully charged. *Burn lights while touring or making long daylight runs*.

ELECTRICAL EQUIPMENT

Lights not steady

1. Discharged battery. *Recharge.*
2. Loose battery terminals. *Tighten terminals.*
3. Loose or dirty connections at switch or lamp. *Go over whole circuit.*

Starter does not turn motor

1. Battery discharged. *Recharge.*
2. Corroded or loose battery terminals. *Inspect, clean tighten and grease terminals.*
3. Starting motor out of adjustment. *Inspect motor and commutator.*
4. Broken wire. *Inspect wiring.*
5. Starting pinion drive stuck. *Turn motor slightly with hand crank or throw gears into "high" and push the car a few inches.*

Generator does not charge

1. Blown fuse. *Renew fuse.*
2. Worn brushes. *Renew if necessary.*
3. Cut-out switch or relay out of adjustment. *Go to reliable repair man.*
4. Open circuit. *Inspect wiring and connections.*

Generator charges too high or too low

1. Generator out of adjustment. *Go to Official Service Station carrying that make of equipment.*

Electrolyte boils out of vents. Case and metal parts eaten

1. Overfilling. *See Instructions for proper filling.*

Case and handles eaten and corroded

1. Charging apparatus out of adjustment. *Regulate generator.*
2. Cracked cover. *Replace cover.*
3. Leaky sealing. *Have battery resealed.*

Electrolyte leaks around posts

1. Hole in vent plug stopped up. *Remove obstruction in vent.*
2. Leaky post sealing. *Have post resealed.*
3. Overfilling. *See instructions for filling.*
4. Holddown rods loose. *Tighten holddowns, and have battery repaired.*

Terminals corroded

1. Leaky terminal posts. Sloppy filling. *Clean all external parts with solution of ammonia or baking soda.*

2. Lead plating gone from terminals. *Clean terminals and tape cables. Give heavy coat of vaseline.*

Metal container badly eaten

1. Leaky jar or cover. Sloppy filling. *Replace broken part.*

2. Boiling due to overfilling or excessive charging. *Clean container and paint with acid proof paint.*

3. Poor ventilation. *See that box is well ventilated.*

PACKARD SIX-CYLINDER MARINE MOTOR
Courtesy of Packard Motor Car Company

STORAGE BATTERIES

PART II

Cleaning a Battery. The starting and lighting batteries are usually contained in an iron box or frame located under the seat or the floor boards. There will be little trouble with the batteries if the box and the frame have been kept dry, but if not, corrosion and leakage of current between the cells will be the result due to

Fig. 6.   Result of Overfilling Battery
Courtesy of Willard Storage Battery Company

rust falling on top of the battery, see Fig. 6. The vent plugs should be secured tightly in place and the outside of the battery should be thoroughly cleaned before opening the cells. Place the battery in a sink and wash with water. Use a stiff bristle brush to remove all dirt. If water will not remove all the dirt, use a rag wet with gasoline.

Electric vehicle batteries usually receive such careful and intelligent attention that the life of the battery is measured by the maximum number of charges and discharges of which the plates are capable under favorable conditions. To prevent any possibility of short-circuiting, a cell is cut out and opened after a certain number of discharges, and if the amount of sediment in the jar is approaching the danger point, the entire battery is opened and cleaned. They are either kept undercharged and thus become badly sulphated, or they are overcharged to a point where the temperature passes the danger mark frequently. When hot, the acid attacks and injures the wood separators so that the average life is about one year. Exceptions to this are found in those cases where the battery has been given proper attention, which results in unusually long life without the necessity of opening the cells for either cleaning or the insertion of new separators. These cases are so in the minority, however, that the battery manufacturers usually recommend that the car owner have his starting battery overhauled in the fall to put it in the best of condition for the winter as well as for the following year. Even where a battery has been

Fig. 7. Drilling Off Connectors
Courtesy of Electric Storage Battery Company, Philadelphia, Pennsylvania

given conscientious attention, the conditions of charging on the automobile are likely to vary so radically that it will be found almost impossible to keep the cells in a good state. Consequently, it is considered the best practice to give all starter batteries an overhauling once a year. The method of doing this is described in succeeding sections.

Replacing a Jar. When a cell requires the addition of distilled water more often than the other cells of the battery, or does not test to the same specific gravity as the others, it is usually an indication that there is a leak in the jar. Failure to give the same specific-gravity reading is not proof of this condition, as the cell may be low from other causes, but the loss of electrolyte is certain evidence of it. The only remedy is to replace the jar at fault.

After locating the cell in question, carefully mark the connectors so as to be sure to replace them the same way. Disconnect the cell from the others in the battery. This may be done either with the aid of brace and bit, which is used to drill down through the post of the connector, Fig. 7, or with a gasoline torch which should be applied carefully to the strap at the post. When the metal has become molten, pry the strap up on the post with a piece of wood. Do not use a screwdriver or other metal for this purpose as it is apt to short-circuit one or more of the cells. Care must also be taken not to apply so much heat that the post itself will be melted as this would make it difficult to reconnect the cell. For one not

accustomed to handling the torch, it will be safer to drill out the post, as illustrated. Lift the complete cell out of the battery box and then use the torch to warm the jar around the top to soften the sealing compound that holds the cover, Fig. 8. Grip the jar between the feet, take hold of the two connectors and pull the element almost out of the jar, Fig. 9. Then grip the elements near the bottom

Fig. 8. Softening Sealing Compound on Cell.

to prevent the plates flaring out while transferring them to the new jar, taking care not to let the outside plates start down the outside of the jar, Fig. 10. After the element is in the new jar, reseal the cell by pressing the sealing compound into place with a hot putty knife. Fill the cell with 1.250 electrolyte to the proper point, the old electrolyte being discarded.

Before replacing the connectors, clean both the post and the inside of the eye of the connector by scraping them smooth with a knife. When the connector has been placed in position, tap it down firmly over the post to insure good contact. To complete the connection, melt the lead of the connector and the post at the top so that they will run together, and while the lead is still molten, melt in some more lead until the eye of the connector is filled **level**. This is termed lead burning and is described at greater length in a succeeding section. Where no facilities are at hand for carrying it out, it may be done with an ordinary soldering copper. The copper is brought to a red heat so that all the tinning is burned off, and no flux of any kind is used. The method of handling the soldering copper and the lead-burning strip to supply the **extra** metal required to fill the eye is shown in Fig. 11.

Fig. 9. Lifting Elements out of Jar
by Hand

Fig. 10. Installing Elements
in Jar

Courtesy of Electric Storage Battery Company, Philadelphia, Pennsylvania

Put the battery on charge from an outside source, and when the cells begin to gas freely, reduce the current to half the finishing rate given on the battery name plate and charge at this rate as long as there is any rise in the specific gravity of the electrolyte in this or any of the other cells. The maximum gravity has been reached when there has been no rise in the specific gravity for a period of three hours. If the gravity of the cell having the new jar is then over 1.280, draw off some of the electrolyte and replace it with distilled water. If the gravity is below 1.270, draw off **some of the electrolyte** and replace it with 1.300 electrolyte. If necessary to put in 1.300 electrolyte, allow the battery to continue charging for about one-half hour longer at a rate sufficient to cause gassing, which will cause the stronger acid to become thoroughly mixed with the rest of the electrolyte in the cell.

Overhauling the Battery. As already mentioned, it will be found desirable to overhaul the majority of starter batteries at least once a year. The expense to the car owner will be less than

Fig. 11.   Reburning Battery Connectors with Soldering Iron
Courtesy of Electric Storage Battery Company, Philadelphia, Pennsylvania

the cost of the frequent attention required by a run-down battery with complete renewal at no distant date, and the service rendered by the battery will be much improved. The best time of year to do this is in the late fall, so that the battery may be at its best during the cold weather. Before undertaking the work, have on hand a complete renewal set of rubber and wood separators as well as sufficient fresh acid of 1.300 specific gravity with which to mix fresh electrolyte. Use the good separators, particularly the rubber ones.

Dismounting Cells. Remove the connectors by drilling, heating, or pulling (in the same manner as a wheel is pulled), and loosen the jar covers by heating or running a hot putty knife around their edges so that they may be lifted off. The covers should be washed in hot water and then stacked one on top of the other with heavy weight on them to press them flat. Lift the jars out of the battery box and note whether any of them have been leaking. A cracked jar should of course be replaced. Treat one cell at a time, by pulling the element out of the jar with the aid of the pliers, meanwhile holding the jar with the feet. Lay the element on the bench and

Fig. 12.   Removing Old Separators
from Elements

Fig. 13.   Pressing Negative Group

Courtesy of Electric Storage Battery Company, Philadelphia, Pennsylvania

spread the plates slightly to permit removing the separators, taking care not to injure the rubber sheets, Fig. 12. Separate the positive group from the negative. If the active material of the negative be swollen beyond the surface of the grid, press it back into position before it has a chance to dry, placing boards of suitable thickness between the plates and carefully squeezing the group between heavy boards in a vise or press, as shown in Fig. 13. Boards of sufficient size and thickness must be used between the plates or breakage will result. Charged negative plates will become hot in a short time when exposed to the air and, in this event, should be allowed to cool before reassembling. Remove any loose particles adhering to the positive plates by passing a smooth wood paddle over the surface but *do not wash the positive plates.*

Treating the Plates. If the positive plates show signs of buckling or stripping of the active matter, or if the negative plates have the light spotted appearance indicative of sulphating, it may be necessary to replace them altogether. In case sulphating appears to be the only trouble, the groups should be reassembled in an open jar with distilled water and given a long, slow charge, testing with the hydrometer at frequent intervals to note whether the specific gravity is rising or not. Twenty-four hours or more may be necessary for this charge, and two or three days will be nothing unusual. This charging, of course, is carried on from the lighting mains through a rectifier or a motor-generator, unless direct-current service is available. If it is necessary to prolong the charge over two or three days, and the specific gravity still continues to rise slowly, it may be preferable to replace the plates.

Fig. 14. Wood and Rubber Separator

Reassembling Battery. Wash all the sediment out of the jars, also wash and save the rubber sheets, unless they happen to be broken, but throw away the old wood separators. The rubber sheets should be placed in clean running water for about a quarter of an hour. Reassemble the positive and negative groups with the plates on edge in order to insert the separators. Place a rubber separator against the grooved side of a wood separator, Fig. 14, and insert a positive plate near the center of the element. The rubber sheet must be against the positive plate, and the wood separator against the negative plate. In this manner insert separators in all the spaces, working in both directions from the center. Care must be taken *not to omit a separator as that would short-circuit the cell.*

The separators should be practically flush with the bottoms of the plates to bring their tops against the hold-down below the strap, and must extend to or beyond the side edge of the plates. Grip the element near the bottom to prevent the plates flaring out while placing the element in the jar. Fill the cell to within one-half inch of the top of the jar, using electrolyte of 1.250 specific gravity. If the negative plates show signs of sulphating, but not enough to call for the special treatment mentioned above, use water instead of the electrolyte. After all of the cells have been given the same treatment and reassembled, return them to the battery box in their proper positions, so that the positive of each cell will be connected to the negative of the adjoining cell and connect temporarily by pressing the old connecting straps in place by hand.

Checking the Connections. Put the battery on charge at its finishing rate (usually about 5 amperes) and, after charging about fifteen minutes, note the voltage of each cell. This is to insure having reconnected the cells properly with regard to their polarity. If this be the case, they should all read approximately 2 volts. Any cell that reads less is likely to have been connected backward. When the cells begin to gas freely and uniformly, take a hydrometer reading of each cell and a temperature reading of one of them. Reduce the current to one-half the finishing rate. Should the temperature of the electrolyte reach 100° F., reduce the charge, or interrupt it temporarily, to prevent the cells getting any hotter. Both hydrometer and temperature readings must be taken at regular intervals, say four to six hours apart, to determine if the specific gravity is still rising or if it has reached its maximum. Continue the charge and the readings until there has been no further rise for a period of at least twelve hours. Maintain the height of the electrolyte constant by adding water after each reading. (If water were added before the reading, it would not have time to mix with the electrolyte, and the reading would not be correct.)

Should the specific gravity rise to about 1.300 in any cell, draw off the electrolyte down to the level of the tops of the plates and refill with as much water as possible without overflowing. Continue the charge, and if the specific gravity again exceeds 1.300, dump out all the electrolyte in that cell, replace it with water, and continue the charge. The charge can be considered complete only when there has been no rise in the gravity of any of the cells during a period of at least twelve hours of continuous charging. Upon completion of the charge, the electrolyte should have its specific gravity adjusted to its proper value (1.270 to 1.280) using water or 1.300 acid, as may be necessary, and the level of the electrolyte adjusted to a uniform ½ inch above the plates.

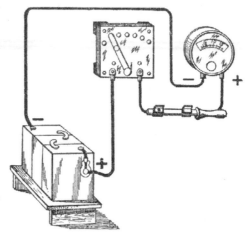

Fig. 15. Wiring Diagram for Discharging Battery through Rheostat

Discharge the battery at its normal discharge rate to determine if there are any low cells caused by defective assembly. The normal discharge rate of the battery is usually given on its name plate. To discharge the battery, the current may be passed through a rheostat, as in Fig. 15, or if no panel board of this type be available, through a water resistance, as shown in Fig. 16. The resistance of a water rheostat increases with the distance between its plates and decreases according to their proximity and to the degree of conductivity of the water itself. If the resistance is too high with the plates close together, add a little acid to the water. It will be necessary, of course, to have an

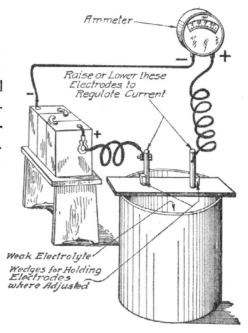

Fig. 16. Wiring Diagram for Discharging Battery through Water Resistance

ammeter in the circuit to show the rate at which the battery is discharging. In case any of the cells are low, owing to being assembled defectively or connected with their polarity reversed, as shown by the voltmeter test (they should all register two volts or slightly over at the beginning of the discharge and should fall off slowly) such cells should be remedied at once. Recharge the battery and then remove the temporary connectors, wipe the inside edges of the jars dry, and put the rubber covers in place. Heat the sealing compound which is supplied for this purpose and apply around the edges of the covers, smoothing it down with a hot putty knife. Care must be taken not to burn the sealing compound when heating it.

Reconnecting Cells. If the old lead connecting straps have been removed carefully, they may be used again, though in many cases it will be found preferable to employ new straps. Before putting the straps in place, scrape the posts clean with a knife and clean out the eyes of the straps themselves. When the connectors have been put in place, tap them down firmly to insure good contact. Before reburning the connectors in place, test each cell with a low-reading voltmeter to make certain that the cells have been connected in the right direction, i.e., that their polarity has not been reversed. It is not sufficient to note that the voltage of each cell is correct, i.e., 2 volts per cell or over, but care must be taken also to note that it is in the right direction. With a voltmeter having a needle that moves in both directions from zero, one polarity will be evidenced by the needle moving over the scale to the right of the neutral line, while if the polarity be reversed, the needle will move to the left. One cell having the proper polarity should accordingly be tested and then, to be correct, the remaining cells should cause the needle to move in the same direction and to approximate the same voltage when the instrument leads are held to the same terminals in the same way for each. Where the voltmeter needle can move in but one direction, i.e., to the right, a change of polarity will be indicated by the needle of the instrument attempting to move to the left and, in so doing, butting up against the stop provided to prevent this. Complete the reassembly of the cells by burning the connectors together, as detailed under the head of Lead Burning.

Renewals. In many cases it will be found necessary upon overhauling a battery to renew the elements. These may be purchased either as loose plates or as groups ready to assemble in the battery. Except in garages doing a large amount of this work, it will not be advisable to buy the loose plates and burn them into groups.

The new groups should be assembled with rubber sheets and wood separators, as directed in overhauling the battery, the jars filled with fresh electrolyte of the proper specific gravity and the battery given a test charge and discharge with temporary connections. The electrolyte should be of 1.250 specific gravity, or seven parts of water to two of pure sulphuric acid by volume. If the test charge has been carried to a point where the specific gravity has ceased to rise for several hours, and the discharge shows no defectively assembled cells, the cells may be permanently connected.

Lead Burning. *Type of Outfit.* In the manufacture of storage batteries, and in garages where a large number of batteries are

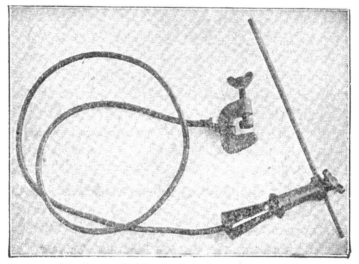

Fig. 17. Arc-Welding Outfit for Burning Connections

maintained, a hydrogen-gas apparatus is employed for this purpose. For the electric-car owner or the garage doing a comparatively small amount of battery repair work, the Electric Storage Battery Company has placed an arc lead-burning outfit on the market. This is low in first cost and, with a little practice, good results can be obtained with it. As the battery itself supplies the power necessary, the only material required is the lead in the form of a flexible strip or heavy wire. The complete outfit is illustrated in Fig. 17. At one end is the clamp for making electrical connection, while at the other is a clamp of different form having an insulated handle and holding a one-fourth inch carbon rod. The two are electrically connected by a flexible cable. This simple outfit can be employed in two ways, the second being preferable for the beginner, at least until sufficient amount of skill has been acquired to use the arc without danger of melting the straps.

First Method of Burning. In the first method, a potential of from 28 to 30 volts (12 to 15 cells) is required.* The clamp should, therefore, be fastened to the positive pole of the twelfth to the fifteenth cell away from the joint to be burned, counting toward the negative terminal of the battery. The carbon then forms the negative terminal of the circuit. Otherwise particles of carbon will be carried into the joint, as the carbon rod quickly disintegrates when it forms the positive pole. The carbon should project 3 or 4 inches from the holder. The surfaces of the parts to be burned should be scraped clean and bright, and small pieces of clean lead about $\frac{1}{4}$ to $\frac{1}{2}$ inch square provided for filling the joint. The carbon is then touched to the strap to be burned and immediately withdrawn, forming an electric arc which melts the lead very rapidly. By moving the carbon back and forth the arc is made to travel over the joint as desired, the small pieces of lead being dropped in to fill the gap as required. Owing to the high temperature generated, the work must be carried out very quickly, otherwise the whole strap is liable to melt and run.

As this method is difficult and requires practice to secure good results, the beginner should try his hand on some scrap pieces of lead before attempting to operate on a cell. Its advantages are that when properly carried out it takes but a short time to do the work, and the result is a neat and workmanlike joint. It is extremely hard on the eyes and smoked or colored glasses must be used.

Second Method of Burning. The second method, utilizing the hot point of the carbon rod instead of the arc, is recommended for general practice. Scrape the parts to be joined and connect the clamp between the third and fourth cells from the joint. With this method it is not necessary to determine the polarity of the carbon. The latter is simply touched to the joint and held there; on account of the heavy flow of current it rapidly becomes red and then white hot. By moving it around and always keeping it in contact with the metal, the joint can be puddled. To supply lead to fill the joint,

---

*This voltage may be obtained from an electric vehicle battery in the garage or from the lighting mains through a suitable resistance, first converting to direct current where the supply is alternating.

an ordinary lead-burning strip can be used, simply introducing the end into the puddle of molten lead, touching the hot carbon. The carbon projecting out of the holder should be only one inch, or even less, in length. After the joint has been made, it can be smoothed off by running the carbon over it a second time.

Use of Forms to Cover Joint. In joining a strap which has been cut in the center, it is best to make a form around the strap by means of a piece of asbestos sheeting soaked in water and fastened around the strap in the shape of a cup, which will prevent the lead from running down. It will be found that sheet asbestos paper is thick enough, but it should be fairly wet when applied. By this means a neat joint can be easily made. The asbestos will adhere very tightly to the metal owing to the heat, but can be removed by wetting it again. When burning a pillar post to a strap, a form may be made around the end of the strap in the same manner, though this is not necessary if reasonable care is used. Two or three pieces of $\frac{1}{16}$-inch strap iron about one inch wide, and some iron nuts about one inch square are also of service in making the joint, the strap iron to be used under the joints, and the nuts at the side or ends to confine the molten lead. Clay can also be used in place of asbestos, wetting it to a stiff paste. As the holder is liable to become so hot from constant use as to damage the insulation, besides making it uncomfortable to hold, a pail of water should be handy, and the carbon dipped into it from time to time. This will not affect its operation in any way, as the carbon becomes hot again immediately the current passes through it.

Illuminating Gas Outfit. Heretofore it has not been possible to do good work in lead burning with illuminating gas, but a special type of burner has recently been perfected by the Electric Storage Battery Company, which permits the use of illuminating gas with satisfactory results. The outfit consists of a special burning tip and mixing valve. Sufficient $\frac{5}{16}$-inch rubber hose should be provided, and the rubber should be wired firmly to the corrugated connections, Fig. 18, as the air is used at a comparatively high pressure. A supply of compressed air is necessary, the proper pressure ranging from 5 to 10 pounds, depending upon the length of hose and the size of the parts to be burned. When air from a compressor used for pumping tires is utilized for this purpose, a suitable reducing valve must be introduced in the supply line. This outfit is designed for use with ordinary illuminating gas and cannot be employed with natural gas.

Connect the air hose to the right-hand cock and the gas hose to the left-hand cock. The leader hose, about five or six feet long, is connected to the lower pipe and to the upper end of the burning tip. When the air pressure at the source is properly adjusted, close the air cock and turn the gas cock on full. Light the gas at the tip and turn on the air. If the flame blows out, reduce the air pressure, preferably at the source. With the gas turned on full, the flame

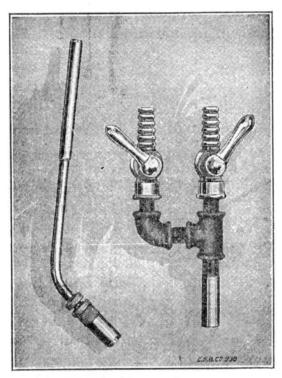

Fig. 18. Lead-Burning Outfit for Use with Illuminating Gas
Courtesy of Electric Storage Battery Company,
Philadelphia, Pennsylvania

will have a ragged appearance and show a waist about ½ inch from the end of the tip, the flame converging there and spreading out beyond. Such a flame is not good for lead burning.

Slowly turn the gas off until the outer portion at the waist breaks and spreads with an inner tongue of flame issuing through the outer ring. The flame will now have a greenish color and is properly adjusted for burning. If the gas is turned off further or if too much air is turned on, the flame assumes a blue color gradually becoming invisible and is then deficient in heating power. When properly adjusted, the hottest part of the flame is just past the end of the inner point. Do not hold the flame too close to the work when burning, as its heating effect is greatly reduced and the flame is spread so as to make control difficult. The burning tip has at its lower end an outer sleeve and lock nut; this sleeve can be taken off in case any of the holes in the tip become clogged. The position of this sleeve is adjustable, the best position varying with the pressure of the flame, and it should be determined by experiment.

Hydrogen Gas Outfit. Hydrogen gas gives a hotter flame and therefore permits of more rapid work, so that where burning is done on a large scale, it is still preferred. The essentials of such an outfit are: first, a hydrogen generator; second, a method of producing air pressure at approximately 2 pounds to the square inch; and third the usual pipe and tips for burning. If hydrogen gas is purchased in a tank and compressed air is available, only the blowpipe, tips, and a reducing valve on the air line are necessary. This is an expensive method to purchase hydrogen, however, so that it is usually generated, and a water bottle is needed between the generator and the blowpipe to wash the gas and to prevent the flame from traveling back to the generator.

For this purpose hydrogen gas is generated by placing zinc in a sulphuric-acid solution. The generator usually employed for vehicle-battery burning requires 50 pounds of zinc, 2 gallons of sulphuric acid, and 9 gallons of water for a charge. Where no compressed-air supply is available, an air pump and an air tank for equalizing the pressure must be used. An outfit of this kind is shown in Fig. 19. In preparing the generator for use, connect up as shown in this cut, taking care that the hose from the generator is connected to the nipple of the water bottle L. Have the water bottle one-half to two-thirds full and immerse it in a pail of cold water up to its neck. Replace the water in the pail whenever it becomes warm. Have stop cock N closed. Put the required amount of zinc, which has been broken into pieces small enough to pass through the opening C, into the lower reservoir. Put on cap X and screw down with clamp D, being sure that the rubber drainage stopper H is well secured in place. Pour the proper amount of water into reservoir A and then pour in the acid, taking care to avoid splashing. *Always pour the water in first.*

In running the hose from K to N, arrange it so that there will be no low points for the water of condensation to collect in; in other words, this hose should drain back at every point to the water bottle. If, however, water should collect in the hose to such an extent as to interfere with the flame and it cannot readily be drained off, kink the hose between T and U and detach it from K; close the stop cock at W and pump until a strong pressure is obtained in the tank; then close

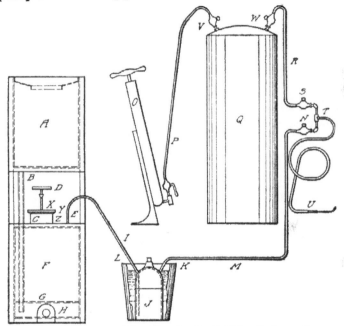

Fig. 19. Diagram of Lead-Burning Outfit, Using Hydrogen Gas

the cock at V, opening those at S and N and, finally, quickly open W; the pressure in the air tank will then force the water out of the hose. The length of the hose from T to U should be such that the mixing cocks at S and N are always within easy reach of the man handling the flame.

In preparing the flame for burning, close the air cock at S and open N wide, hold a match to the gas until it lights, then add air and adjust the gas cock slowly, turning toward the closed position until the flame, when tried on a piece of lead, melts the metal and leaves a clean surface. The tip to be used depends on the work, but most vehicle-battery work is done with the medium tip. Replenish the zinc every few days, keeping it up to the required amount. When a charge is exhausted or the generator is to be laid up for the night, the old solution should be drawn off before making up a new charge and the generator thoroughly flushed out by running water through *A*. The new charge should not be put in until the generator is to be used again. To empty the generator, first pull off the hose at the nipple *K*, then at *E*, and finally the rubber plug at *H*. Care should be taken not to allow the solution to splash on anything and not to dump the generator where the contents will damage cement, asphalt, or wood walks.

Installing New Battery. In not a few instances, it will be necessary to renew the entire battery. As received from the manufacturer, the battery is in a charged condition, i.e., it was fully charged just previous to being shipped, but it must be inspected and tested before being installed on the car. Care must be taken in unpacking it to avoid spilling any of the electrolyte. After cleaning off the packing from the tops of the cells, take out the rubber plugs and see that the electrolyte is $\frac{1}{2}$ inch over the plates. If it is uniformly or approximately below the proper level in all the cells, this is simply the loss due to evaporation. But if low in only one or two cells, this is evidently caused by loss of electrolyte. In case this loss has resulted from the case being turned over in shipment, it will be indicated by the presence of acid on the packing on top of the battery (the acid does not evaporate), and some of the electrolyte will have been lost from all the cells. Replace the amount lost by refilling the cells with electrolyte of 1.250 specific gravity, as already directed.

In case the loss of electrolyte is caused by a cracked or broken jar, the packing under the battery will be wet. Replace the broken jar as instructed in the directions under that heading and add sufficient electrolyte of 1.250 specific gravity to make up for the loss. Should it be found, after replacing the broken jar and giving the battery an equalizing charge, that the specific gravity does not reach approximately 1.275, it is due to not having replaced the same amount of acid as was spilled. To adjust this, draw off the electrolyte from the cell with the syringe and add water or 1.300 acid to bring the specific gravity to between 1.270 and 1.280.

Storing a Battery. There is an amusingly erroneous idea prevalent to some extent that the charge of a storage battery is represented by its electrolyte; that pouring off the electrolyte takes the charge with it; that, in case it is desired to store a battery, all that is necessary is to pour off the electrolyte and store the empty battery and the solution separately; and when it is desired to put the battery back in commission, it is then only necessary to pour the electrolyte back into the cells and, presto! they are ready to start the engine right away. Unfortunately for this theory, the charge is in the active material of the plates and not in the electrolyte.

It is frequently necessary to allow the battery to remain idle for a considerable length of time, in which case it should be put out of commission. If the battery itself is in good condition at the time and if it may be wanted for service again at short notice, this need only consist of giving it a long equalizing charge until the specific gravity has ceased to rise for several hours, then filling the cells to the top with distilled water and putting the battery away in a handy place. It should be given a freshening charge every two weeks or, at least, as often as once a month. If it is actually to be stored, there are two ways of doing this.

One is known as the wet storage method, and the other as the dry, the one to be adopted depending upon the condition of the battery and the length of time it is to be out of commission. The wet storage method is usually applied to any battery that is to be out of commission less than a year, provided that it will not soon require repairs necessitating dismantling it. The dry storage method is used for any battery that is to be out of commission for more than a year, regardless of its condition, and it is also applied to any battery that will shortly require repairs necessitating its dismantling. It will be apparent that this last-named class includes most starter batteries after they have seen several months of service, so that the majority can be placed in dry storage when necessary to put them out of commission.

Examine the condition of the plates and the separators and also the amount of sediment in the bottom of the jars. If it is found that there is very little sediment and the plates and separators are in sufficiently good condition to give considerable additional service, the battery may be put into wet storage by giving it an equalizing charge and covering it to exclude dust. Replace evaporation periodically to maintain the level of the electrolyte $\frac{1}{2}$ inch above the tops of the plates. At least once every four months, charge the battery at one-half its normal finishing rate (see name plate on battery box) until all the cells have gassed continuously for at least three hours. Any cells not gassing should be examined, and the trouble remedied.

When examination shows that the battery will soon require dismantling, it should be put into dry storage. Dismantle the cells in accordance with the instructions already given. If the positive plates show much wear, they should be scrapped; if not, remove any loose particles adhering to them by passing a smooth wood paddle over the surface, but *do not wash the positive plates*. Charged negative plates will become hot quickly when exposed to the air. They should not be allowed to stand in the air until cooled.

Empty all the electrolyte out of the jars into a glass or glazed earthenware jar or a lead-lined tank and save it for giving the negative plates their final treatment before storage. Wash all the sediment out of the jars and wash the rubber separators carefully, then dry them and tie them in bundles. Place the positive groups together in pairs, put them in the jars, and store them away. Then put the negative groups together in the same way, place them in the remaining jars, and cover them with the electrolyte saved for the purpose, allowing them to stand in it for five hours, at least. Then pour off the electrolyte, which may now be discarded, and store away the jars containing the negatives. If the negative plates show any bulging of the active material, they should be subjected to the pressing treatment first, using boards and a vise, as described in a previous section. All of the jars should be well covered to exclude dust.

Make a memorandum of the amount of material required to reassemble the battery, and, when ordering this, provide for extra jars and covers, extra rubber separators, and an entire lot of wood separators with a sufficient excess to take care of breakage in handling. Unless the old connectors were carefully removed, order a new set. When a battery is put in storage, it is well to advise the owner in regard to the material necessary to reassemble, and to request at least a month's notice to procure it.

Charging from Outside Source. Theoretically at least, the starter battery on the automobile should be kept in an ideal condition. It is constantly under charge while the car is running at anything except the lowest starting speeds and should accordingly always be fully charged. The generator is designed to take care of the storage battery and usually has sufficient capacity to light all the lamps in addition. Practice, however, does not bear out this theoretical view of the favorable conditions under which the starter battery is supposed to operate. It will be apparent at the very outset that the method of charging and discharging is not beneficial. To insure long life to a storage battery, it should be fully charged and then discharged to at least seventy-five per cent of its maximum capacity before recharging. It should never be allowed to stand discharged for any length of time. If exhausted, it should be recharged immediately. It should not be charged to half its capacity and then discharged. It should not be overcharged to the point where it continues to gas violently nor where its temperature exceeds 100° F.

All of these are things that should not be done to the storage battery, but it will take only a little experience to enable the garage man to recognize that all these are things which are constantly being done to the majority of storage batteries on gasoline automobiles. Most batteries receive treatment that reaches one extreme or the other, though it will be apparent that the middle course is almost as injurious to the battery. Either a battery is constantly kept undercharged so that it has insufficient charge to spin the engine more than once, and its operation is accordingly unsatisfactory, or it is constantly kept overcharged with the result that the hot acid makes comparatively short work of the plates, and they must be renewed in considerably less than a year of service. The mean course between these two is found in the case of the battery that is only charged to about half its capacity before being discharged again by the use of the starting motor. This treatment results in sulphating.

To keep the storage battery of the starting system in anything like efficient operating condition, it cannot be left on the running board with nothing but the generator of the starting and lighting system to charge it. Hydrometer and voltage tests will be valueless unless the conditions they indicate are remedied, and this cannot be done with the car generator as the sole source of charging current. Here is a typical instance: The battery is in good condition and it is fully charged. On a cold morning, it is drawn on intermittently for almost fifteen minutes by the starting motor before the engine fires. As a result, it is practically discharged. The car is driven only a few miles, stopped and after a rest started again. What charge the battery received by the short run is again lost. The car is run for a little longer time and returned to the garage. The battery has received about one-fourth its normal charge. It stands this way for several days.

The weather being warmer, the engine starts in a much shorter time, but not before the starting motor has exhausted the small amount of charge in the battery. It is not run enough that day to charge the battery nor when taken out again that night, as all the lights are switched on, and under such conditions the battery receives very little current. Multiply this treatment by five or ten representing the number of days the car is driven during the month. At the end of that time, the battery no longer has sufficient charge to operate the starting motor at all and is condemned, as usual, by the car owner as being worthless. This is only one instance of many that are so similar that a few changes in detail would cover them all. No battery ever made could possibly operate efficiently under such conditions. After the car in question had been used a few days, a hydrometer test of the battery would have indicated its need of charging.

Equalizing Charges Necessary. Even where a battery receives almost 100 per cent of its normal charge before being discharged again, there will be numerous occasions on which the charge is not carried to completion. As mentioned under the head of Sulphating, that means so much acid left in the plates at the end of the charge. That acid represents lead sulphate which continues to increase in quantity as long as the acid remains in contact with the active material. To drive it out of the active material into the electrolyte, which is the function of charging, the charge must be carried to completion. This is termed an equalizing charge, and it should be given not oftener than once in two weeks, but at least once a month. To do this, it is necessary to charge the battery from an outside source, as it is seldom convenient to run the engine for the long period of time needed to complete such a charge. Except in cases where the battery is chronically overcharged, as indicated by its violent and continued gassing, it will usually be found necessary

ELECTRICAL EQUIPMENT

to give it an equalizing charge once a month. The constantly overcharged condition is quite as injurious as its opposite, and it can be
cured only by cutting down the output of the generator or increasing
the demand upon the battery for current.

Methods of Charging. The apparatus employed for charging
starter batteries will naturally vary in accordance with the number
that are looked after in the garage. It may range from the makeshift
consisting of a bank of lamps up to an elaborate panel board designed
to provide charging connections for a dozen or more batteries at once.
Where direct current is available—and only a few starter batteries
need this attention—a bank of lamps in connection with a fused
double-pole switch will be found to fill all the requirements. Note
the charging rate (finishing) given on the name plate of the battery
and make the number of lamps in accordance. A 32 c.p. in the
circuit is practically the equivalent of one ampere of current entering
the battery, i.e., it requires one ampere to light a lamp of this size
and type (carbon filament) to incandescence. A number of standard
lamp sockets should be mounted on a board, connected in multiple,
and the group connected in series with the switch and the battery.
(See illustration in résumé of questions and answers on the battery.)
As many lamps as necessary may then be screwed into the sockets.
The more current needed, the more lamps and the higher power
lamps will be necessary. Tungsten lamps may be employed as well
as the carbon-filament type, but as they take so much less current,
lamps of higher candle power will be needed. For example, to
replace a 32-c.p. carbon-filament lamp, a 100-watt tungsten lamp
will be required.

Charging in Series for Economy. Where several starter batteries
have to be charged they may be connected in series, as shown in
Fig. 20, and charge them all at once. The difference between the
110-volt potential of the lighting mains and the 6 to 8 volts needed
to charge a single three-cell battery represents that much waste,
as the drop in voltage has to be dissipated, through a resistance, to
no purpose. In this way, any number of 6-volt storage batteries,
up to twelve, can be charged from a 110-volt circuit (direct-current)
with the same expenditure of current as would be required for
a single battery. This is owing to the fact that, in any storage
battery, the capacity of the battery is the capacity of one cell,

where all are connected in series. Consequently, it will take 10 to 15 amperes to charge one 6-volt battery from the lighting circuit, and when several more units of the same size are connected in series with it, the current consumption will still be the same, but a smaller part of the voltage will have to be wasted through a resistance.

Motor=Generator. Direct current will be found available in comparatively few places to-day, so that some means of rectifying an alternating current, in order to use it for charging batteries, will be necessary. Where quite a number of batteries are to be cared for, the motor-generator will be found to give the highest efficiency, besides proving more economical in other ways. As its name

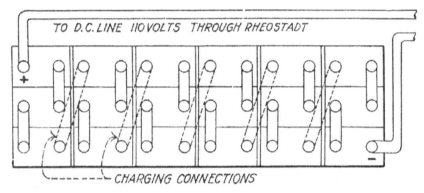

Fig. 20. Batteries in Series Connection for Charging

indicates, it consists of a motor wound for alternating current and fed from the supply mains of the garage, and a direct-current generator which is driven at its normal generating speed by the a.c. motor. There is no electrical connection between the two units. Electrical power in the form of an alternating current is converted into mechanical power in the a.c. motor which drives the armature of the d.c. generator and again converts it into electrical power in the form of a direct current. The first cost of a motor-generator is such that its use is usually confined to large establishments handling quite a number of batteries, though motor generators are now made in much smaller sizes than formerly.

Constant=Potential Charging. One of the oldest systems of battery charging, but one which has only come into recent use to any great extent for automobile batteries, is the constant potential system. This system of charging has many advantages over the series system. Whether one battery or ten is being charged in the series system off of a 110-volt line, the current consumption is the same. This is due to the rheostat using the unused current, and the same amount must be paid for charging one as for more. The batteries need constant watching to see that they do not overheat or boil over. When a number of batteries are charged, the rheostat must be set to take care of the battery requiring the smallest amount of charge, therefore the other batteries do not get as much charging as they need.

In the constant-potential system, no current is wasted and it is taken as needed by the batteries. The battery can be left on charge, for as the battery becomes charged a smaller amount is

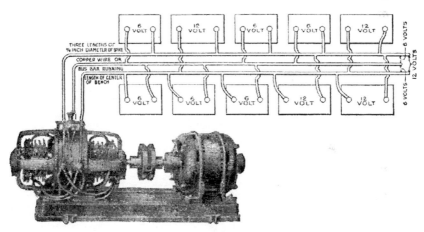

Fig. 21.   Battery Connections for Constant-Potential Charging
Courtesy of Roth Brothers & Company, Chicago

taken by it, and the chance of damage from overcharge is small. It requires about 8 hours to bring a battery to a state of full charge, as contrasted to 24 hours in the series system, and constant watching is not required. The outstanding features of this system are better and cheaper service.

The constant-potential apparatus consists of a motor-driven machine which is made up of two $7\frac{1}{2}$-volt generators on one armature shaft. The windings are separate, wound and insulated from each other, and the windings connected to two distinct commutators. The machine can be used as a $7\frac{1}{2}$-volt or a 15-volt generator. The two parts are connected in series when a 15-volt generator is needed. Only one part is used when a $7\frac{1}{2}$-volt is needed. By referring to Fig. 21, the connections on this battery can be seen. Two wires or bars carry the current, while the third is neutral. This is called the three-wire type in which two combinations of charging current are given. Sufficient current to charge 6-volt batteries can be obtained by connecting either outside wire with the neutral wire. About 15 volts are given by connecting the two outside leads, and will take care of charging 12-volt batteries. When putting batteries on to charge it is best to get the same number of cells on both sides of the line so that the outfit is balanced.

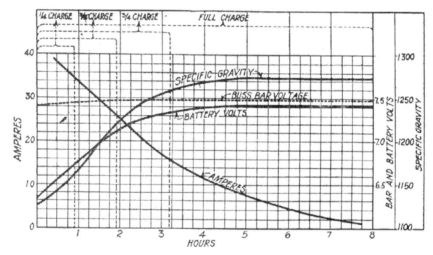

Fig. 22. Potential Charging Chart
Courtesy of Roth Brothers & Company, Chicago

If a battery needs a long charge at a low rate the battery can be placed on another bench and the current put through a special resistance to take care of the extra current.

The batteries are put on charge at a high rate, and the rate is decreased as the batteries become charged, as shown in Fig. 22. It will be seen from this chart that the specific gravity rises as the rate drops and comes to a constant point about the same time as the voltage of the batteries becomes constant. This point is reached after about 6 hours of charging, while the additional 2 hours brings the charge to completion. Fig. 23 shows a charging bench as used in this installation.

Fig. 23. Charging Bench for Potential Charging

A.C. Rectifiers. Where the amount of charging to be done does not warrant the investment in a motor-generator, a rectifier is usually employed. There are several makes of different types on the market: the chemical type, which employs lead and aluminum plates in an acid solution; the mercury-arc type, in which mercury is vaporized in a vacuum by the passage of the current; and others, in all of which the principle is the same. This consists in utilizing the current on but one part of the wave, so that the efficiency of these rectifiers ranges from 60 to 75 per cent. It is accordingly not good practice to employ them except in the smaller sizes. While the mercury-vapor rectifier is made for charging private vehicle batteries, the other types are ordinarily confined to sizes intended for charging small batteries.

A recent addition to the list that is available for this purpose is the Tungar rectifier, made by the General Electric Company. The principle on which this works is the same, but the medium is a new one. This is a bulb exhausted of air and filled with a special gas in which a heavy tungsten-wire filament is brought to incandescence by the passage of the alternating current. This filament is very short and thick, its diameter depending upon the capacity of the rectifier, and it is placed horizontally. It constitutes the cathode of the couple. Directly opposite it, but a short distance away, is the anode of graphite in the form of a button, the lower face of which is presented to the tungsten wire. It is made in three sizes, the smallest of which has a capacity of but 2 amperes and is designed for charging the batteries of small portable lamps, such as are used by miners; and for charging ignition, call bell, burglar alarm batteries, and the like.

Fig. 24. Front View of Large Size G. E. Tungar Rectifier

In the larger size, as shown in Fig. 24, the bulb is mounted in an iron case, on the face of which are mounted the switch for alternating current; an ammeter on the d.c. side, showing the charge received by the battery; and a dial switch for adjusting the voltage to the number of batteries to be charged. There is a compensator with

ELECTRICAL EQUIPMENT

15 taps, and the current is adjustable by steps up to 6 amperes. Anything from a single three-cell battery up to ten of such units (30 cells in all) may be charged at once. The batteries must be connected in series and then it is only necessary to turn the switch

Fig. 25. Interior View of Small Size G. E. Tungar Rectifier
Courtesy of General Electric Company, Schenectady, New York

of the a.c. circuit. In case the alternating-current supply should fail, the battery cannot discharge through the rectifier, and the latter will assume its task again automatically as soon as the current comes on. This is the 6-ampere 75-volt size. It is also made in a

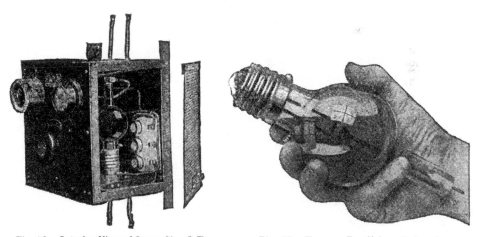

Fig. 26. Interior View of Large Size G.E.
Tungar Rectifier

Fig. 27. Tungar Rectifying Bulb—the
Heart of the Rectifier

6-ampere 15-volt size designed for the charging of a three- or six-cell starter battery in the home garage. Fig. 25 shows an interior view of this size, illustrating the position of the converting bulb, the compensator, the reactance coil, and the fuses, while Fig. 26 illustrates the 6-ampere 75-volt size, showing the panel instrument, i.e., switch, ammeter, and regulating handle, as well as the bulb and fuses. A closer view of the bulb itself is shown in Fig. 27.

To Test Rate of Discharge. If the battery terminals are removable, take off either the positive or the negative terminal, and connect the shunt of the ammeter to the terminal post and to the cable which has been removed, binding or wiring it tightly in place to insure good contact. Where the battery terminals are not easily removable, insert the shunt in the first joint in the line,

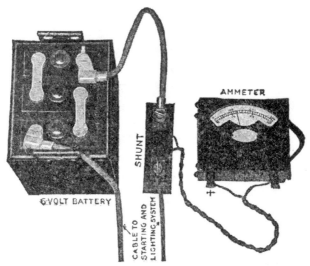

Fig. 28. Setup for Testing Rate of Discharge of Small Storage Battery

Courtesy of Prest-O-Lite Company, Indianapolis, Indiana

as shown in the illustration, Fig. 28. Then connect the ammeter terminals to the shunt. In case the instrument shows a reverse reading, reverse the connections to the shunt, which will be indicated by the tendency of the needle to move backward.

When the ammeter is connected to test for discharge, the starter must never be used unless the 300-ampere shunt is in circuit, as otherwise the instrument is likely to be damaged.

If a shunt of smaller capacity or a self-contained ammeter, that is, one designed to be connected directly in the line is employed and it is necessary to start the engine, either crank by hand or the ammeter should be disconnected before using the starting motor.

When the ammeter is connected to show the discharge and no lights are on, the engine being idle, no current is being used for any purpose, and the pointer of the ammeter should remain at zero. If any flow of current (discharge) is indicated, it shows that there is a ground or a short-circuit (a leak) somewhere in the system. In such a case, apply the usual tests described under the appropriate headings for locating grounds and short-circuits.

With the ammeter connected up as shown in the illustration, the discharge rate of the battery under the various loads it is called upon to carry may be checked up, and, if it proves to be excessive in any case, the trouble may be remedied. For example, with the 300-ampere shunt in the line, the amount of energy consumed by the starting motor may be checked. Without knowing how much current a certain make of starting motor should consume in turning over a given type of engine, it will naturally be impossible to make any intelligent comparisons with the result of the tests. This information, however, is readily obtainable from the manufacturer of the starting system, and it will be found advantageous to obtain details of this nature covering the various systems in general use in your locality, as it will enable you to make these tests valuable in correcting faults. While the starting loads imposed on the electric motor by different engines will vary greatly, the general nature of the load will be practically the same in all cases. When the starter switch is closed, there will be an excessive discharge rate from the battery for a few seconds, the discharge falling off very rapidly as the inertia of the engine is overcome and it begins to turn over, with a still greater drop to a comparatively small discharge the moment it takes up its cycle and begins to run under its own power.

Before undertaking such tests, see that the battery is in good condition and fully charged. Make several tests. Note in each case whether the maximum discharge at the moment of closing the switch exceeds the maximum called for by the maker of the starting system. If a great deal more current is necessary to turn the engine over than should be the case, it is an indication either that the starting motor is in need of attention or that the engine itself is unusually stiff. Atmospheric conditions will naturally have a decided effect on the result of such tests, as an engine that has stood overnight in a cold garage will be gummed up with thick lubricating oil and will require more power to move it at first than if it had been running only a few minutes before. As a general rule, more power will always be needed in winter than in summer, unless the tests are carried out in a well-heated garage. The condition of the engine itself will also have an important bearing on the significance of the tests, as, if the engine has been overhauled recently, its main bearings may have been tightened up to a point where the engine as a whole is very stiff.

Note also whether the discharge rate falls off as quickly as it should when the engine begins to turn over rapidly. If it does not, this also is an indication of tight bearings, gummed lubricating oil, or similar causes, rendering the engine harder to turn over. In the case of a cold engine, stiffness due to the lubricating oil may be remedied by running it for ten or fifteen minutes, and a subsequent test should then agree with the manufacturer's rating. Where the discharge rate does not drop to a nominal amperage within a few seconds from the time of closing the switch, it is simply an indication that the essentials of the engine are not in the best of working order. The carburetor may not be working properly, or the ignition may be sluggish.

In case the discharge rate is very much less than that called for by the manufacturer for that particular engine, it is an indication that the starting system itself is not in the best condition. Poor connections, worn brushes, loose brush springs, a dirty switch, or some similar cause is greatly increasing the resistance in the starting circuit, thus cutting down materially the amount of current that the battery can force through it. In such circumstances, the discharge may not reach so high a rate as that called for by the manufacturer, but to effect a start, even with the engine in normally good condition, a high rate will have to be continued longer, to the correspondingly greater detriment of the battery. In other words, a great deal more current must be drawn from the battery each time the engine is started. Thus, testing the rate of discharge may be made to serve as an indication of the condition of both the starting system and the engine itself. Should it be necessary to make more than eight or ten starts to determine definitely the cause of any variation between the discharge rates shown and those that should be indicated, with everything in normally good condition, the battery should be fully recharged before proceeding any further, as using it for this purpose when almost exhausted is very likely to damage it. Tests of this kind show also whether the efficiency of the battery has fallen off substantially or not, as indicated by its condition after making several starts in succession. When this has been done, the battery may be tested with the voltmeter and hydrometer to ascertain how far it has been discharged. The fact that after having been in service for some time a starting system will not start the engine so many times without exhausting the battery as it would when new may be due either to a loss of efficiency in the battery or to the poor condition of the other essentials of the system. In the majority of cases, however, it will be due to the condition of the battery.

By substituting the 30-ampere shunt for the 300-ampere, the load put on the battery by the lights when switched on in various combinations may be checked and compared with the manufacturer's ratings. Where the discharge rate for the lights is less than it should be, it may be due to the use of bulbs which have seen a great deal of service, the resistance of the filaments increasing with age, or other causes which place more resistance in the circuit, such as poor connections, loose or dirty switches, and the like. Tests may also be made of the ignition system where the battery is called upon to supply current to a distributor and coil by putting the 3-ampere shunt in the circuit. The amount of current required by the ignition system is very small when everything is in normal working order, usually not more than $1\frac{1}{2}$ to 2 amperes. This also can be obtained definitely from the maker of the apparatus. Any great increase in the amount of current necessary would usually indicate arcing at the contact points, which should prove to be in poor condition; a subnormal discharge would signify a great increase in the resistance as in the foregoing cases, and should be evidenced by poor ignition service.

To Test Rate of Charge. To determine the rate at which the battery is being charged (the small dash ammeters are only approximately accurate), reverse the ammeter connections and start the engine by hand. If the car is equipped with a straight 6- or 12-volt system and a dash ammeter is used, see that its reading agrees approximately with the portable ammeter. Should the variation be small, advise the owner so that he may correct his readings accordingly when noting the instrument on the road. In case it is very large, the dash ammeter itself should be adjusted, which can frequently be done merely by bending the pointer.

With the engine running fast enough to give the maximum charging rate, which is indicated by the fact that the ammeter needle stops rising, check the charging rate shown on the portable ammeter, bearing the following in mind: In the majority of cars, the generator is regulated to charge the battery at from 10 to 15 amperes. Some are designed to charge at as low a rate as 7 amperes. Unless the proper charging rate is definitely known, whatever maximum the portable ammeter shows may usually be assumed to be correct. Where the rate is less than 7 amperes it may generally be taken for granted, however, that the battery is undercharging, and the various tests, described in detail under appropriate headings, may be applied to locate the trouble either in the generator or in the automatic cut-out. This applies where the charging rate is too high as well as where it is too low.

The charging rates mentioned above naturally apply only to a 6-volt battery, or to a battery having a greater number of cells, which is connected in series multiple so as to charge at 6 volts. In the case of a six-cell battery permanently connected in series so that it both charges and discharges at 12 volts, the above figures must be cut in half. Twelve-cell batteries are employed in some cases, but the total voltage of the battery is used only for starting, the cells being divided into four groups in series multiple so that each group of three cells charges at 6 volts.

With the generator charging at 10 to 15 amperes, turn on all the lights. If more current is being drawn from the battery than is being supplied by the generator, this will be indicated by the ammeter showing a reverse reading or discharge. It signifies that there is a short-circuit in the lighting switch or the lamps, or in the wiring between the switch and the lamps, or that additional lights, other than those furnished originally with the system, have been added, or larger candle-power bulbs substituted, thus placing too great a demand on the battery.

If the system has been out of adjustment for any length of time, it is quite likely that the battery will shortly need repairs or replacement, because charging at an excessive rate causes the plates to buckle and break through the separators, forming an internal short-circuit, while charging at too low a rate causes a constantly discharged condition of the battery, due to more current being normally called for than is put in. This results in injurious sulphating of the plates.

In case additional equipment has been added, the entire equipment should be turned on, and the total current required should be noted when making discharge-rate tests. Where the generator cannot supply sufficient current to permit the battery to take care of this extra equipment, the battery should be charged from an outside source at regular intervals. It is poor practice to increase the charging rate of the generator, as it is likely to injure the battery through overheating. Where it is necessary to have a higher charging rate than that originally called for by the system, it is preferable to substitute a larger battery. The charging rate of the generator may then be safely increased in accordance with the demand.

In cold weather, it may be necessary to slightly increase the charging rate of the generator in order to compensate for the extra current the battery is called upon to supply. This is owing, not only to the fact that there is a much greater demand on the starting system in cold weather, but also to the fact that the battery is less efficient under winter conditions of operation.

Connections for Two-Voltage Batteries. Where the battery is of either three or six cells, all connected permanently in series, the foregoing suggestions for connecting the testing instruments apply. They must be varied, however, where tests are to be made of batteries connected in series multiple, which may be termed two-voltage batteries since they supply current at one voltage for lighting and at another for starting. In Fig. 29 is shown a battery of this type which is connected so as to charge and discharge through the starting motor at 12 volts, but which discharges at 6 volts to supply the lamps through a neutral lead in the center of the battery. The sketch indicates where to connect the ammeter shunt on charge at 12 volts and on discharge at 6 volts. When testing the starting-motor discharge, it would be connected for 12 volts.

Test the 12-volt circuit with the engine running to get the charging rate; stop the engine, reverse the ammeter terminals and see whether there is any discharge indicating a short-circuit. Also test the discharge rate on the 6-volt circuit with the lights turned off and again with all lights on. These tests should show whether or not there is a short-circuit in the system. Before attempting to

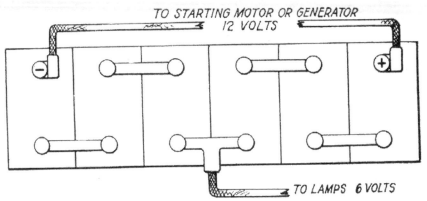

Fig. 29. Battery Connection for 12-Volt Starting Motor and Generator with 6-Volt Connection for Lamps

test the discharge rate of the starting motor, be certain that the 300-ampere shunt is in the circuit. A 12-volt battery will discharge only about half the current necessary to start the engine with a 6-volt battery, but no shunt smaller than the 300-ampere size can be depended upon to carry the load safely and protect the instrument.

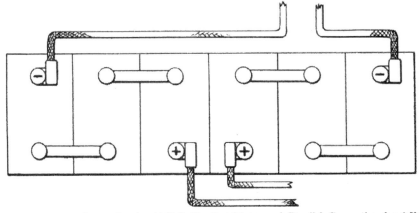

Fig. 30. Battery Connection for 12-Volt Starting Motor and Parallel Connection for 6-Volt Charging and 6-Volt Lighting System

Fig. 30 shows a 12-volt battery connected up in such a manner that it is practically two 6-volt batteries in parallel. The battery is charged at 6 volts, and both the lights and horn are supplied with current at this voltage, but the discharge through the starting motor is at 12 volts. Note the two positive cables leading to the center of the battery. To test the charging rate, the ammeter shunt should be connected first in one of these cables and then in the other, and the two readings added together to obtain the charging rate for the entire battery. The same locations for the shunt, and the same method of adding the readings also apply on discharge. Ammeter readings in the connections shown will indicate whether or not there are any short-circuits, except, of course, in the starting-motor cable.

Voltage Tests. An equally important instrument for the testing of the storage battery is the voltmeter. It is chiefly useful in showing whether a cell is short-circuited or otherwise in bad condition. Under some conditions, it indicates when the battery is practically discharged, but, like the hydrometer, it must not be relied upon alone. It should be used in conjunction with the hydrometer readings to insure accuracy. Since a variation as low as .1 (one-tenth) of a volt makes considerable difference in what the reading indicates as to the condition of the battery, it will be apparent that a cheap and inaccurate voltmeter is likely to be misleading rather than helpful. For garage use, a good reliable instrument with several connections for giving a variable range of readings should be employed. Instructions furnished with the instrument give in detail the method of using the various connections, and these instructions should be followed closely, as otherwise the voltmeter is likely to be damaged. For example, on the 3-volt scale only one cell should be tested. Attempting to test any more is likely to burn out the 3-volt coil in the meter. The total voltage of the number of cells tested must never exceed the reading of the particular scale being used at the time, as otherwise the instrument will be ruined.

Always make certain that the place on the connector selected for the contact of the testing point is clean and bright and that the contact is firm, as otherwise the reading will be misleading, since the increased resistance of a poor contact will cut down the voltage. The positive terminal of the voltmeter must be brought in contact with the positive terminal of the battery, and the negative terminal of the voltmeter with the negative terminal of the battery. If the markings of the cell terminals are indistinct, the proper terminals may be determined by connecting the voltmeter across any one cell. Should the pointer not give any voltage reading, butting up against the stop at the left instead, the connections are wrong and should be reversed; if the instrument shows a reading for one cell, the positive terminal of the voltmeter is in contact with the positive of the cell. This test can be made with a voltmeter without any risk of short-circuiting the cell, since the voltmeter is wound to a high resistance and will pass very little current. This is not the case with an ammeter, however, as connecting such an instrument directly across the terminals of the battery will immediately burn out the ammeter.

Inasmuch as any cell, when idle, will show approximately 2 volts, regardless of whether it is fully charged or not, voltage readings

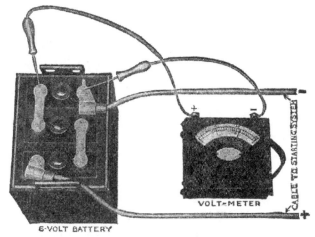

Fig. 31. Proper Setup for Testing Voltage of Batteries

taken when the battery is on open circuit, i.e., neither charging nor discharging, are practically valueless, *except when a cell is out of order.* Therefore, a load, such as switching on the lamps, should be put on the battery before making voltage tests. With the lights on, connect the voltmeter as explained above and test the individual cells, as shown in Fig. 31. If the battery is in good condition, the voltage readings after the load has been on for about five minutes will be but slightly lower (about one-tenth of a volt) than if the battery were on open circuit. If any of the cells are completely discharged the voltage of these cells will drop rapidly when the load is first put on and, sometimes when a cell is out of order, even show reverse readings. Where the battery is nearly discharged, the voltage of each cell will be considerably lower tnan if the battery were on open circuit after the load has been on for five minutes. In the case of an electric-vehicle battery, the lights alone would not provide sufficient load for making an accurate test, so that one of the rear wheels may be jacked up and the brake set lightly until the ammeter on the dash of the car shows 50 to 70 per cent of the usual normal reading. To do this, start the motor on first speed with the brakes loose, and apply the brakes slowly until the desired load is shown by the ammeter reading. Never, under any circumstances, attempt to start with the brakes locked or on hard, as both the battery and the motor will be damaged. In the case of a starting-system battery, the lights alone are sufficient load, as they consume about 10 amperes.

To distinguish the difference between cells that are merely discharged and those that are out of order, put the battery on charge (crank the engine by hand in the case of a starter battery) and test again with the voltmeter. If the voltage does not rise to approximately 2 volts per cell within a short time, it is evidence of internal trouble which can be remedied only by dismantling the cell.

Cleaning Repair Parts. The advent of electric starting and lighting systems has added appreciably to the amount of attention required by machines in the garage, particularly as this essential is a part of the car about which its owner generally knows little. In fact, it is not overstating it to say that fully 25 per cent of all the repair work now carried on in the garage has for its object the keeping of the electrical equipment of the car in good operating condition. Where many cars are cared for and repairs to their electric systems are made as far as possible right in the garage, it will be found advisable to install a method of cleaning parts. Owing to the accumulations of dirt and grease that parts carry after having been in service for a year or more, cleaning them thoroughly before making any repairs makes it possible to detect defects which might otherwise pass unnoticed. The following instructions are reprinted through the courtesy of the makers of the Delco apparatus, and they strongly recommend that the solutions mentioned be used in the exact manner directed, as they are the result of several years' experience in this work, and considerable care has been used in checking them. The sizes of the tanks given are merely indicative of what a very large repair shop would require and are comparative only.

Cleaning Outfit. The cleaning outfit should consist of **three** sheet-steel tanks, Fig. 32, of suitable size (35 gallons **for a large** shop) mounted so that their contents may be kept heated to the desired temperature, three stone jars of approximately 15 gallons capacity, and a sawdust box. Two of the steel tanks should be equipped with overflow pipes so that they can be kept about two-thirds full at all times. These are tanks No. 1 and No. 2. They **are** used for clear hot water for rinsing parts after they have been cleaned.

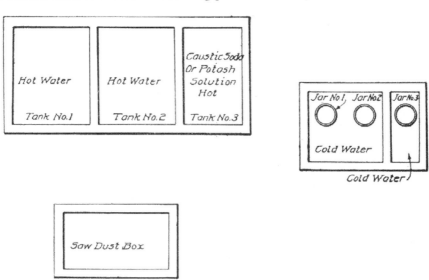

Fig. 32. Layout for Battery Cleaning Outfit

The third tank does not require a drain nor an overflow pipe and is used for the potash or caustic soda solution. This can be used for a long time without changing by simply adding a small amount of soda as the solution weakens. All three tanks are maintained at a temperature of 180° to 212° F., or approximately the boiling point.

The three jars mentioned are used for the acid solutions and are referred to as jars No. 1, No. 2, and No. 3. A wood tank large enough to hold the three jars and divided into two compartments, as shown in Fig. 32, should be provided. This is important, as the parts cannot be rinsed in the same cold water after being immersed in the different acid solutions. The solutions recommended are in tanks 1 and 2, clear hot water; tank 3, a solution consisting of one pound of caustic soda per gallon of water. Jar No. 1 is filled with a solution consisting of four gallons of nitric acid, one gallon of water, and six gallons of sulphuric acid. The water is placed in the jar first, the nitric acid is added slowly, and the sulphuric acid is poured in last. This order must be strictly followed, as it is dangerous to mix a solution of these acids in any other manner. In jar No. 2, the solution is one gallon of hydrochloric acid to three gallons of water, while jar No. 3 contains a solution of one-half pound of cyanide to a gallon of water. Tank No. 2 should be used only for parts which have been in the potash solution and for no other purpose. Tank No. 1 is for general rinsing purposes.

Method of Cleaning Parts. Various metals are cleaned as follows: Steel is boiled in the potash solution until the dirt is removed, which should require only a few minutes. The steel part is then rinsed in tank No. 2 and dried in sawdust. Cast iron parts are boiled in the potash solution to remove dirt, rinsed in tank No. 2, dipped in the acid solution in jar No. 1, rinsed thoroughly in cold clear water, dipped in the cyanide solution, rinsed again in cold clear water, then rinsed in tank No. 1 and dried in sawdust. Copper can be cleaned in the same manner. Polished aluminum should first be thoroughly washed in gasoline, rinsed in tank No. 1, dipped in the acid solution in jar No. 1, rinsed thoroughly in cold clear water, rinsed in tank No. 1, and dried in sawdust. Plain aluminum, unpolished, should be dipped in the potash solution, rinsed in tank No. 2, dipped for a few seconds in the acid solution, rinsed in tank No. 2, dipped for a few seconds in the acid solution in Jar No. 1, rinsed in cold water, then rinsed in tank No. 1, and dried in sawdust.

It will be noticed that when aluminum is put into the potash solution the metal is attacked and eaten away rapidly, so that polished parts of this metal should not be put into this solution, and any aluminum parts should not be left in for a moment longer than necessary. Where the parts are covered with caked deposits of hard grease, they should first be washed in gasoline. Aluminum parts should never be put into the potash solution unless they can be put through the acid immediately after, as the acid dip neutralizes the effect of the potash solution. Parts should only be held in the acid for a few seconds. Paint should first be removed with a good paint or varnish remover unless it is present in very small quantity, and unless the aluminum parts are to go through the potash solution. Enameled work should be washed with soap and water, dried thoroughly, and then polished with a cloth dampened with a good oil, such as Three-in-One. These cleaning methods apply only to solid parts and should never be employed on any plated pieces, as the caustic and acid would immediately strip off the plating. Such parts can be cleaned only in gasoline. It will be apparent, however, that cleaning in this manner will be found advantageous for many parts of the car that have to be repaired other than those of the electric equipment, and, in view of the high cost of gasoline, will be found much more economical as well as much more thorough.

CURTISS AIRPLANE ENGINE

ELECTRICAL REPAIRS

PART I

TESTING EQUIPMENT

The repair of electrical equipment is not often attempted by the ordinary garage repair man because he does not understand the methods of testing the different units or does not have the necessary equipment.

Every repair man should know how to test for trouble in connection with the electrical units and a knowledge of the different parts of the electrical equipment is essential if correct electrical repairs are to be made. If the principle upon which the different units operate is known, a test can readily be made. Of course, there are parts of the electrical system which need special tools and equipment, as in the case of armature repairs, but the simple tests should be made before the unit is sent out for repair in order to determine the cost of the repair.

The best type of equipment proves to be the most economical in the end, and it should be purchased from manufacturers who make a specialty of such equipment. Instruments, such as voltmeters and ampere meters, should always be purchased, and only the best instruments can be relied upon to give accurate readings. In the following pages some equipment is shown that is used for electrical tests. Some parts of this equipment can be made by a person who is handy with tools.

The simple lamp test outfit is the handiest type to use in making general tests. The set, Fig. 1, is for use with outside power, but a similar set can be made for use with the ordinary storage battery. The difference between the two sets is in the type of bulb used in the socket. A 6-volt lamp must be used in a car having a 6-volt battery, and a 12-volt lamp must be used with a 12-volt battery.

A service station or repair shop that can make repairs to electrical equipment will find that a great deal more business will come to the shop than if only mechanical repairs can be made. A repair man who knows how to make accurate tests when hunting trouble in the electrical side of the automobile will find that his services will always be in demand and a study of the following pages on the equipment and methods used for electrical work will be very helpful to all who are interested in the automobile.

Take a porcelain base socket, screw it to a piece of board to form a base. Connect one side of this lamp socket to a standard

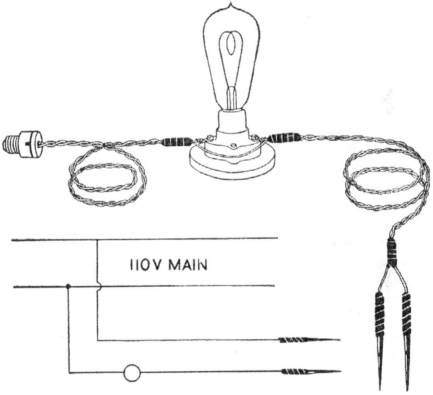

Fig. 1. Handy Testing Set

screw plug. Procure two pieces of brass or steel rod and file or grind them to a long tapering point. These rods should be about 6 inches long and tapering half their length to a sharp point. Connect the other side of the lamp socket to one of these points and connect the second point to the other terminal of the screw plug. Ordinary lamp cord can be used for the connections. For fastening to the test points it should be bared for several inches, wrapped solidly around the metal rods at their blunt ends, and

257

soldered fast in place. The joints should be heavily wrapped with tape or covered with other insulating material to form a handle. as shown in the illustration, Fig. 1. As shown by the diagram forming part of this illustration, it will be seen that the lamp is in series with one of the points, but that when the circuit is closed by bringing the two points together, the lamp is in multiple with the main circuit. The lamp should be of the carbon-filament type owing to its greater durability. As a lamp of this type of 16 c-p. only consumes a little over 50 watts at 110 volts, or approximately half an ampere of current, there is no danger of injuring any of the apparatus on the automobile through its use. Sufficient cord should be allowed on either side of the lamp to permit of connecting it up with the outlet conveniently.

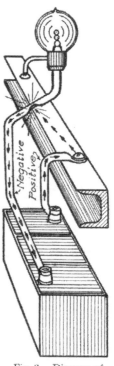

In using this test outfit, the two test points are pressed on places between which no current should pass, and if the lamp lights it indicates that there is a ground between those points. For example, suppose there were a ground between the generator and the switch so that no current reached the latter, the lamp would not light when the test points were placed on terminals 1 and 7 of the diagram, the generator then being in operation. But a little searching along this circuit would soon show where it was grounded, thus making it easy to locate the break or ground. Fig. 2 is a graphic illustration of a ground causing a short circuit,

Fig. 2. Diagram of Ground or Short Circuit
Courtesy of Gray and Davis Company

due to worn insulation. Much more satisfactory results can be obtained with a test set of this nature than with either an expensive hand ringing magneto test set, or with a set consisting of a bell or buzzer and a few dry cells. The former is unnecessarily expensive for the purpose while the latter has not sufficient potential to force the current through grounds or breaks that present too great a resistance, whereas the higher voltage of the lamp test set will cause it to give an indication where the battery set would not. With the aid of such a set, every circuit shown on even the most complicated of wiring diagrams can be tested in fifteen to twenty minutes, maybe less, depending upon how accessible the connections of the various circuits happen to be.

If preferred, owing to greater convenience, a 6-volt lamp can be used in the socket of the test set and current from the car battery can be utilized for testing. In case the car happens to have either a 12-volt or a 24-volt system, connect lamp terminals to but three of the cells. Should the lamp not light to full incandescence it

Fig. 3. Portable Combination Volt-Ammeter for Testing

will indicate that the battery is weak, and a battery that is in good condition should replace the weak one.

In case the battery does not respond to any of the ordinary methods of treatment given then, it will usually be found preferable to refer it to the nearest service station of the battery manufacturer. This is particularly the case where after refilling with distilled water to the proper level and slowly recharging, the battery does not increase in voltage and specific gravity reading with the hydrometer, as it will need overhauling before it can give good service.

Always Test the Lamp. Whether a standard 110-volt lamp or one of the 6-volt type (for which an adapter may be necessary to fit the standard socket) is used, it is a good precaution always to test the lamp itself before going over the wiring on the car. This will avoid the necessity for blaming things generally after failing to find any circuit at all—after fifteen miutes of trying everything on the car—due to the lamp having a broken filament or one of its connections having loosened up.

Special Testing Instruments. For the garage that claims to be fully equipped to give all necessary attention to the electrical system of the modern car, something more than the simple lamp testing outfit is necessary. Portable volt-ammeters such as shown in Fig. 3 are made specially for this purpose. This is a Weston combination volt-ammeter, the voltmeter being provided with a 0–30, 0–3, and 0 to $\frac{1}{10}$ scales for making voltage tests, together with three shunts having a capacity of 0–300, 0–30, and 0–3 amperes, respectively, which are used in connection with the

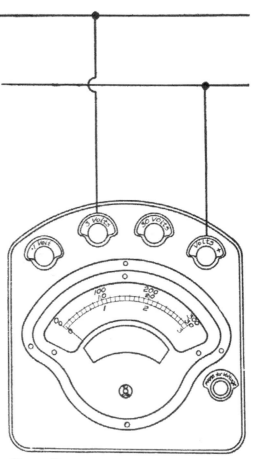

Fig. 4. Diagram Showing 3-Volt Scale Connected across a Circuit

$\frac{1}{10}$-volt scale for making current measurements. A special set of calibrated leads for use with these shunts is also provided. With the aid of such an outfit, accurate tests can be made covering the condition and performance of every part of a starting-lighting and ignition installation. For example, a starting system may be otherwise in perfect working condition, but its operation causes such an excessive demand on the storage battery that the generator is not capable of keeping the latter sufficiently charged. Generator tests, which are described later, having failed to show anything wrong with the dynamo, a test of the starting motor, using the 0–300-ampere shunt of the instrument would doubtless show that an unnecessarily large amount of current was being demanded

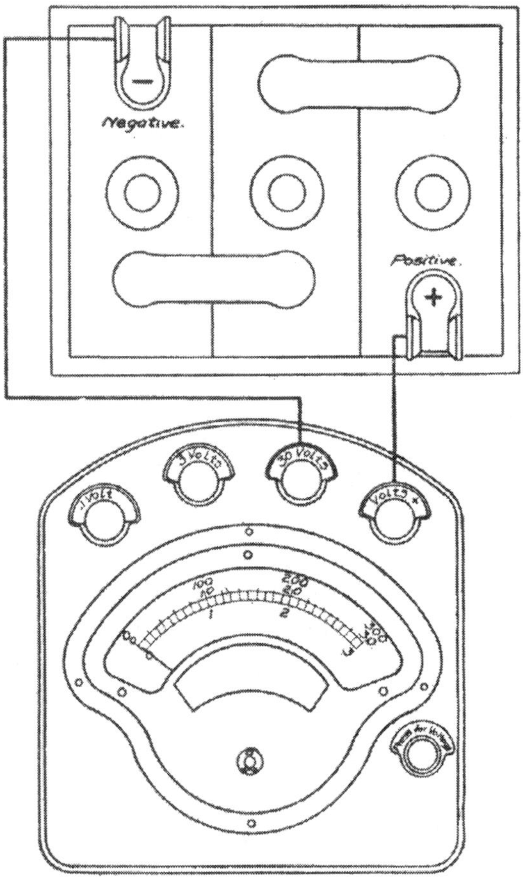

Fig. 5.   Diagram Showing 30-Volt Scale Connected across Storage Battery Terminals

by the motor for its operation, and indicate a fault in the latter.

Voltage Tests. When the instrument is used as a voltmeter it is necessary to select the proper scale for the circuit, and if there is any doubt it is well to start with the 30-volt scale. For testing individual cells of the storage battery the 3-volt scale would naturally be used, while for testing the entire battery, the 30-volt scale would be the proper one to apply. The proper method of connecting the voltmeter to the circuit is shown by the diagrams, Figs. 4 and 5. It is necessary to connect the positive side of the meter to the positive side of the circuit and the other terminal to the negative. Where the polarity of the circuit is not known, this can be readily determined by a trial reading. If the pointer moves to the right, the connections are properly made; in case it moves to the left, it will be necessary to reverse the connections, which should be done at the circuit terminals and not at the meter, to avoid any accidental short circuits.

261

Ammeter Readings. When using the ammeter to determine the amount of current consumed by any of the apparatus, such as the starting motor or the lamps, it is necessary to first select the proper shunt. Should the value of the current to be measured be unknown, it is well always to start with the 300-ampere shunt

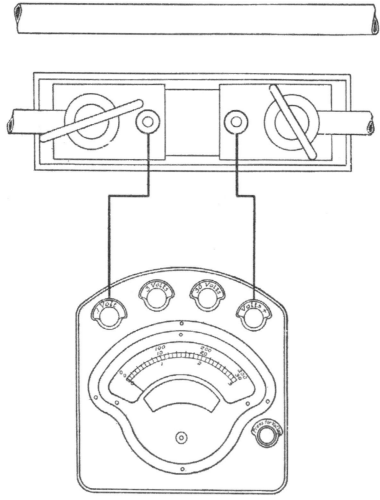

Fig. 6. Diagram Showing Method of Connecting Ammeter to 300-Ampere Shunt

and then insert the 30-ampere shunt in case the reading shows the current to be less than 30 amperes. These shunts are connected in the manner shown by Fig. 6, and as will be plain from this diagram, all shunts are connected in the circuit in a similar manner. The connections always remaining the same, it is only necessary to substitute the different shunts as required by the circuit to be measured. If the polarity be reversed, it is only necessary to shift the connections from the ammeter to the shunt which should be done at the latter, there being no necessity to change the connections of the shunt itself to the circuit.

The 300-ampere shunt must always be used for measuring the starting current, as the latter will rarely have a value of less than 200 amperes when the switch is first closed owing to the necessity of exerting great power at first to overcome the inertia of the gasoline engine, particularly at a low temperature when the lubricating oil has become gummed. Cables of the same size as those employed on the starting-motor circuit of the car should be provided for connecting up the shunt to make the tests. The 30-ampere shunt is employed for measuring the charging current to the battery, while the 3-ampere shunt is used for the individual lighting circuits or for the primary ignition current.

Care should be taken to use instruments of the proper capacity so that no damage will be done to the delicate mechanism of the testing instrument. If an ammeter of 30 ampere capacity is used to test the amperage in a battery of 200 ampere capacity the mechanism inside the instrument will be damaged beyond repair.

Growler Armature Tester. This type of tester is the most efficient, and results are obtained quicker than by other methods. Several makes may be had. In selecting one, be sure that it has sufficient strength to do the work, as some of them are too small or have insufficient saturation to give results.

The principle of the *growler* is the same as that of the transformer, and it operates on alternating current, generally 110 volts. Fig. 7 shows a good design. The two coils *A* form the primary of the transformer; the frame and pole pieces *B*, the magnetic circuit, which is open.

When an armature is placed between the pole pieces, the armature core completes this circuit. The armature conductors form the secondary winding, and if there are no short-circuits in the coils, very little current or voltage is induced in the windings, as in any transformer. Should there be a shorted coil, a heavy current is induced owing to the closed circuit of the short-circuited coil. This sets up a heavy vibration at the slot carrying the shorted coil, which can be felt, or heard, by placing a piece of thin steel or a hack-saw blade over the slot.

Operation. In testing, the armature is slowly revolved in the growler, and each slot is felt with the saw blade, as it comes to the top. If the armature is left on for a few minutes, the short-circuited coil will become hot and will eventually burn out. Commutator shorts due to small particles of copper dragged over the insulation when turning, commonly called "bugs," will be burned off by this heavy induced current. A poorly designed growler will not do this. In testing for an open coil, short-circuit each commutator segment in turn as the armature is revolved; each segment should give a spark owing to the induced current. In case of an open coil, no spark will result. In testing for grounds such as between the commutator and the armature shaft, a grounded winding will cause a spark.

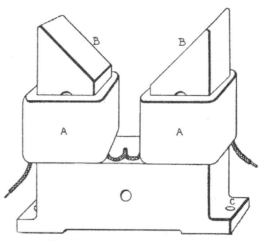

Fig. 7. Growler for Testing Armature

Design. The following is an efficient design of growler that may be readily built in the shop, in case it is not desired to buy one:

In Fig. 8 is shown a lamination of the proper shape and size cut from ordinary sheet iron and with three holes drilled for the holding bolts. There should be enough laminations to build up to a thickness of $2\frac{1}{4}$ inches, and the whole assembly should then be bolted together. Although sheet-iron laminations are the most efficient, the lessened efficiency of cast iron makes very little difference, as the growler is only used for a short time and the cast iron does not have time to heat.

To make the cast laminations, a pattern should be cut from $\frac{1}{4}$-inch pine to the shape of Fig. 8. The small lugs at the bottom are for the feet to bolt to the bench. The holes should be drilled after casting. The pattern should have three coats of shellac and should be sandpapered after each coat has been applied. Nine castings are necessary. Smooth up the castings on the sides and stack them together; hold them with clamps, then drill three $\frac{1}{4}$-inch holes through the whole assembly, as located in Fig. 8; and with the clamp still in place, rivet them together with $\frac{1}{4}$-inch iron rod. Do not set the rivets too tightly as the iron is likely to crack. Drill two $\frac{1}{4}$-inch holes in the legs, as at C, Fig. 7; these holes can be drilled from the bottom very easily.

The assembled frame can now be smoothed up on the emery wheel, especially the surface of the pole pieces B. The coils A

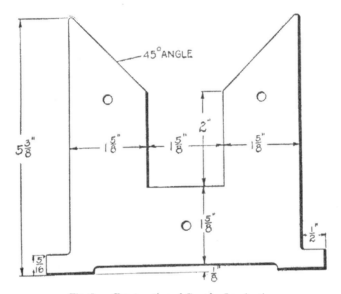

Fig. 8.   Construction of Growler Lamination

are wound up on a wooden form, and each coil consists of 175 turns of No. 14 B.& S. gage copper magnet wire, each wound in the same direction. Leads should be brought out, using lamp cord. The coils are taped as shown in the illustration and are well shellacked. The two coils are placed on the frame, with the two inner leads at the same side; these two leads are connected together, and the two outside leads are brought out and connected to a 110-volt alternating-current circuit through a switch. As it is easy to forget to turn off the growler and as it makes no noise when there is no armature on it, it is well to connect a lamp in the circuit, Fig. 9, using a snap switch to turn it off and on.

ELECTRICAL EQUIPMENT

Undercutting Machine. Most undercutting of commutators is done by hand with an old hack-saw blade and is both slow and unsatisfactory. There are several types of machines for doing this mechanically; some do a smooth job, but others take longer

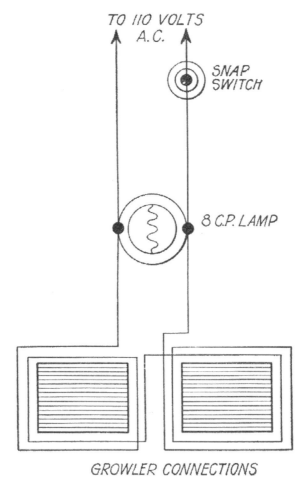

TO 110 VOLTS A.C.

SNAP SWITCH

8 C.P. LAMP

GROWLER CONNECTIONS

Fig. 9. Method of Wiring Growler

and give worse results than the hack-saw blade. The revolving needle gives excellent results and is the quickest of any type. Its adaptability to commutators of various sizes and to different conditions and its quickness in setting up make it very valuable for quick repair and service work.

Its work is clean cut and uniform, with no scratches left on the

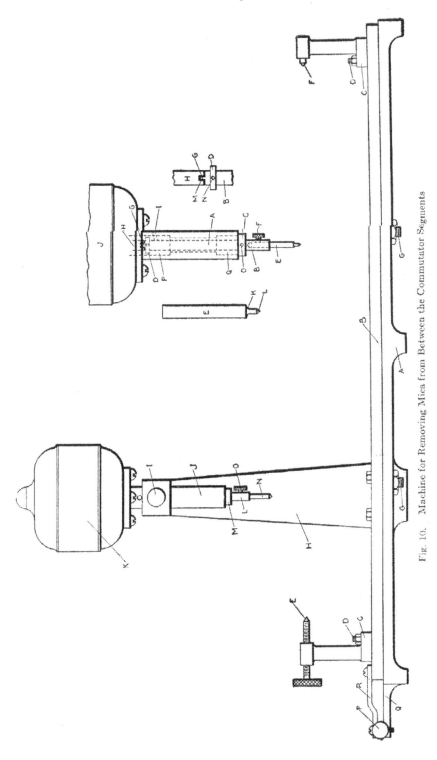

Fig. 10.   Machine for Removing Mica from Between the Commutator Segments

commutator. A design for a machine of this type is given for those wishing to make one, as there are but few on the market at present.

Design. In Fig. 10 is given a side view of a motor-driven machine. The base *A* is made of cast iron 24 inches long, $5\frac{1}{2}$ inches wide, and $1\frac{1}{2}$ inches high; sliding on this base is a carriage

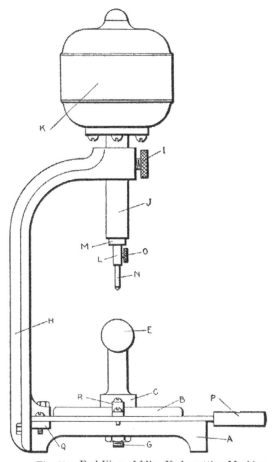

Fig. 11.　End View of Mica Undercutting Machine

B, made 3 inches wide and $\frac{5}{8}$ inch thick, which slides on rails cut on the base. Mounted on the carriage are two center brackets *C;* these are bolted on with the nut *D*. The center screw *E* is adjustable; the center *F* is solid. The column *H* holds the motor and cutter assembly. The motor *K* should be about a $\frac{1}{8}$-horsepower, 110-volt, high-speed universal type, using either alternating-current or direct-current. The motor is mounted on the spindle J and is held in adjustment by the set screw I on the column. The needle N is held in the shaft L by the set screw O.

The armature is placed between centers, the spindle J is adjusted to the proper height, and the carriage is moved back and forth by the handle P through the linkage R, cutting out the mica to the required depth. Fig. 11 shows an end view. The column H is ribbed for strength and is fastened to the base, 8 inches from the end, with four $\frac{5}{16}$-inch standard cap screws, an extra wide leg being cast on the base to support it. The set screw I is $\frac{5}{16}$-inch S.A.E. thread and is knurled. The handle operating the carriage is of $\frac{3}{8}$-inch fiber, and the lever is hinged on the bracket Q, which is cast on the base. The bracket Q is $1\frac{1}{2}$ inches long and has a hole drilled and tapped for 10–32 screws; this bracket should be $\frac{1}{4}$ inch thick and $\frac{3}{4}$ inch wide. The base A has two rails cut on its top, the carriage B being planed to fit. These rails need not extend more than 6 inches on each end, as a lessened surface will reduce friction of the carriage. A bolt, or stud, is mounted rigid in the carriage, and a nut and washer hold it on; the slot should be slightly larger than the stud. The thread on this stud should be rather tight to prevent loosening, while the washer may be a spring or cupped washer to take up any variation in the machining.

The carriage also has a groove cut $\frac{1}{2}$ inch wide, extending within 6 inches of each end in the center of the casting. This is for the center standards C to slide in; by having both centers slide, any armature may be fitted quickly. The standards have a tongue which fits into the groove and is held by a $\frac{7}{16}$-inch carriage bolt with the head turned thin; the squared portion of the bolt prevents turning while adjusting. The rear center is solid in the standard, while the front center is adjustable. The knurled screw E should be of $\frac{7}{16}$-inch stock with an S.A.E. thread, both centers having a 60-degree taper.

The needle assembly, Fig. 10, consists of a spindle A, on which is mounted the motor J screwed to the flange. The shaft B is a piece of $\frac{1}{4}$-inch drill rod, which comes perfectly true and smooth. A collar C is pinned on with a $\frac{1}{16}$-inch pin O; the spindle is bored out to take two bronze bushings P and Q, which are pressed in and reamed to $\frac{1}{4}$ inch. An oil hole I is drilled to oil the upper bearing, the surplus oil running down the shaft and oiling the lower bearing. The shaft is placed in the spindle and a collar is pinned on at the top D. The detail sketch in Fig. 10 shows the end of the shaft, which has a tongue G fitting into a slot M in the motor shaft H, giving a positive, though flexible, drive.

The lower end of the shaft is drilled to take the needle E, which is held in by the knurled screw F. The needles are made of $\frac{1}{8}$-inch drill rod, turned down and having a round shoulder K for strength, the lower shank being of various diameters, depending on the width of the slot to be undercut. It is best to make

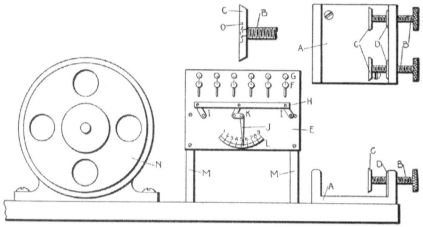

Fig. 12.   Magneto Test Stand

about three sizes of shanks. The point or cutting edge should be pointed and ground three sided, being careful to get each side the same and preserving a true center of the point. After the points are shaped, they should be tempered to a dull blue and finished with an oil stone. When the carriage is assembled on the base, place a little fine valve grinding compound and oil on the rails and grind in the surfaces to a smooth finish; this will ensure easy operation. Holes should be drilled in the base A and the machine fastened to the bench.

Operation. To undercut an armature, place the armature between the centers, moving the centers so that the commutator will come under the needle, and screw up the adjustable center so that the armature will be fairly tight. Select the size of needle suitable for the width of commutator slot, lower the needle so that it will cut away about $\frac{1}{32}$ inch of mica, hold the armature steady with the slot opposite the needle, and steadily draw the needle into the slot, cutting a smooth groove the full length of the commutator; still holding the armature steady, withdraw the needle and cut the next slot, and so on. A little practice will make a smooth quick job. After all the slots are cut, place the armature in the lathe and take off the slight burrs with No. 00 sandpaper.

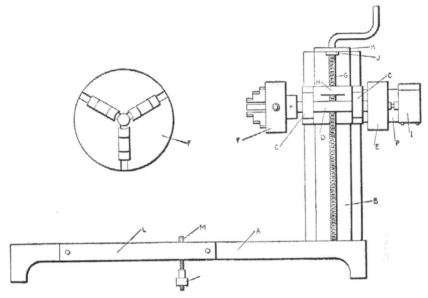

Fig. 13.   Generator Test Stand

Magneto Test Stand. For testing magnetos, a substantial device that may be quickly set up is necessary. Fig. 12 shows a simple design for such an apparatus. The vise A holds the magneto to be tested, clamping it tightly by the two screws B. The magneto has a pulley provided with the standard taper, which is 5 degrees, or if a coupling is on the magneto that may be used for a pulley, a $\frac{3}{4}$-inch leather belt connecting this coupling with the motor pulley. The high-tension wires are connected to the adjustable spark gap, and the magneto is then tested. The motor N should be a variable-speed, 110-volt, and, if possible, direct-current machine. A starting box is used, taking the return spring from the handle and using it for a regulator. This will not damage the resistance, as it is only on a short time and the load is light.

The magneto vise should have a brass base A. The screws are $\frac{3}{8}$-inch S.A.E. thread with a knurled handle, a flat button C being riveted to the screw at the countersunk portion O; this prevents marring the magneto paint. The boss D on the base casting makes the threaded hole stronger. The spark gap is mounted on a fiber base E, $4\frac{1}{2}'' \times 6\frac{1}{2}'' \times \frac{1}{4}''$, fastened to the bench by the

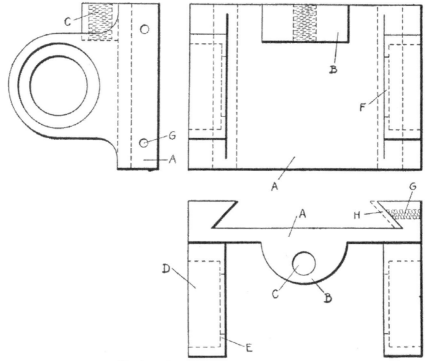

Fig. 14.   Carriage of Generator Test Stand

supports MM. The binding posts G are connected to the gap points F, which can be phonograph needles. The adjustable bar H is $\frac{1}{4}$ inch square, iron or brass, and swings on the links II; the indicator hand J moves on the dial L and is connected to the bar by the link K. These three links are made of $\frac{1}{16}'' \times \frac{1}{4}''$ iron. The link K is so made that when the hand rests on I, the points F should clear the bar $\frac{1}{16}$ inch, and the dial is laid off so that each calibration represents $\frac{1}{16}$ inch; this gives a quick adjustment. The link I on the right-hand side should be connected to the support M, which, in turn, is grounded to the vise A.

Generator Test Stand. To test and regulate generators properly after repairing and before placing on the car, some means must be provided to run the generator at various speeds. Such a test stand must be universal and easily set up. A test stand meeting these requirements is shown in Fig. 13. The baseplate A is cast iron, $10'' \times 16''$, surfaced on the top. Column B is bolted to the baseplate and carries an adjustable head, which holds the driving assembly. The location of the column should be such that the center line of the chuck is in the center of the base. A threaded rod bent into a crank G raises and lowers the head; the rod should be $\frac{7}{16}$ inch with an S.A.E. thread. The lower end of the rod is turned with a $\frac{1}{4}$-inch shoulder and fits into a

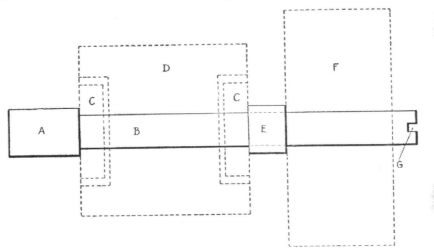

Fig. 15. Pulley Assembly for Generator Test Stand

hole bored in the base; the upper end has a collar J pinned on, and the plate K takes the thrust in lowering the head.

The head has a 45-degree angle groove cut in the body of the casting, Fig. 14, which fits into a similar tongue cut on the column. One side of the body casting A has the groove cut away slightly more to make room for a gib H and two adjusting screws G to take up the wear in the head. These screws G should be 12–24 iron screws and should have lock nuts. The boss B is for the adjusting rod and is threaded to receive it. The shaft runs on two annular ball bearings, the head casting being recessed at D to a press fit while the shoulder E prevents them from working loose. The hole F is for the shaft and is slightly larger than the shaft, Fig. 15. *A* is the end that fits into the chuck collar; *B* is turned to a good light press fit in the bearings; the collar *E* is placed between the outer bearing and the pulley *F* and prevents the shaft from working out; the slot *G* is to drive the speed indicator; *CC* are the bearing seats; and *D* is the body casting. Between *A* and *C* and between *E* and *C* are two thin brass plates to keep the dirt out of the bearings.

The chuck *F*, Fig. 13, is a 4-inch, three-jawed, universal type, fastened to a flange and pinned to the shaft *D*. Any chuck will do for this, as being out of true will not make much difference. The speedometer is made from a Corbin-Brown head, and the scale should have an 80 m.p.h. limit. The hand is taken off and a blank glued to the old dial. The instrument is then recalibrated

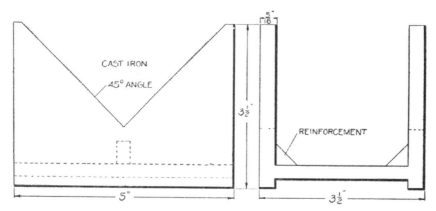

Fig. 16. Mounting Blocks for Generator in Test Stand

with a speed counter to read r.p.m. Having obtained this data on the blank, a neat dial may be drawn and glued on. The speedometer head is held on the carriage by an angle iron made of $\frac{1}{8}'' \times 3''$ iron, the coupling of the head fitting into the slot *G*, Fig. 15. Take care to line up the head so that the coupling will be free at all positions of the shaft. Having the speedometer always operative saves time in testing. The pulley *E*, Fig. 13, should be about 4 inches in diameter and with a 2-inch face, while the motor pulley *A* should be 6 inches.

The generators are held in the stand by a motorcycle chain attached to the screw *M*, Fig. 13, and hooked onto a stud. It is tightened by the hand nut *N*, this screw sliding in a slanting guide *L*; this guide is about 8 inches long and allows for different sizes of generators. There are three studs to which the chain may be hooked. Holes are drilled in the base to fasten the generator to the bench. Square generators line themselves when placed in the stand, while round-type generators are placed in a V-shaped casting, Fig. 16. This is a simple casting requiring no machine work, the bottom edges being filed so that it will set flat on the baseplate.

Generator Test Bench. Fig. 17 shows a test bench that can be made for testing generators. The bench consists of a generator stand; a direct-current or an alternating-current motor, according to the power available; a 6- and 12-volt cut-out; switches of the 10-ampere double and single pole, single- and double throw type; 15-volt meter; and ammeter to read 30-0-30 of the direct-current type. A pair of test points to work from a 110-volt line, a red lamp in series to test the armature and field windings, with binding posts and lamp and socket to light the bench, complete the equipment. Fig. 17a shows the front of the board with the instruments in place, and the back of the board

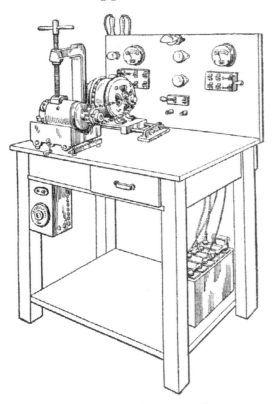

Fig. 17. Electrical Test Bench
Courtesy of Motor Age

with the proper connections for the different units on the test stand. If there is a cut-out on the machine being tested, the cut-outs on the board are not required and the cut-out switch may be closed. The switch can be opened for the use of the cut-outs, if desired, by using the right-hand switch for either 6- or 12-volt generators.

The stand can be used to test the generator as a motor by

simply opening the cut-out shorting switch so that the generator can take current from a battery that is used in conjunction with the test stand. The output of the generator can be tested, also,

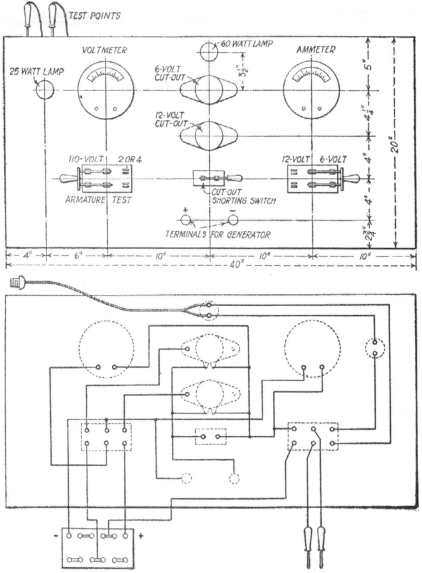

Fig. 17a. Front and Back View of Electrical Test Bench
Courtesy of Motor Age

by driving it with the motor and throwing the desired cut-out into the circuit, and the ammeter will show the current output while the voltmeter will show the voltage of the battery.

The test points can be used on the 110-volt line by placing the left-hand switch in the left position, or used for low voltage test by placing in the right hand position. These test points are handy for carrying out armature and field winding tests as stated. When the switch is at the right hand position the points are connected to the battery.

Ignition Switchboard. For quickness in operation, the single break must be connected so that any type of coil can be tested without using separate ballast coils or leads. This is accomplished by having everything on one switch, as shown in Fig. 18. The

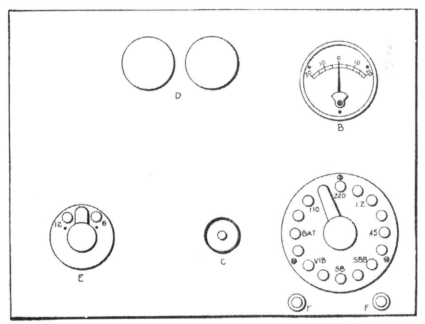

Fig. 18. Ignition Switchboard

switch *A* has eight combinations: 220 volts in series with two 110-volt lamps *D* mounted in sign receptacles so that the lamps project through the board; 110 volts in series with one lamp; a battery contact which gives either 6 or 12 volts, depending on the position of the switch *E*. This switching of the battery current allows either voltage to be used on any of the other switch points. There is also a master vibrator; a single-break tester operated by the handle *C*; the same single break with a 0.45-ohm ballast coil in series; a 0.45-ohm ballast coil; and a 1.2-ohm ballast coil. An ammeter *B* shows the current used.

In Fig. 19 is shown the wiring for the board. The switch *A* is connected to the various units and has the three ballast coils mounted directly on it. The single break *C* has a condenser *I*

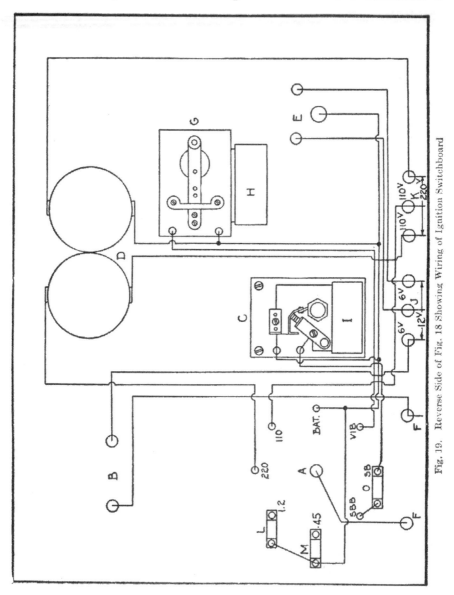

Fig. 19.   Reverse Side of Fig. 18 Showing Wiring of Ignition Switchboard

connected across the points; the master vibrator *G* also has a condenser *H* across the points. The terminal posts *J* connect to the battery and the terminals *K* to the 110- and 220-volt line. The posts *F* are the test leads and should have test clips attached to flexible cables. The whole board may be of wood and enclosed in a box frame, the front swinging on hinges.

The construction of the switch is shown in Fig. 20. The base A is made of $\frac{1}{2}$-inch red fiber, mounted on a mandrel and turned in the lathe to a true circle. It is then placed in the chuck without the mandrel and the two sides faced off; sixteen 12–24 right-hand brass screws are then screwed into the base, Fig. 18. The base is again chucked and the heads are

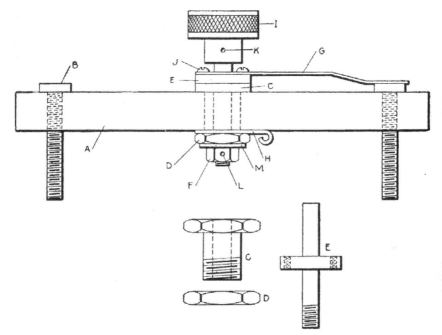

Fig. 20. Construction of Combination Switch for Ignition Test Board

turned off to $\frac{1}{16}$ inch thick. These screws should be 2 inches long so as to extend through the switchboard. Every other screw is cut off flush on the back, as there is a dead point between each two contacts to prevent short-circuits in switching from one point to another.

A center sleeve is made for the switch shaft to rotate in. This is made from a $\frac{3}{8}$-inch S.A.E. cap screw with the head and nut C and D turned thin and a $\frac{1}{4}$-inch hole drilled in it to receive the shaft E. The sleeve C is fastened in the base with a terminal clip H under the nut D; this is for the center connection. The shaft E has a blade of phosphor bronze G screwed to the flange with two 4–36 screws J; the shaft itself is held by the nut F, under which is a washer M; a pin through at L prevents the nut from working loose. A fiber handle I, pinned on at K, completes the switch.

Bearing Puller. There are several bearing pullers on the market, but they are not adaptable to every kind of job and are weak when it comes to a real hard pull. A practical puller is shown in Fig. 21. The base A is of cast iron, having a front vertical standard J and a boss B cast to receive the screw C. This screw is $\frac{3}{4}$ inch with a standard thread. A good snug fit

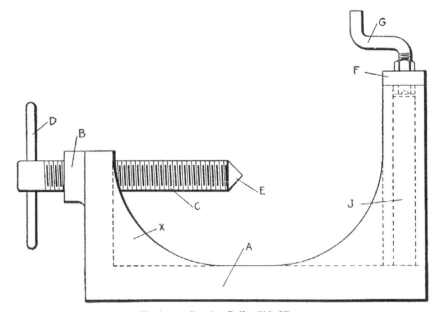

Fig. 21. Bearing Puller Side View

should be made, as wear will eventually cause it to become slightly loose; the crossbar D is used in turning the screw. The plate F on the front standard is held on by two $\frac{3}{8}$-inch cap screws and carries the clamp screw G, which holds the jaws together. The ribs are placed on each end to strengthen the base, and four holes are drilled in the base to bolt it to the bench. Fig. 22 shows the sliding jaws H and I which fit into a slot in the end standard J; the slot is cut from top to bottom. The top plate F carries the clamp screw G which is $\frac{3}{8}$ inch with an S.A.E. thread; the lower end has a groove turned in it. This plate fits on the screw *G* and is held on the sliding block *H* by two 8–32 screws. The block is counter bored to allow the end of the screw to turn free; this device is to raise the block in changing jaws.

The sliding blocks are shown in Fig. 23; these blocks are cut away, as shown, to receive the jaws, which are held by the two small pins *M*. In recessing the blocks, place them in the lathe

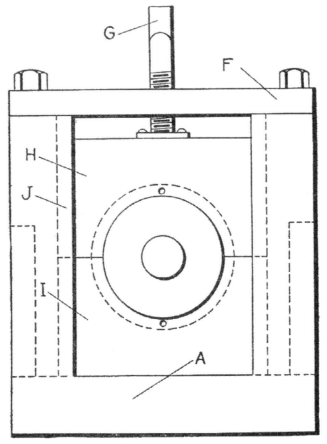

Fig. 22. Bearing Puller End View

with a piece of $\frac{1}{8}$-inch metal between them at *W*; this will make it possible to tighten the jaws in place. The jaws used to grip the bearing are shown in Fig. 24 and should be made of steel, either tool or cold rolled, and case hardened. They are made of round stock of the proper outside size, cut off in lengths, faced off, bored out at *P*, and turned round in the chuck with the shoulder *R*. The jaw face at *Q* is bored and rounded to fit the face of the bearing. The jaws are made for several sizes of bearings, a different set of jaws being made for each, such as 12-millimeter, 15-millimeter, 17-millimeter, etc. The only change in any of these jaws is the size of the face Q. Make the jaws for the largest bearing first and then make up the rest the same, with the exception of the face Q. After the jaws are machined, the holes O are

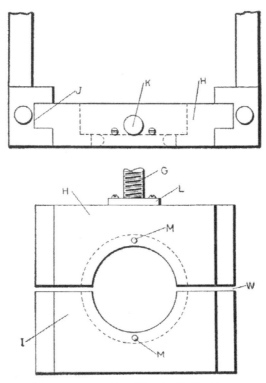

Fig. 23.   Assembly of Bearing Puller Clamps

drilled and the finished ring is cut in half as at S; this can be done in a milling machine or with a hack saw.

As the push rods used in pulling the bearings turn and burr the work, an end piece or point is made, Fig. 25. This end piece E is made of tool steel and hardened. The screw C is drilled as at T, and a ball-bearing U is placed in the hole the end piece rests on. This ball takes the thrust, allowing the end piece to turn. As the screw cannot be used against the work, the push rods shown in Fig. 26 are used. These are made of ¾-inch cold-rolled steel with different shaped ends; A is used for general work,

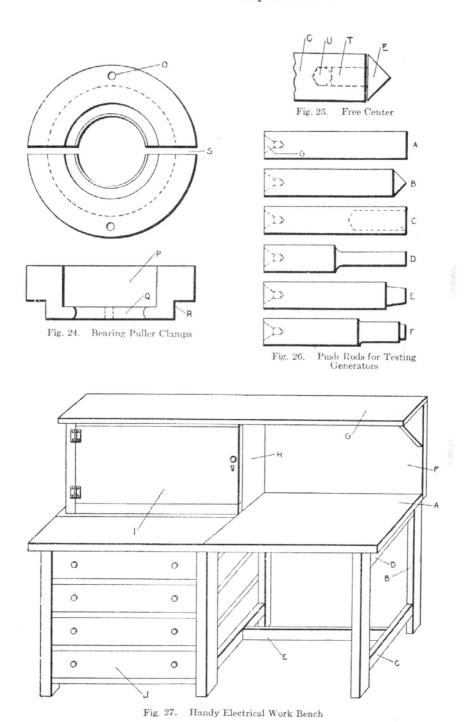

Fig. 25. Free Center

Fig. 24. Bearing Puller Clamps

Fig. 26. Push Rods for Testing
Generators

Fig. 27. Handy Electrical Work Bench

B for shafts with centers, *C* is hollow and fits over magneto drive shafts to protect the threads, *D* is for small bearings, *E* is for Bosch breaker end bearings and *F* is for Eisemann breaker end bearings. Various other shaped rods may be made to meet requirements. These rods should all be case hardened. In using the puller, the bearing is placed in the proper sized jaws and screwed down with the clamp screw, the proper rod being used to push off the bearing.

Work Bench. To work with neatness and precision a neat and handy one-man bench is required. It helps create the right atmosphere as a dirty and disorderly shop is sure to produce poor

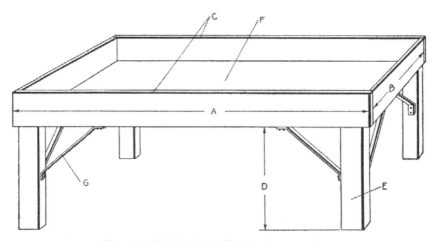

Fig. 28. Wash Rack for Cleaning Generator Parts

workmanship. Where the benches are separate, no workman is crowded, and the tendency to keep the shop clean is greater. A very convenient bench of this type is shown in Fig. 27. This is made of dressed pine, the top being of 2″×12″ planks two wide; the legs *B* and the crosspieces *C* and *D* are 2″×4″ with the top of the bench 32 inches from the floor. A crosspiece *E* is placed for a foot rest, the other half of the bench being used for the drawers *J*. The bench has a back *F*, 18 inches high with a shelf *G* of 8-inch board. To the left is a tool cupboard with a locking door *I*. On the board back *F* are hung the tools that are used most. The portion of the bench used for work should be covered with 28-gage sheet steel. The gas furnace can be placed at the extreme left. The test switches and lights can be placed at *II* on

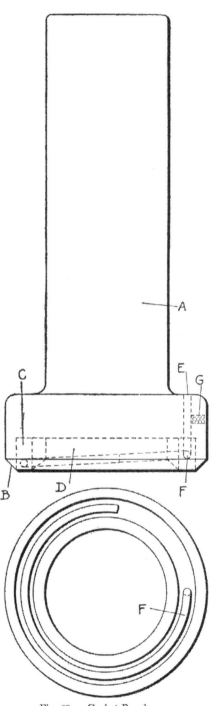

Fig. 29.   Gasket Punch

the end of the cupboard, the wires being run inside the cupboard. These benches may be used singly or built double with a right and left unit to fit between a window.

Wash Rack. A serviceable wash rack is shown in Fig. 28. This is placed wherever convenient and a pail is set under it to catch the drip. The sides C and the bottom are made of 1-inch pine; the legs E are $2'' \times 4''$. The iron brackets G support the legs, which may be any desired height. The length A should be 3 feet, and the width B, 18 inches; if made too large the rack collects trash. The inside is lined with 28-gage galvanized iron with a drain hole at F. Some shops put casters on this rack and move it from bench to bench.

Small Tools. As the gaskets used in insulating magneto bearings are sometimes hard to get, a punch to make them is shown in Fig. 29. The handle of the punch A may be made of tool steel or of soft steel with a steel cutter. A groove is cut at C to form an edge B, while the center is turned out at D, leaving two cutting edges to form the gasket. By relieving the cutting edges on the outside, it makes a clean-cut gasket. In order to get the finished gaskets out of the punch, an extractor is placed in the slot.

The hole E is drilled, and a wire circle F is placed in the hole and is held by the set screw G; this wire is bent so that it will force the gasket out as soon as the pressure is taken from the punch. There are several sizes of these gaskets, such as insulation

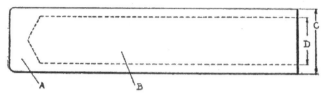

Fig. 30. Cone Bearing Drift

for 12-, 15-, and 17-millimeter bearing cups, and shims for the same sizes, the 15-millimeter being used the most.

Cup Drift. In Fig. 30 is shown a drift for driving on cone bearings. The body A is made of cold-rolled steel of the size needed for the drift. It is drilled out at B to the desired size; the dimensions C and D should be to fit 15-millimeter and 17-millimeter bearings. As these are very handy tools around the shop, a variety of sizes should be made.

Bearing Cup Puller. As it is very hard to get a bearing cup out of an end plate, such a puller as shown in Fig. 31 is quick and efficient. The body A is made of cold-rolled steel, the lower end being shaped to a sharp angle and slotted so that it will

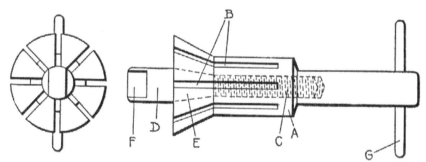

Fig. 31. Cone Puller

expand. These slots B may be milled or cut with a hack saw. A $\frac{7}{16}$-inch hole C is drilled and threaded with an S.A.E. thread, and a taper bolt D is screwed into the hole. This screw has a taper E which expands the body of the puller, a flattened portiok

F being made for a wrench. A **T** handle is placed in the shank at *G*, and the whole tool is case hardened. In using this puller, the screw is backed out and the sharp angle points placed back of the cup. The screw is then turned up tight and the whole assembly struck sharply on the bench, striking the screw, when the cup will be forced out without damaging the cup or the end plate.

ELECTRICAL REPAIRS

PART II

Ohm's Law. Where new wires have to be installed in electrical repairs, a thorough knowledge of the relation existing between current, pressure, and resistance is of great benefit to the repair man, especially when armature winding enters into the repair work. Certain sizes of wires have a known resistance to the flow of current. Therefore, to get the desired result, we must have a correct size wire to get a certain pressure with a certain quantity of flow.

In 1827, a scientist named Ohm discovered that a certain definite relation existed between electrical current, pressure, and resistance. He arranged these relations into a law, called Ohm's Law, which forms the basis for most of the electrical measurements of steady currents. The law is stated as follows: *The strength of a current equals the pressure divided by the resistance.*

The three units of electrical measurement are: Amperes—rate of flow; volts—pressure causing current to flow; ohm—resistance to flow. In making calculations symbols are used instead of the terms. Amperes are represented by the letter I, volts by the letter E, and ohms by the letter R, which denotes the resistance in the circuit. If any two of these quantities or units are known, the third can be found. The formulas for these calculations are as follows:

$$\text{Amperes} = \frac{\text{volts}}{\text{ohms}} \text{ or } \frac{E}{R}$$

$$\text{Ohms} = \frac{\text{volts}}{\text{amperes}} \text{ or } \frac{E}{I}$$

$$\text{Volts} = \text{ohms} \times \text{amperes or } R \times I$$

The following are examples of the calculations: A circuit has a 50-volt pressure with a resistance of 5 ohms in the circuit. How many amperes will flow in the circuit?

$$I = \frac{E}{R} \text{ or } \frac{50}{5} = 10$$

ELECTRICAL EQUIPMENT

To find the number of ohms, proceed as follows:

$$R = \frac{E}{I} \text{ or } \frac{50}{10} = 5$$

To find the number of volts:

$$E = R \times I \text{ or } 5 \times 10 = 50$$

These same units are used to find the power of an electrical machine. The unit of power is the *watt*. One horsepower is equivalent to 746 watts. The formula for this calculation is as follows:

$$P = \frac{I \times E}{746} \text{ or } \frac{\text{amperes} \times \text{volts}}{746}$$

Substituting from the above calculation we have power $= \dfrac{50 \times 10}{746}$

or $\dfrac{500}{746}$, which is a little more than $\frac{1}{2}$ horsepower.

Take another example: A starting motor takes 250 amperes at a pressure of 6 volts. What is the horsepower developed by the motor?

$$P = \frac{250 \times 6}{746} = 2 \text{ plus, which is the horsepower developed by the}$$

starting motor.

Wiring. *Necessity for High-Tension Cables.* In early days much trouble was experienced with poorly insulated and poorly mounted wires. This was particularly the case with the secondary circuits, the insulation of which was frequently inadequate to carry currents at the high potentials employed, so that there was more or less leakage. This was further aggravated by the chafing, or rubbing, of these wires against moving parts. The former trouble was eliminated by the adoption of specially constructed cables which are tested to carry 30,000 volts. Cables of this type are illustrated in Fig. 32, which also shows the cables employed for electric lighting and starting installations, where the chief difficulty has usually been the selection of a cable of too small a carrying capacity for the current used.

The importance of using heavily insulated cables for both the primary and secondary cables of the ignition, and more particularly the latter, has come to be generally understood, and cables especially designed for this service have now been in use for a number of years; but the importance of using wiring of ample capacity, in the lighting and starting circuits, is not so well appreciated. In the former instance, the problem was one of insulation only, the amount necessary to prevent leakage of the secondary current not being fully realized in the early days; nor was the necessity for thoroughly protecting the primary cables from the effects of oil and water taken into account. Trouble from these sources, however, have long since been a matter of the past; even the well-insulated cables now in general

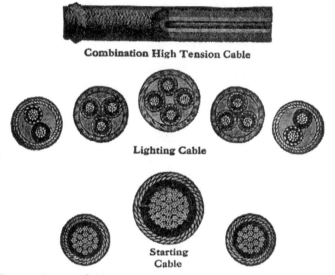

Fig. 32.   Types of Cables Employed in Electrical Equipment of Automobiles

use become oil soaked in time, but, when faulty ignition is thought to be due to them, they are promptly replaced.

In many of the early electric starting and lighting systems, the wiring has been as poorly adapted to the purpose as was that of the pioneer ignition systems. This was not on account of improper insulation but owing rather to poor design or to a lack of consideration of the importance that proper wiring has on the efficient operation of the system. No electrical system of this kind is any better than its storage battery; and, as the amount of energy that can be husbanded in the latter is limited, every effort must be made to avoid waste in its use. What constitutes waste in a standard lighting system using current at 110 to 115 volts, and what may be so termed where the available potential is only 6 volts, are two very different things. A voltage drop of one to 5 volts in an incandescent lighting system is negligible. A drop of 5 volts below the 110-volt standard will cause a perceptible dimming of the lamps, but the life of the lamp filaments themselves will be greatly increased, other factors remaining the same, so that the loss in efficiency is not of such great moment.

Importance of Voltage Drop. But, in an electric starting and lighting system, the loss of even a fraction of a volt due to the wiring represents a substantial falling off in the power. As mentioned in the introductory, the unit of potential, or voltage, times the unit of current flow, or ampere, equals the watt or power unit, and there are 746 watts in an electrical horsepower. Take the case of an electric-starting motor with an unusually long connection between the battery and the electric motor. Assuming that the length and diameter of this wire is such that there is a loss of *1 volt* between the battery and the motor and that, at the moment of starting, 300 amperes are required to *break away* the engine, i.e., free the pistons and bearings when the lubricating oil has thickened from the cold so as to bind them. In the actual power consumed, this voltage drop represents 300×1, or 300 watts, equivalent to more than $\frac{3}{7}$ horsepower.

The loss of but $\frac{1}{2}$ volt, other factors remaining the same, is equivalent to almost $\frac{1}{6}$ horsepower, or about what a strong man can exert for a limited time. This appears to be getting things down pretty fine, but in the case of the Dyneto system, the manufacturers specify that the cable between the starting motor and the storage battery must be large enough to transmit *400 amperes with a total loss not to exceed $\frac{1}{4}$ volt*. With this amount of current, the voltage drop in question represents 100 watts, or nearly $\frac{1}{7}$ horsepower. Of course, this loss only takes place at the instant of starting, but that is just the time when the highest efficiency and the full power of the battery is required. Moreover, the starting motor frequently has to be operated a number of times, especially in cold weather when the battery efficiency is at its lowest, before the engine will start. Even at the lower-current values necessary for turning the engine over after it has been broken away, a drop of one volt represents an appreciable power loss, as the current consumed is anywhere from 50 to 100 amperes. It will be apparent from this why the manufacturers lay such emphasis on their instructions not to lengthen connections, if avoidable,

ELECTRICAL EQUIPMENT

TABLE I
American Wire Gage (B. & S.)

No.	Diameter in Mils	Diameter in Mm.	Circular Mils	Ohms per 1000 Ft.	No.	Diameter in Mils	Diameter in Mm.	Circular Mils	Ohms per 1000 Ft.
0000	460.00	11.684	211600.0	.051	19	35.89	.912	1288.0	8.617
000	409.64	10.405	167805.0	.064	20	31.96	.812	1021.5	10.566
00	364.80	9.266	133079.4	.081	21	28.46	.723	810.1	13.323
0	324.95	8.254	105592.5	.102	22	25.35	.644	642.7	16.799
1	289.30	7.348	83694.2	.129	23	22.57	.573	509.5	21.185
2	257.63	6.544	66373.0	.163	24	20.10	.511	404.0	26.713
3	229.42	5.827	52634.0	.205	25	17.90	.455	320.4	33.684
4	204.31	5.189	41742.0	.259	26	15.94	.405	254.0	42.477
5	181.94	4.621	33102.0	.326	27	14.19	.361	201.5	53.563
6	162.02	4.115	26250.5	.411	28	12.64	.321	159.8	67.542
7	144.28	3.665	20816.0	.519	29	11.26	.286	126.7	85.170
8	128.49	3.264	16509.0	.654	30	10.03	.255	100.5	107.391
9	114.43	2.907	13094.0	.824	31	8.93	.277	79.7	135.402
10	101.89	2.588	10381.0	1.040	32	7.95	.202	63.2	170.765
11	90.74	2.305	8234.0	1.311	33	7.08	.108	50.1	215.312
12	80.81	2.053	6529.9	1.653	34	6.30	.160	39.7	271.583
13	71.96	1.828	5178.4	2.084	35	5.61	.143	31.5	342.433
14	64.08	1.628	4106.8	2.628	36	5.00	.127	25.0	431.712
15	57.07	1.450	3256.7	3.314	37	4.45	.113	19.8	544.287
16	50.82	1.291	2582.9	4.179	38	3.96	.101	15.7	686.511
17	45.26	1.150	2048.2	5.269	39	3.53	.090	12.5	865.046
18	40.30	1.024	1624.1	6.645	40	3.14	.080	9.9	1091.865

TABLE II
Carrying Capacity of Wires

B. & S. Gage	Circular Mils	Rubber Insulation Amperes	Other Insulation Amperes
18	1,624	3	5
16	2,583	6	8
14	4,107	12	16
12	6,530	17	23
10	10,380	24	32
8	16,510	33	46
6	26,250	46	65
5	33,100	54	77
4	41,740	65	92
3	52,630	76	110
2	66,370	90	131
1	83,690	107	156
0	105,500	127	185
00	133,100	150	220
000	167,800	177	262
0000	211,600	210	312

and then only to use wire of the same size and kind. This, of course, does not apply to the starting motor connection, as that should never be lengthened without increasing the diameter of the wire to compensate for the increase in length.

Calculating Size of Cable. It is not advisable to do so where it can possibly be avoided, but, when made necessary by the fitting of an enclosed body, the following formula should be used for calculating the size of cable that should be employed:

$$\frac{\text{Maximum current} \times 10.7 \times \text{number of feet of wire}}{.25} = \text{diameter or cross-}$$

section of wire in circular mils

For example, in the case cited above, where the maximum current at the instant of starting is 300 amperes and the distance between the battery and the starting motor is four feet (measured from battery to switch and from the latter to the starting-motor terminal), the size of wire necessary would be:

$$\frac{300 \times 10.7 \times 4}{.25} = 51,360 \text{ circular mils}$$

As shown in the table on page 37, which gives the corresponding sizes of the B & S gage, the nearest to this is No. 3 wire of 52,634 circular mils cross-section, but, to allow for a factor of safety, either a No. 2 or a No. 1 wire would be used for such an installation. Now, in case it becomes necessary to take the battery from the running board close to the engine and place it under the floor of an enclosed body, increasing the length of wire needed to 8 feet, the cross-section of the wire required would be 102,720 circular mils, the closest gage number to this being the No. 0 cable. In other words, doubling the length of the cable would make it necessary to double its cross-section in order to prevent exceeding the minimum permissible drop in the voltage. This will make plain why some of the amateur experiments in re-locating the essentials of an electric starting system have had such disastrous effects on its efficiency.

Effect on Lights. In the case of the lamps, the effect of an increased drop in the voltage is not so serious; though, because of the very low-battery voltage available, what would otherwise be a negligible loss assumes important proportions. On the 3-cell 6-volt battery now so generally used, the lamp filaments are designed to burn to full brightness on a potential of 6 to 8 volts, this variation being provided to compensate for the difference in the battery voltage when fully charged and when partly discharged, as the voltage of the battery decreases as it discharges, dropping to but 1.50 volts per cell when practically exhausted, or a total of $4\frac{1}{2}$ volts. Even if receiving this full voltage, the 6-volt bulbs would burn very dimly, but there must be deducted from it the voltage drop due to the wiring and the switches. This is the reason why the brightness of the lamps (with the generator idle) affords such an excellent indication of the state of charge of the battery.

It will be apparent from the above that a drop in potential of but one volt in the lighting circuit would cause a serious loss of efficiency at the bulbs. Assuming that the headlights consume 4 to 5 amperes, and applying the above formula on the basis of a maximum distance of 10 feet from the battery, it is found that a No. 16 wire is necessary; but, in order to provide a large factor of safety, nothing smaller than No. 14 wire is ordinarily employed for the lighting circuits, and, in some cases, it is No. 12.

Importance of Good Connections. Under the head of "Resistance", however, attention has been called to the fact that not alone the length and size of the connecting wires, but also all switches and joints are factors in calculating the total resistance of a circuit. Consequently, it is poor practice ever to make a joint in a wire where a single length may be employed. Whenever a wire is broken by accident, the trouble should always be remedied by replacing it with an entirely new piece rather than by making a joint in the old wire. Loose connections also add greatly to the total resistance in a circuit, as well as connections in which the contact faces of the terminals are dirty or corroded. In replacing or tightening connections, care should be taken to see that the parts in contact are scraped or filed bright and that both the terminal nut and its lock nut are screwed down firmly. The switches are also an important factor where voltage drop is concerned and switch blades or contacts that are dirty or corroded, or that are not held firmly in contact when closed, will be responsible for an appreciable drop in the voltage that will become increasingly perceptible as the battery becomes discharged.

ELECTRICAL EQUIPMENT

Some Ignition Cable Pointers. At the beginning of the auto-motive industry, but little attention was paid to high-tension spark-plug wires. Today, however, automotive engineers are giving this subject more serious consideration, realizing the importance of this unit in the proper operation of the internal-combustion motor. As these wires are required to carry a voltage ranging from 6000 to 18,000 volts, it will be necessary to insulate them thoroughly. The material to be used should be a compound which has high dielectric characteristics. The reason for this is that continual satisfactory operation of the ignition depends upon the quality of this material.

Installations Used. Three general installations are used in automobile work: (1) open wiring between distributor and spark plugs, the wires being supported by brackets or running free; (2) wiring in fiber or other insulating conduits; and (3) wiring in grounded metal conduit.

Installation No. 1 can be successfully used on those motors where the distance between the distributor and the spark plugs is short and thus the wires will be prevented from striking the motor or other metal and injuring their insulation.

The disadvantages of this installation, however, are lack of mechanical protection and a development of electrostatic surface capacity when insulated brackets are used. If the wires are run through holes in brackets larger than the wires, the insulation will be chafed and weakened.   On the other hand, if the wires are clamped in position, the thickness of the insulation will be lessened because of compression.

Installation No. 2 offers mechanical protection, but it has the great disadvantage of allowing the electrostatic charge to attain a high pressure before discharging to the ground.

Installation No. 3 can be used advantageously on the majority of four- and six-cylinder motors. This method also offers mechanical protection of the wires and greatly reduces the strength of the electrostatic charge, but this type of assembly is likely to cause more trouble because of the poor insulation of the porous cables. Invisible pores may be present in the insulation and allow the current to discharge through these pores into the conduit or ground. thereby weakening the current at the plug if a spark occurs in that unit. This installation also offers another advantage as cross fire is practically eliminated. The current lost through poor insulation will go to the ground and not take a path through another porous lead into the wrong combustion chamber.

High-tension wire failures are generally due to one of the following causes: mechanical stress, heat, chemical action, dielectric stress.

Mechanical Stress. A conductor of sufficient strength to withstand ordinary handling and vibration and possessing sufficient flexibility is secured by using copper stranded wire with an insulating material whose base is rubber. Of course, injuries resulting from handling high-tension wires should be taken into consideration. Wires should be guarded to secure proper protection. Faults to be avoided in eliminating unnecessary mechanical stresses are unsupported wires, tight wires, sharp bends, sharp edges, tightly clamped brackets, or brackets with holes too large.

Heat. There is a wide variation of heat under the automobile hood, and while these temperatures are seldom high enough to endanger the rubber insulation, they are well above those conducive to its normal life. When the motor is in operation, the temperature seldom exceeds 175° F., but this temperature may rise to about 200° F. for a short period after the motor is stopped. Oxidation is also greatly increased by the additional heat.

Chemical Action. Gasoline is a very destructive agent when in contact with rubber, although this action is not long, as the vaporization is so rapid. Oil, however, does not evaporate so readily and when once in contact, continues to act on the rubber, greatly weakening its insulating strength.

Dielectric Stress. The voltage of the high-tension current passing through these leads has a wide range, depending upon the width of the spark gap and the pressure in the cylinder at the time the spark occurs. Various tests indicate the voltage to be between 6000 and 18,000. The dielectric stress is generally sufficient to cause a brush discharge on the surface of the insulating wall of the high-tension lead at points where this lead comes in close proximity to grounded metal parts. This is especially true when wires are contained in a grounded metal conduit. This brush discharge or corona produces ozone and oxide of nitrogen, and these gases are very detrimental to the insulation. For instance, the gases will start cracks on the surface, generally near the bend in the cable.

Exhaustive investigations have shown that this cracking in the insulation is a phenomenon requiring the combination of several factors, namely, mechanical stress, electrification, and the presence of air. It is well known that ozone actively attacks rubber, and when the rubber is under mechanical stress, the products of reaction are pulled apart, forming small cracks which, when started, rapidly increase in size until the insulation is open to the cable.

Plain and Braided Cables. Braided covers over the insulation simply conceal this cracking; they do not prevent it. Braided covering also absorbs oil, thus producing an undesirable action as previously stated. The proper conductor must be of sufficient strength to prevent its breaking under ordinary conditions, and the insulation must be sufficiently durable to withstand mechanical, thermal, dielectric, and chemical conditions. Insulation will gradually fail as the porosity of the wall increases. This porosity may increase to a point where it will interfere with proper spark-plug functioning and even then the defect will not be visible.

Plain and braided cables formerly were extensively used, but a larger per cent of assemblies are now being equipped with plain cables. Braided cables are generally used where it is necessary to provide additional protection against mechanical injury; also in a few cases when the temperature is somewhat above 225° F., in which case the insulation softens and the cable is in danger of being seriously damaged at its pointed support. With the foregoing exceptions, plain cables have distinct advantages over braided cables for the reason that more insulation can be provided with a given diameter, thus ensuring a larger factor of safety in dielectric strength. Then again, plain cables have an electrostatic capacity, smooth finish, and high surface insulation.

Make-up of Cables. The size of the conductor cannot be computed on its carrying capacity. With a magneto system, the current will not exceed 0.4 ampere and with the battery systems it is probably never in excess of 0.1. These high values are sometimes reached when compression is low and the width of the spark-plug gap is small. It is true that a very small wire would carry this current, but it is necessary to use a larger wire on account of insufficient mechanical strength in the smaller wire. High tension cables such as Kerite have a large number of these qualities.

Ford Magneto. The Ford magneto consists of a stationary spider on which are placed sixteen coils of flat copper ribbon, each coil wound in the opposite direction to the next and the whole assembly connected in series, thus making the coils alternately north and south poles. One end of this coil circuit is grounded

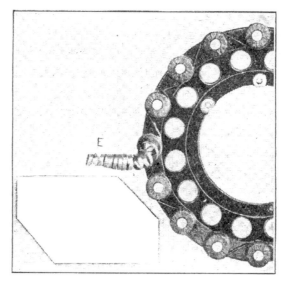

Fig. 33. Copper Ribbon Coils of Ford Magneto

through a copper rivet in the spider, and the other end is soldered to a terminal block at the top of the spider. The current is carried out through a terminal post on the flywheel cover by means of a pointed spring attached to the post and bearing on the terminal block.

The magnetic field is produced by sixteen magnets fastened to the rim of the flywheel. The magnets are placed with their north poles together and their south poles together. Over each pole thus formed is placed a flat iron pole piece. The magneto is assembled with a $\frac{1}{32}$-inch clearance between the magnets and coils, and this clearance is adjusted by means of metal shims. Fig. 33 shows the coils.

Capacity. As this magneto has no commutator the current produced is alternating, with sixteen reversals per revolution. The voltage produced is from 6 to 30, depending upon the load and the speed. The ignition requires 1 ampere and the headlights about 3; as this magneto was designed to take care of this load only, an increased load on the magneto is inadvisable. Numerous devices have been made to charge a battery from this magneto, but the majority of these devices are unsatisfactory owing to an insufficient current capacity to offset the rectifying losses.

Testing. Through use, the current is decreased either by weak magnets or by partial grounds in the coils. In making a test with an alternating voltmeter, the voltage is taken with the engine running at a car speed of about 25 miles per hour. With the ignition only as a load, the voltmeter should show about 20 volts when the magneto is up to strength.

Recharging. When the magnets become weak, it is necessary to recharge or replace them. They may be recharged without removing them from the car, with the flywheel off but with the magnets still attached, or with the magnets removed from the flywheel; new magnets may be used.

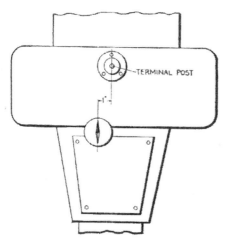

Fig. 34. Position of Compass

Recharging in Car. Recharging in the car is done by sending a current through the coils, causing each coil to become a separate magnet charger, charging each magnet which is placed opposite to it. As it takes direct current to charge a magnet properly, there must be a direct current supply. Two 6-volt starting batteries may be satisfactory to use, the connections being made between the batteries and the magneto with No. 6 wire. In order to saturate the magnets, 40 amperes should flow through the coils. Since about 1917 the resistance of the Ford magneto coils has been 0.25 ohm. Applying 12 volts to the coil from two storage batteries connected in series will allow 48 amperes to flow through the coils.

Before the current is applied to the magneto, the flywheel must be set in proper relation to the coils. This is done by putting a compass over the flywheel, Fig. 34. Take out the forward floor boards; disconnect all wires from the terminal post; place the compass slightly back and 1 inch to the left of the post; raise the left-hand side of the hood so that the compass will be in sight while cranking. Then crank the engine slowly until the compass needle points with the north to the front of the car. It is well to shake the compass a little after it is pointing straight to be sure of a correct reading. Now place the positive battery wire with the clip on the terminal post, and then touch the large nut on the exhaust pipe several times with the lead. Do not hold the contact more than a second as it may burn off a connection on the inside of the magneto because of the heavy flow of current.

The first application of the current charges the magnets, but several applications give the owner, who may be a spectator, the assurance of a job well done. Remove the charging wires and replace the ignition wire on the terminal post, then connect the test instrument and note the rise in strength. In some cases it will be found that the magneto is weaker or entirely dead; this may be due to any one of four causes:

> Poor setting of magnets with compass
> Reverse setting
> Polarity of charging current reversed
> Magneto coil connections reversed

The first condition is caused by the needle of the compass sticking, thus giving a false reading; therefore, reset and charge again. If it fails to come up, reverse the setting; that is, set with the south pole up instead of the north pole as in the original setting.

The second condition is generally caused by the compass needle becoming reversed; therefore, recharge the compass needle correctly on the magnet charger, and be sure that the dark end of the needle points north. To correct this second condition, reverse the setting of the magneto as before described and again charge.

To remedy the third condition, test the polarity of the charging wires; if it is reversed, change back and charge again, first reversing the setting.

The fourth condition is caused by the coils being connected in the opposite direction at the factory. The remedy is to reverse the setting and again charge.

In some cases the magnetism has practically disappeared; then the only remedy is to charge in any position and continue the charging process until a polarity is found.

Recharging on Flywheel. In recharging without removing from the flywheel, it is handy to use a small 6-volt charger having Ford charging pole pieces. Find the north pole of the charger and mark it with chalk; then find the north pole of the magnets and mark; place the north pole of the charger to the south pole of the first magnet and apply the current for one second. Skip the next magnet, as that is of opposite polarity; go around the wheel

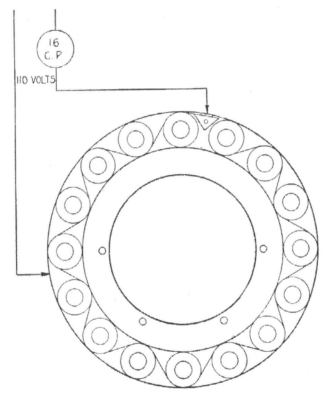

Fig. 35.   Testing Coils for Grounds

and charge the seven other magnets of the same polarity as the first magnet. Now reverse the wires on the charger, and charge the remaining magnets in like manner.

Recharging out of Car. If the magnets are removed from the flywheel, the first operation is to sort out the right- and left-hand magnets and place them in separate piles. Start with one pile and charge it to its proper polarity and again pile separately or place on the flywheel in alternate sequence. Charge the other pile in the reverse direction; that is, simply turn the magnet over when charging, thus charging the magnet in the opposite direction; replace on the flywheel in the remaining spaces.

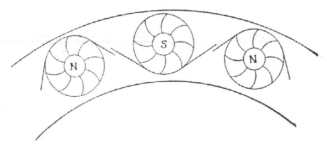

Fig. 36.   Winding of Old-Style Coils

Repairing Magneto Coils.   The coils on the spider after a time become grounded by fine particles of metal and carbon in the

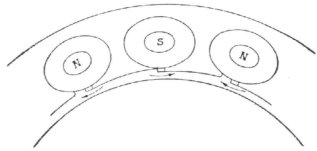

Fig. 37.   Winding of New-Style Coils

oil which work through the coil insulation and ground a portion of the magneto.   Where a magneto fails to come up on charge, it is

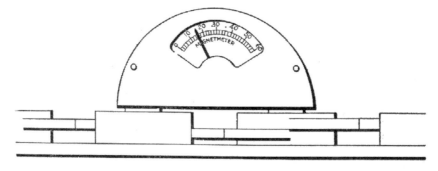

Fig. 38.   Testing for Shorted Coils

generally owing to this cause, and while washing out the crankcase rarely remedies the trouble, still it helps to prevent further trouble.

The spider must be removed and the grounded portion reinsulated. The coils are tested by applying 110 volts with a lamp in series as in Fig. 35, first unsoldering the ground connection. If the lamp lights, a ground is present; slight grounds will cause a white smoke at the point of trouble but heavy grounds will not. By applying about 12 volts from a battery to the grounded coil, the ground will generally show up. If this fails, unsolder in the middle and test each half, when the ground may soon be found. The grounded coil should be forced off by using two screw drivers as levers.

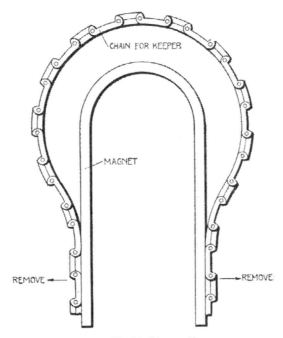

Fig. 39. Flexible Magnet Keeper

The old tape should be cut off and new tape put on, using cotton tape $\frac{3}{4}$ inch wide, wound with a lap of half the width of the tape; more than this will be too thick.

Where the fiber end pieces are broken, be sure to cut new ones from $\frac{1}{32}$-inch fiber. After taping, shellac well. In replacing the coils, connect each coil so that the polarity of adjoining coils will be opposite, the old style being shown in Fig. 36 and the new style in Fig. 37. After all the grounds are cleared and a final test is made, the ground connection may be replaced on the spider. A 6-volt battery current should now be applied to the whole assembly and each coil tested with a compass for polarity, thus proving that each pole is of opposite polarity to the poles on either side of it. This is very important.

To be sure that there are no shorted coils, the 6-volt current should be left on and each coil tested with the magnetmeter as in Fig. 38. The coil is now finished and should be given one more coat of shellac.

Testing and Charging Magnets. The permanent magnets used in magnetos are generally made of tungsten or chrome steel. Tungsten magnets were in extensive use until the cost of this metal became so great during the World War that it was necessary to develop a less expensive material. A few prominent manufacturers are having excellent results with properly treated chrome steel, and as it is less expensive, it is considered the ideal magnet material.

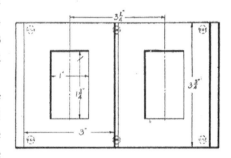

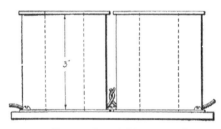

Fig. 40. Construction of Magnet Recharger

Keeper. A keeper must be used when the magnet is removed from the magneto or when the armature is removed from the field. A careful test has shown that a magnet will lose about thirty per cent of its strength if a keeper is not used while removing the magnet from the charger to its proper position on the magneto, or vice versa; the magnet was again removed and replaced without a keeper, with an additional loss of two or three per cent. The magnet was then allowed to stand on a shelf for three or four days without a keeper; on testing it was found to have lost an additional five or ten per cent. The same magnet was charged, a keeper being installed before removing the magnet from the charger, and it was then tested for strength. After the magnet had stood for six months, a test showed the strength to be the same as on the first day.

From the foregoing it will be noted that thirty per cent—the greatest amount of lost strength—was lost at the instant the magnet was removed, either from the charger or from the magneto without a keeper. There are a number of testers on the market, but several of them are of little use as the first loss occurs before the tester can be placed in operation. The aforementioned test was made by measuring the voltage between the brushes of a direct-current constant-speed generator, the magnets to be tested forming the field of the generator. Any loss in magnet strength would cause a lower voltage reading.

A prominent manufacturer recommends that a keeper be constructed from an old silent chain. After annealing, the chain is put over the magnet, Fig. 39, in such a way that the magnet can be placed in position before it is necessary to remove the keeper.

Testing. There are several ways of testing a magnet, such as with a compass, by the scale method, or by a voltage test as above described. When a compass is used, it is placed on a table with the needle at rest and pointing north; the magnet to be tested is placed in a line at right angles to the needle and about 3 feet from it and the deflection noted. This method is inaccurate as the deflection does not vary much from weak to strong, and it takes too much time.

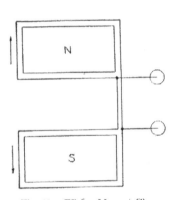

Fig. 41. Wiring Magnet Charger

The scale method is not entirely satisfactory as there is a loss during the test. The magnet has a keeper; this keeper is pulled away until it leaves the magnet and the pull in pounds noted.

Charger. In charging a magnet it is necessary to saturate it in order that it will retain the maximum charge. This can best be done with a charger having a heavy field and a short magnetic circuit with sufficient cross-section of iron to keep down the reluctance. It has been found by experience that to obtain the strongest magnet, there must be a short magnetic circuit. Therefore, if the magnet projects into the coils as in a solenoid, the magnetic circuit has been reduced to the length of the magnet plus the keeper on the bottom. If we have, in addition, a core in each coil 3 inches long, 6 inches of length have been added to the magnetic circuit, and the result is poor saturation.

A satisfactory magnet charger may be obtained at a low price in any voltage from 6 to 220, or one may be made as follows:

Two brass spools are made, Fig. 40, with a hollow center $1'' \times 1\frac{3}{4}'' \times 3''$, to which are soldered the end pieces. To operate on 6 volts, these spools are wound full of No. 14 magnet wire, with the coils wound in opposite directions, Fig. 41, and the two coils connected in multiple. If 110 volts is used, wind with No. 22 wire and connect in series.

Charging. In charging, the magnet is held above and at right angles to the charger and the current applied for a second, when the magnet will swing to the position it should occupy in the charger to receive a proper charge. Place the magnet in the coils, apply current for one second and the magnet is charged; any longer application is a waste of current and time.

If a keeper be placed on a magnet and pulled toward the top of the magnet, most of the magnetism will vanish because of the distortion of the magnetic lines of the circuit.

Testing Magneto Armatures. It is an easy matter to make a test of the strength of secondary current in magneto armatures and such a test will always give an indication as to the condition of the windings on the armature. To satisfactorily make this test it is

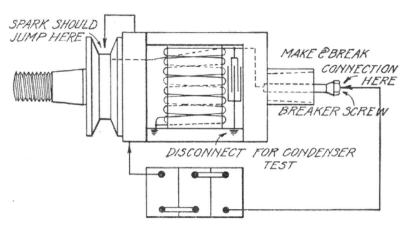

Fig. 42. Testing Secondary Spark

necessary to remove the magneto armature from the magneto and remove the breaker mechanism from the armature. After the breaker mechanism has been removed, replace the long screw which holds the breaker mechanism in place back in the end of the armature, as shown in Fig. 42.

Next take a piece of high tension wire and attach it to the magneto frame and bend it around so that it is about one-quarter inch from the brass part of the collector ring. Take a six-volt battery and connect a piece of wire to each terminal. Hold the negative wire to the armature frame and then make and break a contact on the end of the long breaker screw in the end of the armature with the wire which is attached to the positive side of the battery. This induces a current in the secondary and, if the armature is in good condition, a spark should jump from the collector ring to the wire each time the contact is broken. If the spark does not jump this gap, there is something wrong in the armature winding, and tests should be made to find out which one of the windings is faulty. If the condenser is defective and the armature windings are in good condition, the spark will not jump the gap at the collector ring, and a test for a defective condenser must be made.

Magneto Primary Winding Test. In this test use a six-volt battery with an ammeter in series as shown in Fig. 42-a. Connect

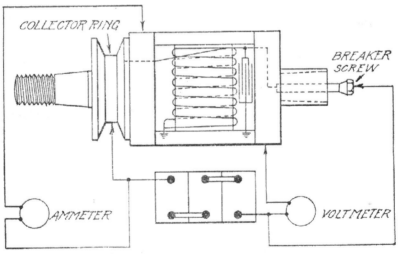

Fig. 42-a. Testing Secondary Winding with Voltmeter and Testing Primary Winding with Ammeter

one battery terminal to the ammeter, and from the other ammeter terminal make a connection to the magneto frame. From the other battery terminal make a connection to the long breaker screw.

If there is a reading of six to ten amperes, the winding is O.K. If there is no reading, then there must be an open circuit in the primary winding. If the reading is more than twelve amperes, it indicates a short circuit. There is only one remedy for a defective armature and that is to install a new one.

Magneto Secondary Winding Test. The secondary winding, being a fine winding, an ammeter cannot be used to make the test as enough current cannot flow through the winding to show a reading. To make this test use a six-volt battery with a voltmeter in series with the battery. Connect one terminal of the voltmeter to the battery and the other terminal of the voltmeter to the frame of the armature. From the other battery terminal make a connection to the collector ring. If the secondary winding is in good condition, there should be a reading of about two and one-half to three volts on the voltmeter. If there is no reading, the winding is broken somewhere, giving an open circuit. If the reading is high, then the windings are short circuited.

In making these tests it should be remembered that there will be a variation in the maximum readings for different models and different makes of magnetos as the windings vary; so if an accurate check is required, the reading should be taken from an armature of the same model and make which is known to be in perfect condition. The reading should be compared with that of the armature being tested.

Magneto Condenser Test. The condenser on the ordinary shuttle type magneto cannot be removed for testing as it is incorporated in the armature. One side of the condenser is grounded on the frame of the armature and this part must be disconnected before the test can be made; if it is not disconnected, the test lamp will light through the primary winding and a false indication will be obtained.

Condenser tests use the 110-volt lamp test sets, as shown in Fig. 1, page 2. Place one test point on the end of the long screw and the other test point on the disconnected side of the condenser and, if the lamp lights, the condenser is out of order.

If the lamp does not light, test the condenser for open circuit in the following way. Attach a piece of wire on the long screw in such a way that it does not touch the frame of the magneto and bend it around until it is near the disconnected side of the condenser.

Touch the test point to the screw and the condenser terminal, as in the previous test, and then touch the wire on the screw to the disconnected side of the condenser terminal, as shown in Fig. 42-a. If the condenser is in good condition, there should be a short, small, and snappy spark between the two wires as they come together.

In magnetos where the condenser can be removed, such as the Dixie, the condenser test can be carried out in the same manner as for a condenser in a battery ignition.

Testing High Tension Coils for Battery Ignition. Before the windings in the high tension coil can be tested, the different terminals of the winding and the condenser connections must be found. The following test may be made to locate the different windings and connections, and after these have been located and marked, the test can be made to find the condition of the coil winding and condenser.

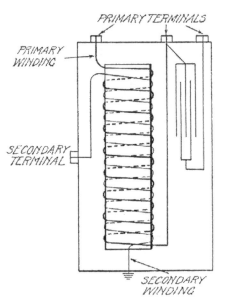

PRIMARY TERMINALS

PRIMARY WINDING

SECONDARY TERMINAL

SECONDARY WINDING

Fig. 43. Coil with Three Primary Terminals with Condenser Incorporated

High tension coils are of two types: one, in which the condenser is incorporated in the coil; and the other in which the condenser is not incorporated but is attached to the breaker point.

Of the first type there are those which have three primary connections on the external surface, as shown in Fig. 43; and those which have two primary connections on the external surface, as shown by Fig. 43-a.

The plain coil which has no condenser incorporated, as shown in Fig. 43-b, usually has only two primary external connections.

It should be remembered when making the test that the high tension external terminals are usually placed in the center of the coil and are heavily insulated, and the other end is usually grounded at the base. Secondary windings on the high tension coil cannot be tested with such low tension current as 6 or 12 volts because of the many turns of fine wire used for the secondary winding.

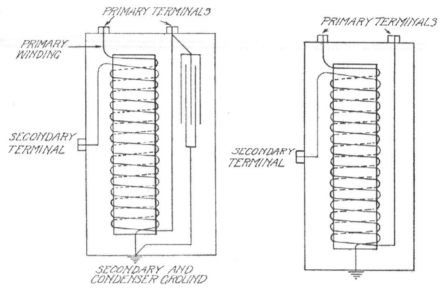

Fig. 43-a. Coil with Two Primary Terminals with Condenser Incorporated   Fig. 43-b. Coil with Two Primary Terminals without Condenser

Before tests can be made on these coils the different windings must be located. This can be done with either a 6- or 12-volt battery.

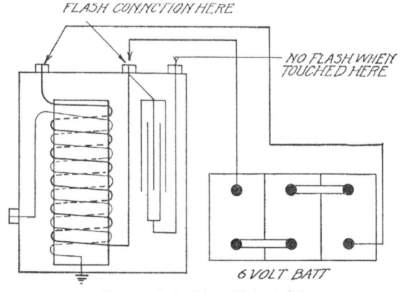

Fig. 43-c. Finding Primary Winding in Coil

ELECTRICAL EQUIPMENT

To locate primary windings in any of these coils: Attach a piece of wire to each of the battery terminals, as shown in Fig. 43-c, and touch one primary terminal on the coil with one wire attached to the battery; with the other battery wire make a flash connection to the other primary terminals on the coil. When a short flashing spark is obtained, the ends of the primary winding have been found. This will account for two of the primary terminals.

To locate condenser and primary connections on three terminal coils: Having found two of the primary terminals, the third is the one to which the dead side of the condenser is attached, and there will be no flash shown at this terminal when the foregoing test is being made. The other side of the condenser is connected to one of the other primary terminals and to find out which one make the following test: Connect a piece of wire to the secondary terminal and bend it so that the free end is about three-eighths inch from the base of the coil. Next take one of the wires attached to the battery and cut off some of the insulation. Attach this wire to the dead terminal and allow the end to hang over and touch one of the other primary terminals. Now, take the other battery wire and make a flash connection to the vacant primary terminal. If there is a good spark at the gap between the end of the wire attached to the secondary and the base of the coil, the condenser connection has been found. The one side of the condenser is connected to the dead terminal and the other side is connected to the terminal on which the flash connection is being made when the heaviest spark is obtained at the end of the wire connected to the secondary terminal.

To locate condenser and primary terminals on two terminal coils: The test is made in exactly the same way as with the three-terminal coil excepting that the dead side of the condenser or ground will be on the base of the coil. In the two-terminal coil all that is necessary is to find the two ends of the primary winding for with this coil the condenser is placed at or near the breaker point.

To test primary windings on high tension coils: When making this test on primary windings of coils, with three primary terminals, care should be taken in making the connections because if one connection is made on the condenser dead side terminal, no reading will be given and the wrong impression as to the condition of the coil will be obtained.

To make the test connect an ammeter in series with a six-volt battery. Connect one wire from the battery to one end of the primary and connect the other end of the primary to one terminal of the ammeter and the other terminal of the ammeter to the vacant battery terminal, as shown in Fig. 43-d.

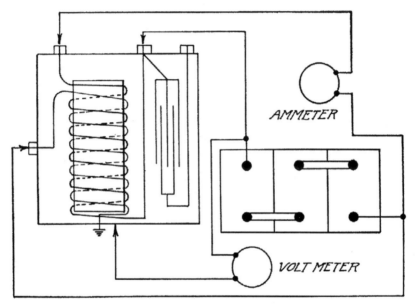

Fig. 43-d. Testing Primary Winding with Ammeter and Testing Secondary Winding
with Voltmeter

If there is no reading on the ammeter, the winding is open-circuited. If there is a high reading, this indicates that the windings are short-circuited. If the ammeter shows a reading of about 8 amperes, the winding is in good condition.

When using the ammeter, care should be taken not to damage the instrument. It is a good plan to be sure that there is enough resistance in the circuit to limit the current flow to the capacity of the instrument being used.

To test secondary windings on high tension coils: Either a voltmeter in series with a 6-volt battery may be used for this test or the 110-volt lamp test set may be used. With the voltmeter test one lead from the battery should be placed on the end of the secondary winding. A wire from the voltmeter should be attached to the base of the coil and the other voltmeter terminal should be connected to the battery, Fig. 43-d. If the winding is in good condition, the voltmeter should show a reading of about $2\frac{1}{2}$ volts; if the winding is short-circuited, the reading will be higher; and if open-circuited, there will be no reading.

With the 110-volt test the test points should be placed one on the base of the coil and the other on the secondary winding terminal. If the lamp lights, the windings are short-circuited. If the lamp does not light and there is a small spark when the test points are removed from the secondary terminal, the winding is correct. If the lamp does not light and there is no spark when the connection at the secondary terminal is broken, then the winding is open-circuited. The reason why the lamp does not light even though the winding is in good condition is because the resistance of the secondary winding is so high that there is not sufficient current flowing to cause the lamp to light. If the secondary windings are short-circuited, the resistance is lessened and enough current then flows to cause the lamp to light.

To test a condenser incorporated in high tension coils: For this test the 110-volt lamp test should be used. In the preliminary test the terminals on the coil to which the condenser is attached will have been found. Attach a wire to each of the terminals of the condenser and bend them around so that they are close together. Next place the lamp test points on these terminals and, if the lamp lights, the condenser is faulty and short-circuited. If the condenser is in good condition, a sharp, snappy spark will be obtained as the two wires attached to the condenser terminal are brought together.

To test a condenser not incorporated in coils: This test may be made by judging the condition of the spark or by the direct application of current. Where the condenser is enclosed in a coil the best test is the spark test. Have the switch on and while an assistant turns the crank, watch the spark. If there is a faint spark at the condenser points as they open, the condenser is in good condition. If the spark is heavy, the condenser is faulty. This same test can be used on a condenser that is attached to a magneto armature. Another test that can be made in regard to the condition of the spark is as follows: Use the 110-lamp test outfit and connect the grounded side of the condenser to one test point. Connect the other test point to the low tension terminal of the coil and form a connection at the two points. Break the connection, and if the condenser is in good condition, there will be a short, snappy spark. If it is faulty, the spark will be heavy and a deeper yellow.

The direct-current application test is shown in Fig. 44-a. To find if there is a short circuit in the condenser, use the lamp test outfit. Place one test point on each of the condenser terminals. If the lamp lights, the condenser is short circuited.

The test for a grounded condenser is shown in Fig. 44-b, and each side of the condenser is tested. Place one test point on the

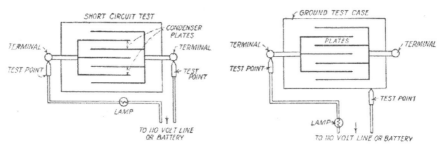

Fig. 44-a.   Short-Circuited Condenser Test
on D. C. Current

Fig. 44-b.   Grounded Condenser Test
on D. C. Current

case of the condenser and the other on the condenser terminal. If the lamp lights, that side of the unit is grounded. Test the other side of the condenser in like manner. One side of the condenser is used to complete the ground in some units, and the lamp will light on this test. If the lamp lights on touching the test point to the case and the external terminal, the unit is out of order.

Testing High Tension Coils under Working Conditions. *Astatic Gap.* The astatic gap has three points, Fig. 45. Point A is connected to the high-tension lead of the coil or armature, while the point B is insulated and is the static point. The function of the static point is to maintain an even resistance between the points A and C, thereby giving a definite resistance for a given distance; this is of prime importance to provide a reliable test.

The action of the static point is to produce a capacity at the points in tune with the oscillations of the high-tension discharge. As the secondary current from any high-tension coil is of high frequency, although greatly damped because of the amount of iron in the coil or armature, the introduction of a capacity or condenser action into the circuit has a direct bearing on the gap.

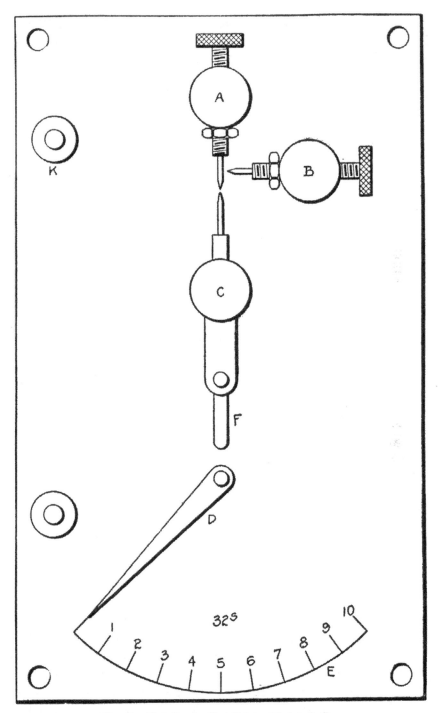

Fig. 45.   High-Tension Test Points with Astatic Gap

ELECTRICAL EQUIPMENT

The distance between the points A and B should be 0.002 inch. The two terminal posts should be connected on the back of the fiber base by a small wire. The body of the posts A, B, C should be $\frac{5}{8}$ inch in diameter, especially the static point; too small a mass will not furnish sufficient capacity to work properly. Phonograph points are good for this purpose and are easily mounted. Lock nuts should be used on screws A and B and also on C if necessary.

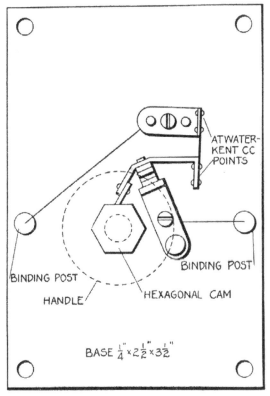

Fig. 46. Breaker-Point Test Set

Vibrator. A master vibrator is placed in series with a 6-volt storage battery and the coil to be tested, the high-tension lead being connected to the terminals on A and C and grounded to the primary of the coil. With the spark jumping the gap, the point C is opened until the spark will just jump it continuously. If the gap measurement is taken with a good coil a standard is obtained.

After the vibrator is once set it should not be changed; any change in adjustment will mean a change in the quality of the spark. As some high-tension armatures have such a high primary resistance that a vibrator will not operate through them, a single-break interrupter may be used to overcome this difficulty.

Single-Break Test. A simple cheap breaker may be made as in Fig. 46. A piece of $\frac{1}{4}$-inch red fibre $2\frac{1}{2}''\times3\frac{1}{2}''$ forms the base; Atwater-Kent type CC points are used for contacts; the hexagon cam is made from a $\frac{3}{8}$-inch hexagon iron rod turned down to a shoulder $\frac{1}{4}$ inch in diameter and projects through the base, with a fiber handle about an inch in diameter attached. A condenser is connected across the points, and the whole assembly mounted on the test board. To test with this apparatus, the coil is connected as in Fig. 47; the battery coil primary and breaker are connected in series; the coil secondary is connected to the gap, and the spark is noted. As this type of breaker has no resistance to speak of and is operated by hand, the coil has plenty of time to saturate its core, the spark produced being uniform.

Special Dial Gap. For quick results, utilize the special dial gap, Fig. 45. This gap has a fiber base $\frac{1}{4}''\times3\frac{1}{4}''\times5\frac{1}{2}''$, on which are mounted two stationary points marked A and B and a grounded movable point C; below is a pointer D, which moves on the scale

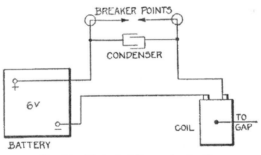

Fig. 47. Method of Connecting for Test

E. The movable point C slides in the slot F and is held by a plate and two rivets. The lower part of the body C projects through and forms one rivet, while the other projects through the plate about $\frac{1}{4}$ inch, and the cam bears on it, as well as the spring, holding the plate assembly against the cam. Point A is connected on the back to terminal K.

The dial E is cut in the fiber and white lead put in the cuts. This dial is laid out in ten divisions, marked 1, 2, 3, 4, etc., and moving the pointer one division causes the gap to change $\frac{1}{32}$ inch. In using this apparatus, the dial makes it possible to get a quick positive reading. A table can be made up to show just what each type of armature or coil should test, thus eliminating all guesswork.

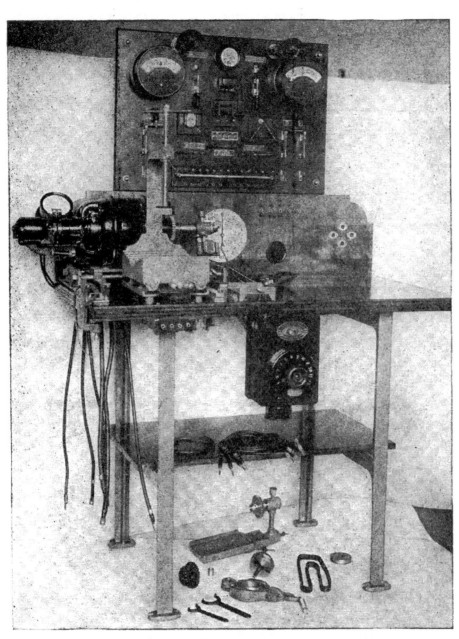

WEIDENHOFF ELECTRICAL TEST BENCH COMPLETE

ELECTRICAL REPAIRS

PART III

TESTING WIRING

Locating Grounds. By referring to any of the Delco diagrams of the one-wire type, it will be noted that certain parts of the circuits are normally grounded, i.e., they are connected to the common return represented by the chassis of the car. For example, the negative battery terminal, one terminal of each lamp, one motor, one generator brush, one timer contact, one terminal of the horn push button, and one terminal of the condenser in the coil are grounded. Before testing the wiring for grounds, it will be necessary to remove these normal, or intentional, grounds. This is carried out, in the order in which they are mentioned, by disconnecting the negative battery lead and removing all the lamps, placing a piece of cardboard between each generator and each motor brush, including the third brush of the former and the commutator against which it ordinarily bears, disconnecting the leads from the horn button and from the distributor, and raising the base of the ignition coil so that it is insulated from the top cover of the generator motor. The system will then be in the condition shown in Fig. 48.

One of the test points is then placed on the frame of the car and the other point on the negative terminal A of the battery. If the lamp lights, it will indicate a ground somewhere on the switch or in the motor windings (all of the switch buttons being pushed in). Then, with one test point still grounded on the frame of the car, test with the other point the different terminals of the combination switch. If the lamp lights during this test, it will indicate a ground on that particular circuit, which can be remedied without any particular difficulty.

Locating Shorts. To test for short-circuits between wires that are normally insulated from each other, place one test point on the end of one wire and the second test point on the end of the other, as shown in Fig. 49. If the lamp lights, it will indicate a short-circuit

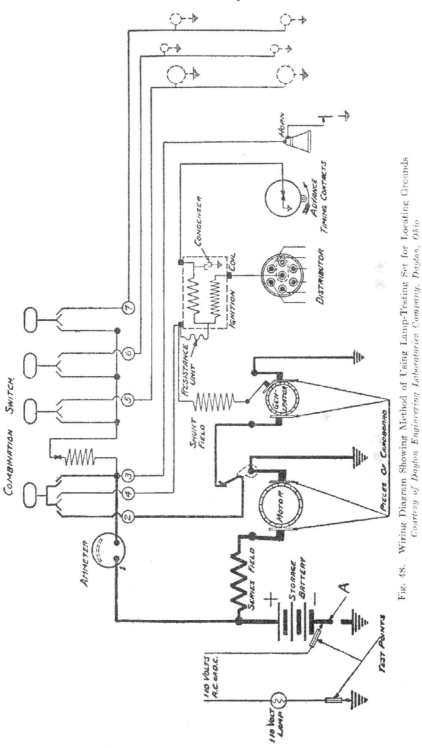

Fig. 48. Wiring Diagram Showing Method of Using Lamp-Testing Set for Locating Grounds
Courtesy of Dayton Engineering Laboratories Company, Dayton, Ohio

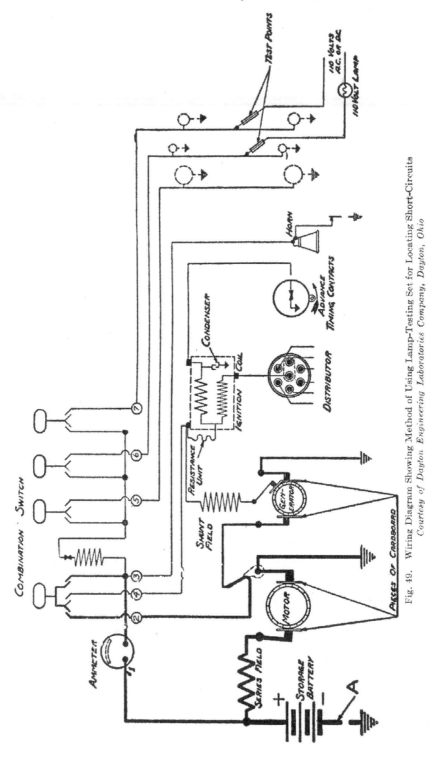

Fig. 49. Wiring Diagram Showing Method of Using Lamp-Testing Set for Locating Short-Circuits
Courtesy of Dayton Engineering Laboratories Company, Dayton, Ohio

between these two wires, which can then be carefully inspected to locate the exact position of the fault. Failure of the lamp to light when the test is made will indicate that the wires in question are in good condition; the tests can then be applied to other parts of the circuits which should be insulated from each other.

Locating Breaks in Wires. Where the failure of the apparatus in a particular circuit makes it apparent that a wire, or lead, may be broken, it may be tested by placing one of the points on each end of the wire in question. The lighting of the lamp will indicate that there is a complete circuit through the wire, while its failure to light is evidence of a break in the wire. If at all difficult to locate the break, the easiest method of repairing is it to replace the wire with a new lead of the same size and type of insulation. The method of carrying out this last test is illustrated in Fig. 50 and it is naturally applicable to any of the wires, not only of this type of installation but of any other lighting and starting system. In making this test, care must be taken not to apply the points at places on the terminals where a ground connection will result, as this will complete the circuit through the lamp without the current passing through the wire supposedly under test. This method of locating grounds, short-circuits, or open circuits will be found much better than the use of a buzzer, bell, or magneto, and it is recommended wherever a 110-volt current is available. However, where it is not available, a lamp, bell, buzzer, or the portable voltmeter may be used in connection with the storage battery on the car, after detaching its usual connections to the system.

Ground in Starting or in Lighting 2=Wire Circuits. When the blowing of a fuse in any lighting circuit is due to a ground, or a similar fault is suspected in the starting system, it may be tested for either with the lamp outfit or with the low-reading voltmeter, as follows:

Disconnect one battery terminal, taping the bare end to prevent contact with any metal parts of the car, and connect one side of the voltmeter to this terminal. Attach a length of wire having a bared end to the other terminal of the voltmeter, as shown in Fig. 51. Connect the bared end of the free wire to some part of the car frame; making certain that good electrical contact is made. Disconnect the generator and starting motor completely, open all lighting switches, and be sure that the ignition switch is off. If there is no ground in the

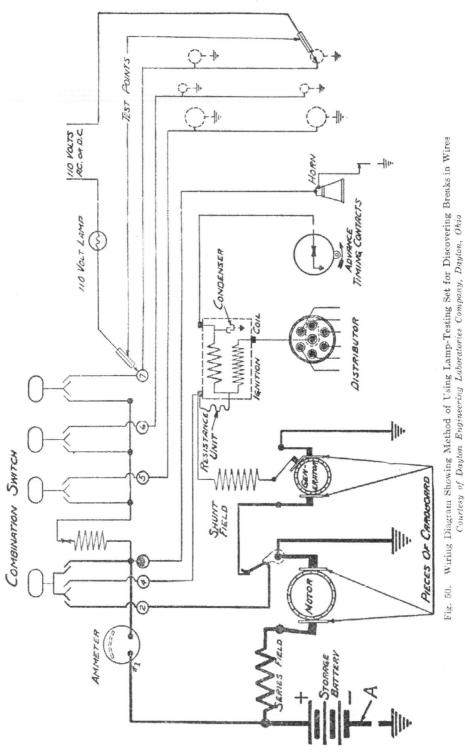

Fig. 50. Wiring Diagram Showing Method of Using Lamp-Testing Set for Discovering Breaks in Wires
Courtesy of Dayton Engineering Laboratories Company, Dayton, Ohio

circuit, the voltmeter will give no indication. Be sure that none of the disconnected terminals are touching the engine or frame; to insure this, tape them.

Should the voltmeter give a reading of 4 volts or more, it indicates that there is a ground in the wiring between the battery and the junction box, or in the wiring between the junction box and the generator or the starting motor. If the voltmeter reads less than 4 volts but more than $\frac{1}{2}$ volt, all wiring and connections should be carefully inspected for faults. This test should be repeated by reversing the connections, that is, by reconnecting the wires on the side of the battery circuit that has been opened and disconnecting the other side.

Localizing Any Ground. To localize any fault that the reading of the voltmeter may show, reconnect the wires to the starting motor

Fig. 51. Testing for Grounds with Voltmeter in
Two-Wire System

and close the starting switch; any reading of the voltmeter with such connections will indicate that the ground is in this circuit. Should no ground be indicated with these connections, disconnect the starter again and reconnect the generator; if the voltmeter records any voltage, the ground is in the generator circuit. With both starter and generator disconnected, the voltmeter being connected first to one side of the battery and then to the other, operate the lighting switches, the ignition switch, and the horn, one at a time, and note whether the voltmeter needle moves upon closing any of these switches. A voltage reading upon closing any of these switches will indicate a ground in that particular circuit.

Short=Circuit Tests. To test for short-circuits, substitute the ammeter for the voltmeter, but do not connect the instrument to

Fig. 52. Testing for Short-Circuits with Ammeter in Two-Wire System

the battery. The shunt reading to 20 amperes should be employed, one side of the ammeter being grounded on the frame as previously described, and the other being connected with a short wire that can be touched to the open side of the battery, Fig. 52. Disconnect the starter and the generator and open all the switches, then touch the bare end of the wire to the battery terminal on the open side as shown. Any reading, no matter how small, will indicate a short-circuit (two-wire system) in the wiring between the battery and junction box or between the latter and the starter, or generator. If the ammeter reading shows a heavy current, there is a severe short-circuit.

Localizing a Short=Circuit. The short-circuit may be localized in the same manner as described for the voltmeter test, i.e., connect the starter and test; disconnect the starter, connect the generator and test. A reading on the generator test may be due to the contacts of the cut-out sticking together. If the cut-out contacts are open and the ammeter registers, there is a short-circuit in the generator windings.

ELECTRICAL EQUIPMENT

Disconnect the generator again, remove all the lamps from the sockets, and turn on the lighting-circuit switches one at a time, touching the wire to the battery terminal after closing each switch. A reading with any particular switch on indicates a short-circuit in the wiring of the lamps controlled by that switch. Only one switch should be closed at a time, all others being open. This test should be made also with the ignition switch on but with the engine idle. The ammeter should then register the ignition current, which should not exceed 4 to 5 amperes. If greater than this, the ignition circuit should be examined.

Cautions. Do not attempt to test the starter circuit with the ammeter as it will damage the instrument. To test the starter circuit, reconnect as for operating, removing the ammeter. Close the starting switch; a short-circuit in the wiring will result either in failure to operate or in slow turning over of the engine. See that the switch parts are clean and that they make good contact. If the short-circuit is in the winding of the starting motor, there will be an odor of burning insulation or smoke.

The battery must be fully charged for making any of these tests. While the effect either of a ground or of a short-circuit will be substantially the same, its location and the remedy will be more easily determined by ascertaining whether it is the one or the other.

Lamp Troubles. When short-circuits, grounds, or open-circuits are suspected as the cause for lights failing to burn, it is advisable to examine the different lamps in the system before starting to test or to pull out any of the wiring. In the single-wire or grounded system, the circuit is completed by grounding the lamp through the reflector. They often become rusted or dirty, failing to make good electrical contact and the lamp will not light. The lamp sockets may become rusted or dirty with the same result and the wires will break inside the lamp causing an incomplete connection. The plunger springs in the sockets may get weak, making poor connection, and the socket will have to be renewed. Cleaning and making good connections will often cure other troubles. If the bulbs are not of the same voltage in the dash and tail lamps which are in series connection, one lamp will burn brighter than the other or may not burn at all. The lamps should be half the voltage of the battery. If the system is 6 volts, the lamp bulbs should each be 3 volts.

ELECTRICAL EQUIPMENT

Testing Cut=Out. If the battery is not charging properly, the generator being in good condition, or it is discharging too much current through the cut-out, the latter should be tested and adjusted to remedy the trouble. The cut-out is designed to close when the voltage across the terminals of the voltage coil is $6\frac{1}{2}$ to $7\frac{3}{4}$ volts. To check this a voltmeter should be connected across the terminals, noting the reading at the point that the contacts close. It is designed to break the circuit when the discharge current is less than 1 ampere, preferably as close to the zero mark as possible to reduce the arc on breaking the contacts. This can be checked by placing an ammeter in the circuit in series with the current coil of the cut-out, noting the value of the current at the moment that the contacts separate. When properly adjusted the air gap should be $\frac{1}{32}$ inch.

To adjust the cut-out, the influence of both the air gap and of the spring tension must be taken into consideration. The air gap has little or no effect upon the point of cut-out, this being governed almost entirely by the spring tension, whereas the point of cutting in is governed by both the air gap and the spring tension. The following examples will illustrate the adjustments necessary in cases of excess voltage and current, excess voltage alone, insufficient voltage and excess current, and insufficient voltage alone.

Where the relay cuts in at 8 volts and cuts out when the discharge current is 2 amperes: Decrease the air gap, as this will lower the voltage of the cut-in point, but it will also increase the discharge current on cutting out. To overcome the latter, increase the spring tension slightly, noting the effect on the ammeter until the latter registers less than 1 ampere on cutting out.

Where the relay cuts in at 8 volts and cuts out at 1 ampere: Decrease the spring tension as this will cause the relay to cut in at a lower voltage and also to cut out after the current starts to discharge through it.

Where the relay cuts in at 6 volts and cuts out at 2 amperes: Increase the spring tension, causing the relay to cut in at a higher voltage and also to cut out at a discharge-current value of less than 2 amperes.

Where the relay cuts in at 6 volts and cuts out with a discharge current of 1 ampere: Increase the air gap slightly and also increase the spring tension so as to cause the relay to cut in at a higher voltage and also cut out at a discharge current of less than 1 ampere.

In this connection *cut in* signifies the closing of the contacts when the voltage coil becomes energized as the generator starts up; *cut out* indicates the opening of the generator battery circuit when the current from the battery reverses the polarity of the current coil of the relay, thus opening the circuit and cutting out the generator from the battery circuit when the generator slows down and there is insufficient voltage from charging the battery. While these instructions apply particularly to the Delco relay or cut-out, all devices of this nature operate on the same principles.

Before making any adjustments, the contact points should be examined. If they are blackened or pitted, take two narrow strips of emery cloth about $\frac{3}{8}$ inch wide and both the same length. Place them together, emery sides out, insert between the contacts and while an assistant holds the points together, draw back and forth. If no assistance be obtainable, use a single strip and apply alternately to each contact point until its face is bright all over and true so that when the two points come together they touch evenly all over their surfaces. Do not take off any more than is necessary for this purpose, particularly where the contacts are platinum, as this simply wears them away uselessly and they are very expensive to replace. After cleaning, test for cutting in voltage and cutting out current and it frequently will be found that no adjustment is necessary.

These instructions regarding the cleaning of contact points apply with equal force to all instruments having contacts by means of which the circuit is frequently made and broken, for even platinum is burned away by the electrical action of the current which tends to carry the metal of the positive contact over to the negative in finely divided form this making a hole, or crater, on the positive and a cone, or peak, on the negative.

If the contacts are too badly burned to permit of their being put in good condition in this way, it will be necessary to replace them. After the relay has been reassembled with the new contacts, it should be adjusted in accordance with the instructions already given. When the contacts are correctly adjusted, both pairs will make contact at the same instant and clear across the 'ine of contact so that when the relay is held up to the light, it is impossible to see light passing through any portion of the line of contact. When adjusting the relay make sure that all insulating bushings are in good condition and that the connections and coil terminals are free from breaks or grounds, as these would cause uncertainty in its operation.

Testing Circuit=Breaker. In case the circuit-breaker vibrates constantly, it indicates a ground in one of the circuits. Should it continue to vibrate when all of the buttons of the combination switch have been pushed in, the ground will almost invariably be found in the horn or its connections. In case no ground can be found in any of the circuits with the aid of the testing lamp, and the circuit-breaker still continues to vibrate, connect the portable testing ammeter in the circuit, using the 30-ampere shunt. Then hold the circuit-breaker closed and note the ammeter reading when it opens. This must be done quickly as the current necessary to keep it operating is small so that the ammeter reading will quickly drop to a value of 3 to 5 amperes. However, the circuit-breaker should not open on a current of less than 25 amperes. If the ammeter reading indicates that it does so, increase the tension of the spring until the current necessary to operate it shows that it is properly adjusted. In case the instrument shows that the circuit-breaker is opening at the proper point but still continues to vibrate, another series of tests for a ground must be made as the latter is the cause of the trouble.

Testing Armatures. In reading the foregoing instructions as well as those that follow here concerning the Delco system, it should be borne in mind that they apply in principle, and in many cases in actual detail, to the majority of other systems described. In other words, all starting and lighting systems are based on the same principles and, while many of them differ in detail and in design, the application of the instructions in question will very frequently be evident by comparing them point for point and modifying the instructions to compensate for any slight differences in design or wiring.

Armature troubles are of much less frequent occurrence than the majority of defections, such as worn brushes, dirty commutator, or the like, which temporarily put the system out of commission, so that every part of the system which might be at fault should be investigated before attempting to test the armature for faults. To carry out these tests, the voltmeter and the lamp-testing set are necessary. Where no previous experience has been had in making tests with these aids, it will be well to become familiar with the detailed instructions given for their use in connection with the dtermination of other faults, as already described. It is not necessary to remove the dyna-motor from the car for this purpose. When tests of the remainder of the system indicate no faults and when grounds in the armature-

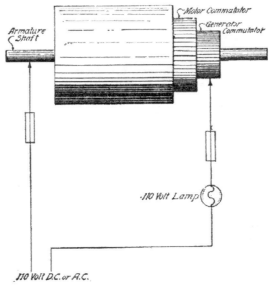

Fig. 53. Diagram for Locating Grounded Generator Coil with Lamp-Testing Set

windings or short-circuits between them are not suspected, raise all the brushes from the commutator and slip pieces of cardboard between the brushes and the commutator so as to insulate them from each other. These instructions cover the single-unit Delco machine, so the foregoing applies as well to testing for short-circuits between generator and motor armature windings. For greater simplicity, the possible faults and the tests for locating them are treated under different heads, as follows:

(a) *Grounded Generator Coil.* On one-wire systems of the single-unit type, the presence of a grounded generator coil will materially reduce the charging rate to the battery and will also result in slow cranking of the engine. To determine whether a generator coil has become grounded, place one of the test points on the frame or on the armature shaft, both of which are grounded, and the other on the generator commutator, as shown in Fig. 53. If the lamp lights, it indicates a ground on the commutator. The test of the generator of a two-unit set would be carried out in exactly the same manner.

(b) *Grounded Motor Coil.* According to the nature of the fault, a grounded motor coil may either prevent operation of the starting

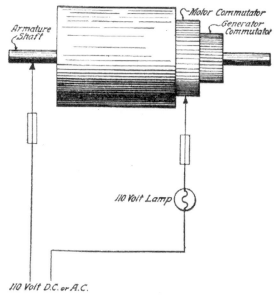

Fig. 54. Diagram for Locating Grounded Motor Coil with Lamp-Testing Set

motor altogether or it may result only in an excessive consumption of current for starting. The test is carried out in the same manner as described for the generator, except that the second point of the test set is placed on the motor commutator, Fig. 54. It will likewise be evident that an independent starting motor can be tested in the same way.

(c) *Short-Circuits between Motor and Generator Armature Coils.* In most cases short-circuits between motor and generator armature coils will decrease the speed of cranking and will cause the armature to continue to run after the engine has been shut down. This test is carried out by simply placing one test point on the generator commutator and the other on the motor commutator. If the lamp lights, it indicates a short-circuit between the generator and motor windings, Fig. 55. This test is naturally only applicable to single-unit machines having two independent windings on the same armature core, as in the case of the Delco, the type in question.

(d) *Open- or Short-Circuited Generator Armature Coils.* When testing for open- or short-circuited generator armature coils, the gen-

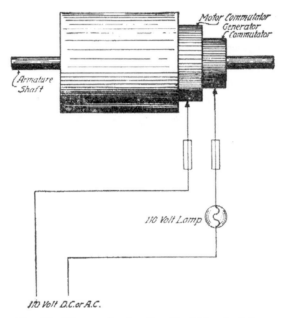

Fig. 55. Diagram for Locating Short-Circuits between Motor and Generator Armature Coils

erator brushes should be left in contact with the commutator, but the storage battery should be disconnected from the system, carefully taping the loose battery terminals before proceeding. Then disconnect the shunt field from the brushes and tape these terminals so that they do not accidentally come in contact with the frame or other parts of the unit. Connect up a dry cell and the portable ammeter, using the 30-ampere shunt, as shown in Fig. 56. Turn the armature over slowly by hand. If the commutator is clean and bright and the brushes are making good contact with it, a very noticeable change in the ammeter reading will indicate an open- or a short-circuited armature coil. To determine whether the coil is open- or short-circuited, the following tests can be made:

(1) *Open-Circuited Coils.* Connect the brushes to the terminals of the dry cell so that a current of about 10 amperes is flowing through the brushes. The field should be entirely disconnected and its terminals either taped or held out of the way. Then, with a special pair of points connected to the voltmeter using the 3-volt scale, measure the voltage across each two adjacent commutator bars. If there is an open-circuited coil in the armature, the voltage reading will increase considerably, Fig. 57.

(2) *Short-Circuited Coils.* If there are no open-circuited coils and the preceding tests indicate that there is trouble with

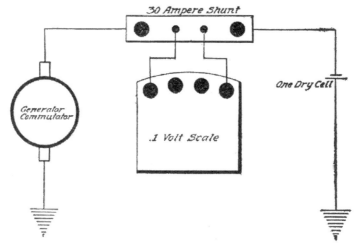

Fig. 56.   Diagram for Testing Open or Short-Circuited Generator
Armature Coil with Ammeter

the armature, it should be tested for short-circuited coils. This should be done only after the preceding tests have been made, as and open-circuited coil might cause the .1-volt scale of the voltmeter to burn out if this test were made first. The armature is connected as indicated in (1), but for this test the .1-volt scale instead of the 3-volt scale of the voltmeter is used, Fig. 58. The voltage drop between adjacent commutator bars is then measured by slowly turning the commutator over by hand. The readings should be approximately the same. If any of them drop nearly to zero, it will indicate that one or more of the armature coils are short-circuited. In taking these readings, care must be observed to keep the points

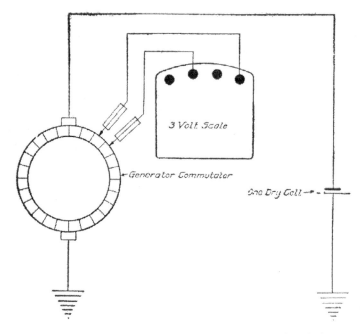

Fig. 57. Diagram of Set-Up when Coils Are Open-Circuited

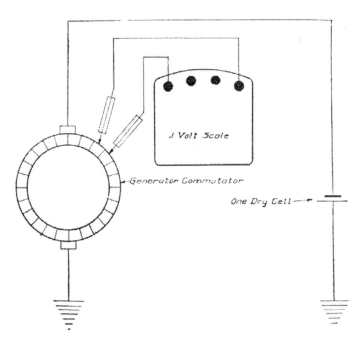

Fig. 58. Diagram of Set-Up when Coils Are Short-Circuited

always on adjacent commutator bars and not allow them to span more than two bars at any time; otherwise, the voltage drop may be sufficient to injure the voltmeter.

Should any of these tests indicate open- or short-circuited coils in the armature, it is advisable to send the armature to the manufacturer for repairs, or to install a new armature. Unless the fault is plainly visible, as where a coil-terminal connection at the commutator bar has broken or become short-circuited, the average establishment will find the repair entirely beyond its facilities to make, so that time and expense will be saved by promptly referring it to the factory. Special equipment and skill in the handling of such

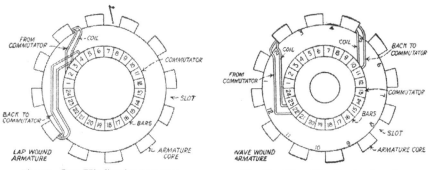

Fig. 59. Lap Winding for Armature   Fig. 60.   Wave Winding for Armature.

repairs are indispensable and are beyond the province of the garage man. These tests can also be used for testing generator and starting-motor windings where two units are used separately.

Armature Winding. It is necessary to remove the damaged coils for repairs after the armature windings have been tested, and the short-circuits, grounds, and open circuits in the coils have been found. It usually means that the armature must be entirely rewound for in order to reach the damaged coils, others must be disturbed. There are two types of windings, "lap" and "wave," but there are many connections and combinations used.

The segments in the commutator are termed "bars"; the grooves in which the coils are placed are called "slots"; the coils are spoken of as so many "turns" per coil and so many coils per slot.

The wire generally used in armature winding is covered with enamel or a double layer of cotton. Silk is often used for it makes a thinner wire. This is important for the wire must not stand above the top of the slot. The wires vary in thickness in practically every unit. If a repair man wishes to make a specialty of armature work, he must carry a large stock of wires and ribbons of all sizes. It is much cheaper to send the armature to the makers and receive a

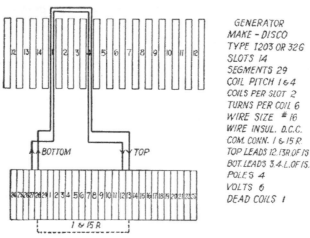

GENERATOR
MAKE – DISCO
TYPE 1203 OR 326
SLOTS 14
SEGMENTS 29
COIL PITCH 1 & 4
COILS PER SLOT 2
TURNS PER COIL 6
WIRE SIZE # 16
WIRE INSUL. D.C.C.
COM. CONN. 1 & 15 R.
TOP LEADS 12.13R.OF 1S
BOT. LEADS 3.4.L.OF 1S.
POLES 4
VOLTS 6
DEAD COILS 1

Fig. 61. Armature Rewinding Diagram
Courtesy of Chittenden

correctly rewound armature in exchange. Special equipment is necessary and it does not pay the average garage man to do this work.

Two typical winding diagrams are given with an explanation of the terms used. Fig. 59 shows the "lap" winding, and Fig. 60, the

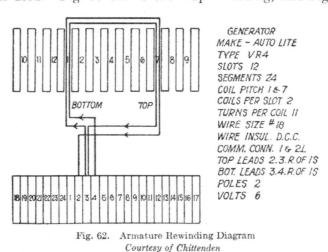

GENERATOR
MAKE – AUTO LITE
TYPE VR4
SLOTS 12
SEGMENTS 24
COIL PITCH 1 & 7
COILS PER SLOT 2
TURNS PER COIL 11
WIRE SIZE # 18
WIRE INSUL. D.C.C.
COMM. CONN. 1 & 2L
TOP LEADS 2.3.R.OF 1S
BOT. LEADS 3.4.R.OF 1S
POLES 2
VOLTS 6

Fig. 62. Armature Rewinding Diagram
Courtesy of Chittenden

"wave" winding. The two charts, Figs. 61 and 62, show one method used in giving the data for rewinding and the specifications for a "lap" and a "wave" winding, respectively. The data in Fig. 62 means:

1. "Slots 14"—there are 14 slots or grooves in which the coils are placed.

2. "Segments 29"—there are 29 bars in the commutator.

3. "Coil pitch 1 and 4"—the coils pass through the slots numbered 1 and 4, or that the number of slots between the coils are 4 including the two outside slots.

4. "Coils per slot 2"—there are 2 coils to each slot, giving 4 coil sides to each slot.

5. "Turns per slot 6"—there are 6 turns of wire for each coil.

6. "Wire size 16"—a wire of number 16 Brown and Sharpe gauge is to be used.

7. "Wire insul D.C.C."—The wire must be insulated with a double layer covering of cotton.

8. "Comm conn 1 and 15"—there should be 15 bars between the connections of the wire and the commutator. The first and last bars are included in this number.

9. "Top leads 12 13 R of 1S"—the coils that are to be put in the top half of the slot should be connected to commutator bars 12 and 13 and to the right of the slot chosen as slot 1 for the beginning connection.

10. "Bott leads 3 4 L of 1S"—the coils that are to be in the bottom half of the slot should be connected to the bars 3 and 4 and to the left of the slot chosen as slot number 1.

11. "Lead"—the number of bars to the right or left of the slot through which the coil passes.

12. "Poles 4"—a 4-pole machine.

13. "Dead coils 1"—there is one coil not connected to the commutator.

The commutator bar that is in direct line with the slot numbered 1, is also numbered 1. They are used as the starting point for the numbering and the winding connections.

Let us trace the path of the wire as shown in Fig. 62. The coil starts at bar 27, which is the number 4 bar, and to the left of slot 1 through which it passes. It is carried to slot 4 and passes through it from the top of the slot. It is wound in this manner until there are 6 turns in the coil and is then connected to bar 12 which is the 12th bar to the right of slot 1.

If a coil is connected to bar 29, it would pass through the bottom of slot 2 and over to slot 5 with 6 turns in it and connected to bar 14. It will be seen that there are 4 slots between the the coils and 15 bars between the connections at the commutator. Always count the beginning slot or bar. This same method is carried throughout the winding until each slot has two top and two bottom leads in it and each commutator bar has two coils connected to it.

Commutator Maintenance. In the course of time, the commutator bars of the generator will wear down until they are flush

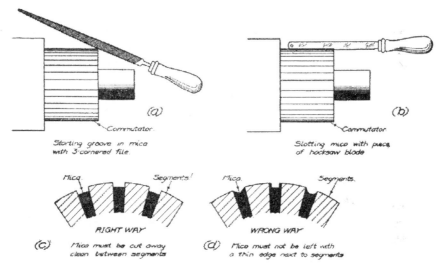

Fig. 63. Method of Undercutting Mica Insulation on Commutator
Courtesy of Auto Electric Systems Publishing Company, Dayton, Ohio

with the mica insulation separating them. When this occurs there will be excessive arcing in the brushes which, in turn, will cause the copper to be burned away until it is level with, or below, the surface of the mica. This condition will be indicated by a rusty black color on the commutator bars. To prevent this condition, the commutator should be cleaned occasionally with sandpaper as directed. If the mica is *high*, it should be undercut as follows:

The armature is removed from the machine and placed in a lathe, truing up both commutators until they are perfectly concentric. This should be done carefully and then as fine a cut as possible taken to avoid wasting the copper needlessly. When the commutators have been trued up in the lathe, cut out mica between the commutator bars of the generator only. For this purpose a piece of hacksaw blade should be fixed in a handle, as shown in Fig. 63, and its teeth ground off until they will cut a slot that is just slightly wider than the mica insulation. The cut need not be more than $\frac{1}{32}$ inch deep. In this way a rectangular slot, free from mica, will be obtained between each two adjacent commutator bars. After undercutting the mica, the edges of these slots should be beveled very slightly with a three-corned file in order to remove any burrs which would cause excessive wear of the brushes.

It is unnecessary to undercut the mica on the motor commutator, as, wherever metal or metallic brushes are used on Delco machines, they are sufficiently hard to keep the mica flush with the surface of the copper as it wears down without any undue arcing at the brushes, whereas in the case of generators provided with carbon brushes, the carbon is not hard enough to do this. After completing the undercutting, the commutator when viewed from the end should show clean-cut retangular slots between the bars, as in the left-hand view, Fig. 63. The machine should then be re-assembled and the brushes sanded-in to the commutator, as previously described. This operation of fitting the brushes to the commutator will be necessary whenever anything has been done to the commutator, when new brushes are installed, or when the third-brush location is readjusted to vary the ouput of the machine on generators having this type of regulation.

These instructions for fitting the brushes, cleaning the commutator, and undercutting the mica of the commutator of any machine equipped with soft-carbon brushes, apply with equal force to all makes of generators and starting motors employed on automobiles. Next to the battery the brushes and commutators will be found to demand most attention—or to put it in another way, they will be found to constitute a cause of trouble only second in importance to the battery. It must not be assumed, however, that all blackening of the commutator is caused always by high mica. Any one of the following conditions may cause the commutator to assume an appearance similar to that produced by high mica: (1) generator brushes of improper size or material, as where replacements other than those supplied by the manufacturer of the machine have been installed; (2) insufficient spring tension on brushes—all springs slacken up in time and they should be examined at intervals to see that the brushes are being held firmly against the commutator; (3) overloading of the generator caused by partial failure of the regulating device or other cause; and (4) an open- or short-circuit in the generator windings, or a short-circuit between generator and motor windings in a single-unit machine like the Delco.

Sometimes, when the armature has been overheated, the solder will work from between the commutator bars making them loose and causing the commutator to become black and give poor generation. If the commutator is not perfectly round, it will cause the ammeter needle to vibrate at high engine speeds. Any connections loose in the circuit will cause the same trouble.

Seating the Brushes. To insure proper operation of the machine either as a generator or as a motor, it is necessary that the brushes fit the commutator exactly and that they make good contact over their entire surface. If they do not, sparking will occur and the commutator will become burned and blackened, cutting down the efficiency of the machine. The brushes are the only wearing parts of a direct-current generator or motor, and, as this wear on them is constant, they will require attention at intervals to keep them in good condition. Whenever sufficient wear has taken place to make the contact uneven, the brushes must be fitted to the commutator or *sanded-in*. Cut a sheet of No. 00 sandpaper in strips slightly wider than the brush. Emery cloth must *never* be used for this purpose. It is metallic and will tend to cause short-circuits in the commutator. The strip of sandpaper is wrapped around the commutator so as to make contact with at least half of its circumference in the manner illustrated in (a) and (c) of Fig. 64. The smooth side of the paper is laid on the commutator so that the sanded side rubs the brush. By drawing the sandpaper back and forth, it is possible to fit the brush very accurately to the commutator. It will be obvious that if the sandpaper be applied to the commutator, as shown in (b) and (d) of the same illustration, that the brush will only touch at its center and there will be excessive sparking between the gaps thus formed.

A high squeaking note caused by the operation of either the generator or motor is an indication that either the brushes or the commutator need sanding-in as the latter will become roughened from the wear. It should be smoothed up by taking strips of the same grade of sandpaper sufficiently wide to cover the commutator, applying them by wrapping in the same manner but with the sanded surface on the commutator bars. This can be done most effectively by running the machine through its other commutator

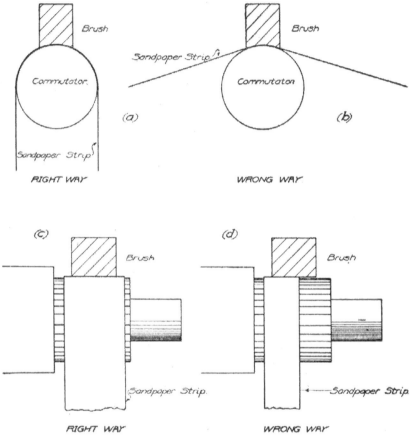

Fig. 64. Method of Sanding-In Brushes
Courtesy of Auto Electric Systems Publishing Company, Dayton, Ohio

for a few moments while holding the sandpaper strip in place on the first. If, after this smoothing up, the mica insulation between the bars of the commutator is flush with the surface of the copper bars, it must be undercut. On most of the Delco machines it will be found possible to sand-in the upper and lower brushes separately by this method, but in a number of cases on account of the construction of the machine, it will be found advisable to sand-in both motor brushes, as well as both generator brushes at the same time. It is unnecessary to lubricate either the motor, the generator brushes, or the commutators, as this simply results in gumming them and causes grit and dirt to collect on the commutator and cut grooves in both it and the brushes.

Brushholder Tests and Troubles. When fitting new brushes, care should be taken to see that they slide freely in the holder, for if they stick, the brush will not make good contact with the commutator. The brush must not be too loose or it will twist or

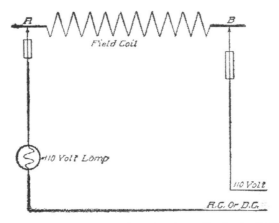

Fig. 65. Diagram for Locating Open Circuits in Field Coils with Lamp-Testing Set

cock in the holder which will not allow full brush contact and low generator output will result.

The following test can be made for a grounded brush holder: insulate the brush by putting some paper between it and the commutator. Place one test point on the holder and the other test point on the frame of the machine. If the lamp lights, it indicates that the holder is grounded. In the case of the third-brush holder the windings must be disconnected from the brush while making this test or the brush taken completely out of the holder.

Testing Field Coils. The tests of field coils are simpler than those of the armature, and they apply in large measure to practically any system.

Open-Circuits in Fields. To test for open-circuits in fields, the test set is the only apparatus required, and the points should be placed as shown in Fig. 65. By placing one point on each terminal of the particular winding to be tested, failure of the lamp to light will indicate that the coil is open-circuited, as the wire of the coil will afford a path for the current, unless broken. The fact that the lamp may not light to full brilliance in some of these coil tests is no indication of trouble, as the difference is simply due to the additional resistance represented by the coil itself. In case an open-circuited coil is found, the only remedy is to return it to the manufacturer for repair or replacement.

Grounded Fields. To test for grounds in the field windings, place one test point on the frame of the machine and the other on a terminal of·the field coil. Before doing this, however, all intentional ground connections made by the terminals should be removed.

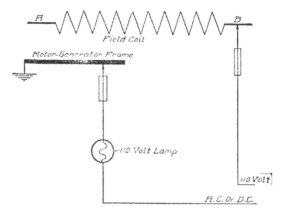

Fig. 66. Diagram for Locating Grounded Fields

These can be located by referring to the winding diagram. If the lamp lights, it will indicate a ground. The manner of applying the test points is shown in Fig. 66.

Short-Circuits between Windings. To test for short-circuits between windings not normally connected, as for example the shunt and series winding of a field coil, place one test point on the terminal of one winding and the other test point on the terminal of the other field winding, as shown in Fig. 67. If the lamp lights, it will indicate a short-circuit between the windings. The field coils can also be tested with a voltmeter, the 30-volt scale being used in connection with a 6-volt storage battery for this purpose, Fig. 68. As all lighting generators have more than one winding on their fields, i.e., shunt and series windings (the latter termed "bucking coils" when reversed), these tests are equally applicable to all makes.

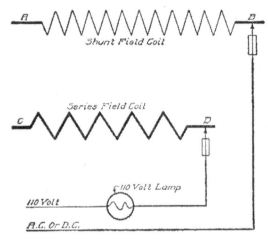

Fig. 67.   Diagram for Testing Short-Circuits between Windings

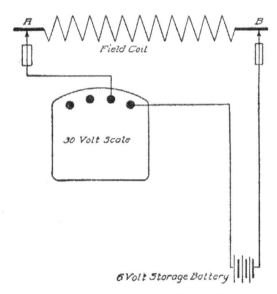

Fig. 68.   Voltmeter Test Diagram for Open-Circuited Field

Voltmeter Field Tests. The method of employing the voltmeter for making field tests, shown in Figs. 68 and 69, is as follows:

To test for an open-circuited field, connect up as shown in Fig. 68. The positive terminal of the voltmeter is connected to the positive terminal of the battery. An insulated copper wire of convenient length, with the insulation stripped off for about one inch at each end, is then attached to the terminal of the voltmeter marked "30 volts," and a similar wire is attached to the negative terminal of the battery. The free ends of these wires are then used in the same manner as the points of the test set, except that the voltmeter reading is the indication sought instead of the lighting of a lamp. Before making the test, touch the free ends of the wires together. This reading will be the total voltage of the storage battery, and it should be kept in mind when making the tests.

If, instead of touching the free ends of the wire together, they are placed on the terminals of a high resistance, the voltmeter reading will naturally be much less. In other words, the value of the voltmeter reading will always depend upon the amount of resistance offered by the coil or other circuit that is being tested. When there is no circuit, as with the free ends held apart in the hands, there will be no indication on the voltmeter scale. An open-circuited coil will accordingly be indicated by a zero reading of the voltmeter when the two free ends, or points, are placed upon the terminals of the coil, Fig. 68. If, on the other hand, the voltmeter reading is nearly half of that of the battery voltage, the coil is in good condition. This test corresponds to that with the lamp-testing set using the 110-volt current, illustrated in Fig. 65. It is a method which also permits one coil to be checked against another of the same kind, as the readings given by the two coils should be approximately the same. Where neither a 110-volt current nor a portable voltmeter are available, these tests may be carried out with the aid of a 6-volt bulb in connection with the storage battery, as shown for the voltmeter tests. In this case, the lamp will light brightly when the free ends of the wires are brought together, but it will dim in proportion to the amount of extra resistance added to the circuit, as represented by the coil under test. While not so accurate as the tests with the voltmeter, comparative tests are also possible with the low-voltage lamp, a very perceptible difference in the lighting of the lamp indicating a greatly increased resistance. When using current from a storage battery for testing, care must be taken to have the points of the test set, or ends of the wire, clean and bright, and to make good, firm contact. If necessary, places on the machine at which the test points are to be applied should

ELECTRICAL EQUIPMENT

first be scraped or filed clean, otherwise, additional resistance will be inserted by the poor contact at the points, as for example, where the latter are applied to a painted surface.

To test for grounds in a field, after having removed all ground connections, as mentioned in a previous paragraph, place one end,

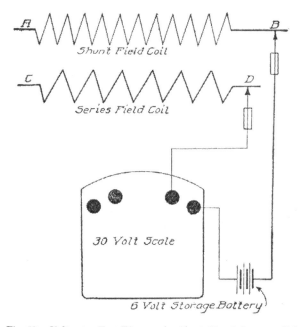

Fig. 69.   Voltmeter Test Diagram for Short-Circuit between Coils

or point, on a terminal of the field coil and the other on the frame of the machine. The method of making the test is identical with that shown in Fig. 66, except for the substitution of the voltmeter for the 110-volt light circuit. If the coil is free from grounds, the voltmeter needle will remain at zero; in case, there is a ground, there will be an indication on the instrument and the worse the ground the greater the value of this reading will be. This test corresponds to that illustrated in Fig. 54.

Short-Circuits between Coils. The test for short-circuits between coils is similar to that shown in Fig. 55 and naturally applies to all lighting generators where the two windings of the fields are concerned. Place one end, or point, on the terminal of one winding and the other end on the terminal of the other winding, as shown in Fig. 69. If there is no connection between the coils, as should be the case, the voltmeter needle will remain stationary. Any movement of the voltmeter needle indicates a short-circuit and the greater the value of the reading, the more complete is the short-circuit between the two coils.

In order to make these tests without removing the machine from the car, disconnect the storage battery and tape the disconnected terminals; then, insulate all the brushes by placing pieces of cardboard between them and the commutators. Disconnect all wires leading to generator terminals, and likewise, all wires leading to field-coil terminals. By referring to the circuit and wiring diagrams for the particular car under consideration, all these leads can readily be identified, and after disconnecting them, the field coils of the machine can be tested. When the tests indicate that the field coils are not in perfect condition, it will ususally be found advisable to remove the field coils from the machine and send them to the manufacturer for repair or replacement, for unless the fault is plainly apparent, which will seldom be the case, the repair will usually be found to be beyond the average garage facilities.

STUDEBAKER BIG SIX, FIVE-PASSENGER BROUGHAM

349

FORD CAR ELECTRICAL SYSTEM

Ignition. Outside of stationary gas engines, the Ford engine is about the only one now using a low-tension inductor type magneto. To use the current generated by the magneto for ignition purposes, it is necessary to use a spark coil or induction coil to step the low-tension current up to the necessary voltage to jump the spark plug gap.

The action of the coil is no different to the ordinary spark coil or induction coil as far as the principle of induction is concerned. Instead of using a set of contact points to close and open the primary circuit, a commutator or timer is used. There is a set of vibrator blades on the coil on which the contacts are placed and the condenser is incorporated in the coil. The current generated by the magneto is alternating and cannot be used for lighting purposes This fact makes the installation of a direct-current generator necessary for lighting and battery charging purposes.

The battery can be used for ignition purposes as well as the magneto but its prime use is for starting and lighting work. The Ford magneto and ignition, as well as the lighting system, are thoroughly discussed in this section, but it should be remembered that the operation, principles, troubles, and cures discussed in other sections apply equally as well to the Ford.

The tests that are used on other starting motors and generators for locating troubles can be equally well applied to the Ford generator and starting motor.

Induction Coils. The Ford induction, or ignition, coils are located in the coil box on the dash of the car. On the earlier models which were not equipped with the starting system at the factory an ignition switch was placed on the outside of this box. On the late models the ignition switch is located on the cowl and forms a part of the lighting switch. There are four coils in this box, Fig. 1 showing the box in cross section. Each coil furnishes a spark to each cylinder of the motor.

box, Fig. 1, showing the box in cross section. Each coil furnishes a spark to each cylinder of the motor.

If the electromagnet is wound with a number of turns of fine wire over the primary winding, Fig. 1, a transformer is produced. A spark of very high voltage will be induced in this winding

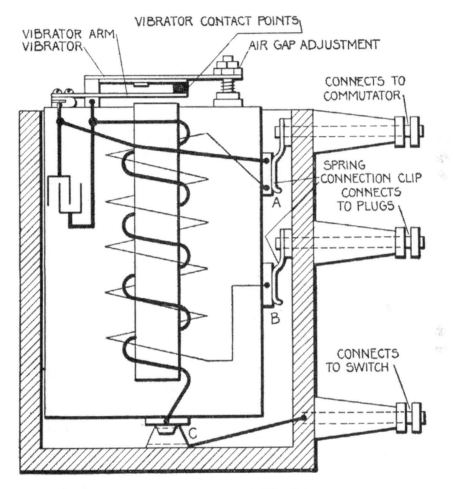

Fig. 1.   Cross-Section of Coil-Box Unit

when the circuit in the primary winding is broken. The current induced in this secondary winding is as many times stronger than that flowing in the primary winding as the number of turns of wire in the secondary is greater than the number of turns in the primary. For instance, if there are 100 turns in the primary winding and 100,000 turns in the secondary winding, the voltage of this secondary current will be 1000 times the voltage of the primary current, if the resistance in the external circuit of the secondary is not changed.

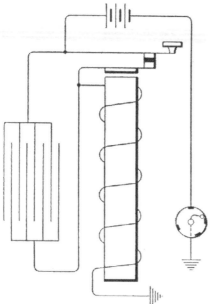

Fig. 2.   Connection of Condenser in the Coil

In the case of an ignition coil, the change in voltage is very great as the current from the secondary winding must have sufficient pressure, or voltage, to jump the gap at the spark plug. This current has a very low amperage, however, for it never exceeds $\frac{2}{10}$ ampere and generally it is about $\frac{1}{100}$ ampere. The voltage finally depends on the compression and the spark-plug gap.

Vibrator. The vibrator is used to cause frequent continuous breaking of the primary circuit, as a strong current is induced in the secondary winding when the circuit of the primary is broken. By referring to Figs. 1 and 2, it will be noted that the vibrator is directly above the end of the core. When the core becomes a magnet, it will attract the vibrator *A*, pulling it down and opening the circuit at the point *B*. The opening of this primary circuit causes the core to lose its magnet-

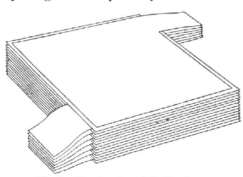

Fig. 3.   Construction of the Condenser

ism, and the vibrator is then drawn up by a spring, again closing the circuit at the points *B*, and the core again becomes magnetized. This series of events continues at the rate of many times a second with the result that the core of the coil alternately becomes a magnet and then an ordinary unmagnetized piece of iron. When the primary circuit is broken the magnetism instantly disappears causing a secondary current to be induced in the secondary winding, and each impulse gives a current of sufficient strength to jump the gap between the points of the spark plug.

Condenser. The condenser, Figs. 2 and 3, acts as a reservoir in storing up, or absorbing, a certain portion of the current at the time the points separate. It may be likened to a surge tank or diaphragm, Fig. 4, which allows the water in a water system to move into a by-pass when the main outlet is quickly shut, thereby preventing the breakage of the water pipe. The condenser is contained in the coil unit and is composed of sheets of tin foil and paraffin paper in alternate layers; every other sheet of tin foil is connected to one of the vibrator points; the remaining sheets are connected to the other vibrator point. The con-

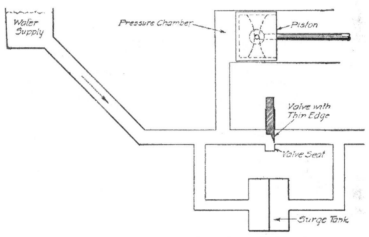

Fig. 4. Diagram Showing Hydraulic Analogy of Ignition System

denser prevents the vibrator points from burning rapidly and at the same time causes the magnetism to disappear quickly. A certain amount of current is induced in the primary winding at the time the circuit is broken, and this eddy current tends to again magnetize the core. This continuous action, if unremedied, would prevent the quick demagnetization of the core and cause a very inefficient secondary current. The condenser absorbs the eddy currents, thereby allowing a strong spark to be produced at the spark plug. It is almost a sure sign that the condenser is defective when the vibrator points start to burn and a white spark appears at these points. If, after examining the points and replacing them with a new set, the spark still continues, it is evident that the condenser has broken down. It will then be necessary to install a new coil as the condenser cannot be repaired.

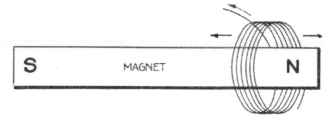

Fig. 5.   Principle of Induced Current

Ford Magneto. If magnetic lines of force are cut by a coil, a current is induced in the coil. By referring to Fig. 5 it will be noted that the coil is being moved backward and forward on

Fig. 6.   Magneto Coils and Magnets

the end of a permanent magnet. This action induces a current in the coil in the reverse manner that a soft-iron core was made an electromagnet by allowing a current to flow through the coil.

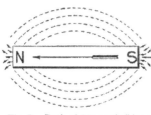

Fig. 7.   Path of Magnetic Lines of Force

A Ford magneto utilizes this same principle in generating a current for ignition —for ignition and lights on early models. Fig. 6 shows the magneto coils and their relation to the magnets. There are sixteen stationary coils and sixteen magnets that are fastened on the flywheel and revolve at a distance of $\frac{1}{32}$ inch from the cores of these coils. The rapid cutting of these magnetic lines of force by the coils—the magnets moving—induces a current in the coils of variable voltage, the voltage depending upon the speed at

TABLE I
Output of Early Ford Magneto at Various Speeds

R.P.M.	Volts	Amperes	R.P.M.	Volts	Amperes
200	8.0	3	800	20.0	—
300	9.2	—	900	22.8	—
400	12.2	—	1000	24.3	—
500	14.2	—	1200	27.0	—
600	16.4	—	1500	30.0	5
700	18.8	—			

which the motor is operating. The amperage also varies with the speed of the motor but does not vary as much as the voltage. The magneto will generate sufficient current to operate the ignition satisfactorily at all motor speeds.

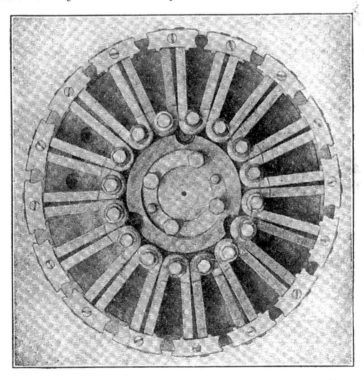

Fig. 8. Mounting of the Magnets

Magnetic lines of force pass from the north pole to the south pole of a magnet, Fig. 7. When these lines of force travel through a coil in a certain direction, the current will flow from that coil from a certain terminal in one direction only. If the direction of these lines of force is changed, the direction of the induced flow of current will also be changed. The horseshoe magnets form a magnetic circuit between their poles; they are mounted with like poles together, Fig. 8. Small steel plates [are mounted at the ends of the magnets so that the lines of force will pass through the cores of the coils a greater length of time than

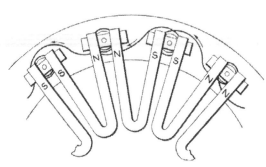

Fig. 9. Current Induced in One Direction

if the ends of the magnets were bare. Alternate coils are wound in opposite directions so that a current of the same polarity will be induced in all sixteen coils at the same time. When the south poles of the magnets are opposite a coil that is wound in one direction, Fig. 9, the current will flow in the direction indicated by the arrows. North lines of force are then flowing through the core of the adjacent coil, and as this coil is wound in the opposite direction to that of the first coil, the current will flow in the same direction. When the magnets are turned one-sixteenth of a revolution, north magnetic lines of force will be flowing through the first coil and south magnetic lines through the second coil. The direction of the induced current will then be changed, this reversal taking place sixteen times in every revolution. This position is shown in Fig. 10.

Table I shows the output in volts and amperes of the early Ford magneto at various speeds.

Timer. The timer is used to distribute the primary ignition current to the proper coil at the time a spark is desired to explode a gas charge in a cylinder.

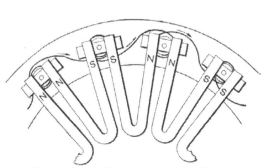

Fig. 10. Current Induced in Opposite Direction

By referring to Fig. 11, it will be noted that there are four contacts around the inner part of the timer equidistantly spaced.

A roller is mounted on the front end of the camshaft which makes contact with these segments, thereby completing the primary circuit through the spark coil, causing the vibrator to operate, and producing a secondary spark at the spark plug. A diagram of the ignition circuit is shown in Fig. 12. The coil box on all Ford cars is provided with a battery terminal so that a battery can be utilized for ignition purposes if desired. On the cars equipped with a starting system at the factory, the starting battery is connected to this terminal. The Ford Motor Company recommends that the car be started with the ignition switch in the battery position and run on the battery until the engine warms up. The magneto should then be used for ignition as it

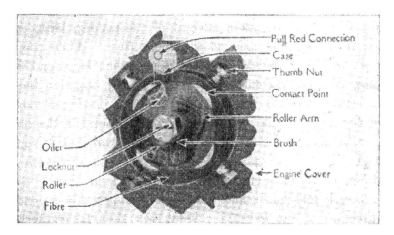

Fig. 11. Ford Timer

is designed to meet this service. The battery connection is made through the lighting and ignition switch.

Path of Ignition Current. By referring to Fig. 12, it will be seen that when the switch is on **BATTERY,** the current leaves the positive pole of the battery, passes to the starter switch, to the second terminal on the terminal block, and through the ammeter to the battery terminal on the back of the switch. The current then travels to the busbar in the bottom of the coil box, through the primary winding of coil No. 1—the timer contact is on segment No. 1—through the vibrator points to terminal No. 1 on the timer, to the timer roller, and to the ground, and returns to the negative post of the battery. As the current flows through the primary winding of the coil, the vibrator starts to operate and a current of high voltage is induced in the secondary winding every time the vibrator points open. This high-tension current flows to the spark plugs and returns to the other end of the secondary winding through the timer and the timer wires.

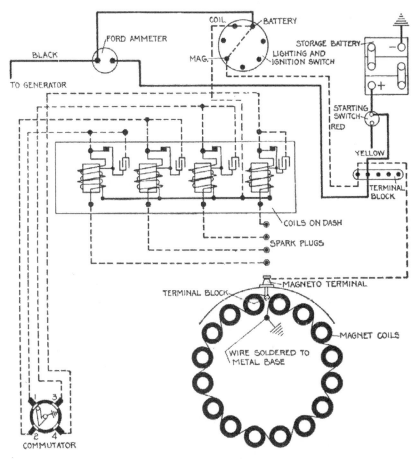

Fig. 12. Ignition Wiring Diagram

When the switch is turned to **MAG**, the current is taken from the terminal of the magneto and flows to the first terminal of the terminal block, to the magneto terminal on the back of the switch, and across the switch and to the busbar in the coil box. The remainder of the magneto circuit is the same as the battery circuit except that the magneto current returns to the grounded end of the magneto coils instead of to the battery.

ELECTRICAL EQUIPMENT

Testing Dash Coils. If it is thought that the ignition coils are out of adjustment when the motor misses or is hard to start, they can be easily tested from the front seat. The cylinders that are missing can also be located by this method.

Remove the coil-box cover and speed up the motor to a car speed of about 12 m.p.h. Then press down on vibrators Nos. 1 and 2 and note the action of the motor. If two explosions are distinctly heard at the exhaust, it is a sign that Nos. 3 and 4 are operating all right. If, however, there is just one explosion, it is a sign that one of these cylinders is not working properly. This fault can be located by the process of elimination. Release No. 1 vibrator and hold down No. 3 instead; if only one cylinder is then firing, it is a sign that either No. 4 or No. 1 is defective. Either one can be eliminated by holding down its vibrator. If the motor stops, it should be tried again with the throttle open a little more. If vibrator No. 4 is then depressed and the motor stops firing, it is a sure sign that No. 1 cylinder is missing; this, however, may not be coil trouble. To eliminate any possibility of coil trouble, one of the properly working coils should be lifted out and exchanged with the supposedly defective coil. If the cylinder still misses, the spark plug should be examined; if the spark plug is all right, the motor should be examined

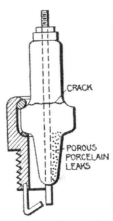

Fig. 13. Damaged Spark Plug

for loss of compression, valve trouble, dirty commutators, loose connections, or broken wires.

Spark Plugs. In Fig. 13 is shown a partial section of a spark plug. The center electrode is made of heat-resisting metal so that it will not fuse and melt away. The porcelain or electrode insulator is made of material that will not crack with either heat or cold. It must also withstand any sudden change in temperature without cracking. If the porcelain does crack or become porous, as in Fig. 13, it is useless to try to use it as the spark will pass through the pores instead of jumping the gap at the points. The current always takes the path of least resistance and the resistance of a spark gap under pressure is much greater than that of the path through the porous porcelain.

Care of Ignition System. The timer should be removed at regular intervals and inspected. Any old grease containing a great deal of grit and cuttings should be carefully removed. The contacts should be inspected to make sure that there are no uneven or worn places such as shown in Fig. 14. If the timer is in this condition, the motor is likely to miss when running at a fair rate of speed. The timer roller will enter the low places and bounce over the contact. The roller spring should be carefully examined as the end of this spring may be worn almost in two, and if it is replaced in this condition, it is sure to cause trouble.

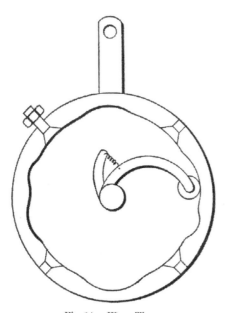

Fig. 14. Worn Timer

Timer Wires. The timer wires are enclosed in a loom to prevent them from being damaged mechanically and to keep them free from oil. They should be carefully examined to see that there are no bare wires exposed, especially where they connect to the timer. If there is an accidental ground in these wires, the motor will miss, backfire, or "kick" when it is cranked.

STARTING AND GENERATING SYSTEM
GENERATORS

Function. The generator produces an electric current that replaces current used from the storage battery. When the starter is used, current is discharged from the storage battery, and this current must be replaced as the battery would be exhausted if this were not done. The lights also take current from the battery when they are in use if the generator is not generating sufficient current to supply them. Fig. 15 shows the assembly of the starter drive and an outside view of the generator.

It has been stated that if an electric current is passed through a conductor, which may be in the form of a coil, a magnetic field

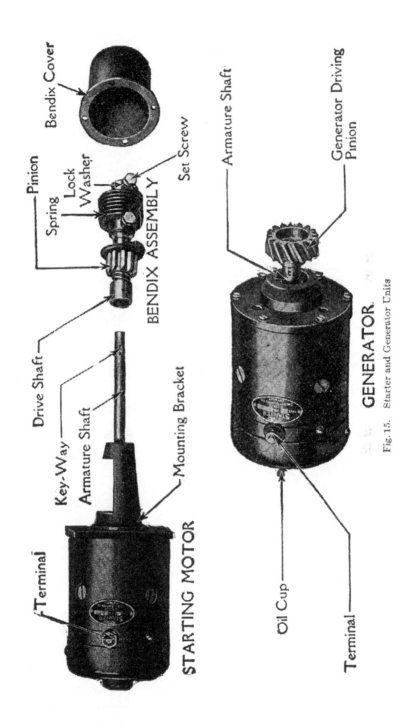

Fig. 15.   Starter and Generator Units

is produced about the conductor. The introduction of an iron bar in the coil greatly increases the magnetic effect because it is much easier for the magnetism to travel through the iron than through the air inside the coil of wire. For this reason, the iron core is always used in the electromagnet.

It is also true that if a conductor is passed between the poles of a magnet through the magnetic field, an electric pressure is generated, or induced, in the conductor which will cause current to flow. The greater the number of magnetic lines of force cut per second by this conductor, the greater will be the amount of current flowing through it. These magnetic lines of force can be increased by winding the field coils with a greater number of

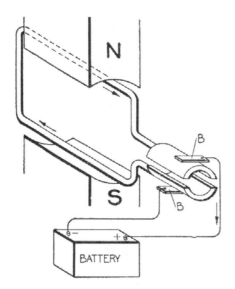

Fig. 16. Simple Generator

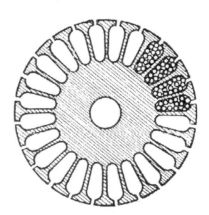

Fig. 17. Windings of Modern Armature

ampere turns; by using a higher voltage on the fields; or by increasing the speed of the generator.

A simple generator is shown in Fig. 16, in which a loop of wire is revolving between the poles of a magnet. In order to carry the current that is induced in the loop of wire into the external circuit, a commutator is provided. This consists of two segments, each being connected to an end of the wire loop. Two brushes *B* run on this commutator to collect the current. In all modern generators a number of loops or coils of wire are mounted in a rigid manner on a laminated iron core, forming the armature, Fig. 17. The brushes are so placed on the commutator that the current collected by them flows from one brush through the external circuit and back to the other brush.

Regulation. Since the voltage generated in the armature of a generator is proportional to the number of magnetic lines cut per second, it is evident that by regulating the speed at which the armature travels, we can regulate the voltage generated. It is also evident that by regulating the field strength, and thus changing the magnetic lines flowing through the armature, we can regulate the voltage generated. The latter method is used in the Ford generator. If this voltage were not held within certain limits, the lights on the car would be burned out as the high voltage would force enough current through the lamp filaments to melt them and cause an open circuit.

Third Brush. The Ford generator decreases the field strength by the use of the third brush. The field winding is connected between the grounded main brush and the small third brush which bears on the upper side of the commutator, Fig. 18. The position of this brush may be changed so that it is nearer to or farther from the grounded main brush.

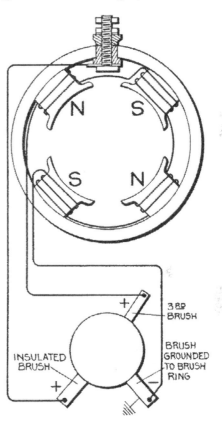

Fig. 18.   Generator Field Connections

The distance between these two brushes determines the maximum strength of the current delivered at the generator.

The action of the third brush is as follows: When the generator is operating at a low rate of speed, the magnetic lines of force pass in a straight line from the north field pole to the south field pole, Fig. 19. It will be noted that the third brush is bearing on the commutator segments that are in the direct path of these magnetic lines of force. When the speed of the generator is increased these magnetic lines are distorted, Fig. 20. This causes the coils that are connected to the commutator bars on which the third brush bears to be out of the direct path of the magnetic lines. The voltage generated at the bar on which this third brush bears will then be decreased, and as decreasing the strength of the field coils decreases the total number of magnetic lines cut by the armature, the output of the generator will be reduced.

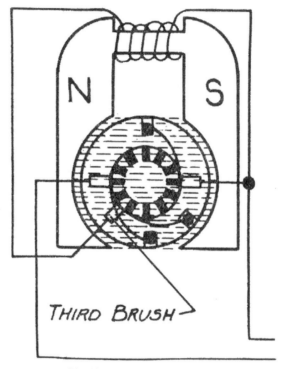

Fig. 19. Path of Lines of Force

To regulate the output of the Ford generator, all lights should be turned off and the motor should be run on the magneto. The generator should be warm when the change is made. Remove the cover that closes the opening in the rear end of the generator housing. This is done by taking out two round-headed screws that hold this cover in place. The hexagonal nut holding in place the bolt that clamps the third-brush holder to the brush ring is reached through the opening in the rear-end housing. It is at the right of the generator terminal when facing the rear end of the generator. A small, thin, open-end wrench is the best one to use in turning this nut. Loosen it and then tap the third-brush holder so as to move it in the slot in the desired direction. Moving the third brush in the same direction as the armature is rotating increases the charging rate; moving it in the opposite direction decreases the charging rate, Fig. 21. The engine should be running at about 800 r.p.m. and when the desired output is obtained, the nut should be tightened. The engine should then be run at different speeds to make sure that

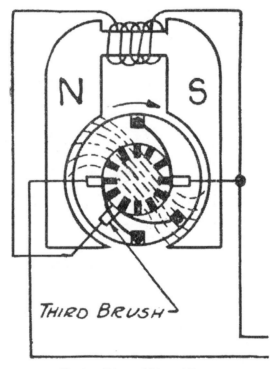

Fig. 20. Distorted Lines of Force

the current does not reach a value greater than that indicated before the nut was tightened. The brush should be set so that the highest reading is between 10 and 12 amperes. It is good practice to *sand-in* the third brush after it has been set in its new position until all points of the brush touch the commutator. The method of sanding-in the brush is shown in Fig. 22.

Shunt=Wound Generator. The Ford generator is shunt wound, which is to say, only a portion of the current generated passes through the field coils, or the shunt, of the generator. The connections of the shunt fields are shown in Fig. 18. On each of the four field poles is wound a single field coil, and these coils are connected in series with each other. The joints between the coils are made by soldering the wires together and covering the joint with tape. The resistance of the four field coils when cold is about 2.45 ohms.

Proper Generator Operation. The cutout should close when the generator is running at about 600 r.p.m., or at a car speed of 10 m.p.h. At this speed the voltage of the generator should be a little higher than that of the battery so that the generator can charge the battery just as soon as the points close. As the speed of the engine increases, the output of the generator will continue to increase until the generator is running at 1200 r.p.m. or a car speed of 20 m.p.h. At this speed the current reaches its maximum value; at higher speeds the charging rate decreases. This decrease is caused by the almost complete distortion of the magnetic lines of force, which distortion decreases the voltage at the third brush.

A charging rate of 10 amperes is the best for average driving conditions. The cutout will not open and disconnect the generator from the battery until the voltage of the generator has dropped slightly below that of the battery, when the battery will begin to discharge into the generator. This will be indicated by the pointer of the ammeter coming to the **O** line and moving on the discharge position to 1 or 2 amperes. This discharge current should not exceed a few amperes and should flow for only an instant before the cutout points open.

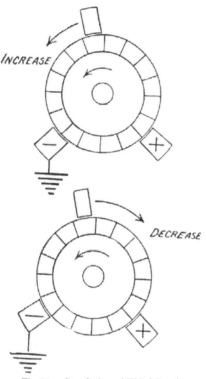

Fig. 21.   Regulation of Third Brush

Cutout. The purpose of the cutout is to automatically connect the battery to the generator when the voltage of the generator is greater than that of the battery, and to disconnect the battery from the generator when the voltage of the battery is greater than that of the generator. This action is necessary to prevent the battery from discharging into the generator when the motor is not running.

To accomplish this automatic action, two windings are placed on the cutout core, Fig. 23. One is of heavy wire and carries all the current generated by the generator, and the other is of small wire connected so

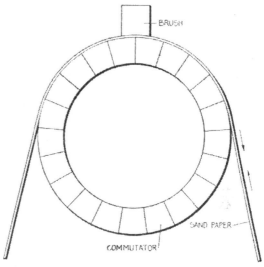

Fig. 22. Method of Sanding-In a Brush

that it will receive the full voltage of the generator. The small wire, or voltage coil, performs the duty of closing the contact points when the generator voltage is slightly greater than that of the battery. The small amount of current generated at low speeds flows through this fine winding and magnetizes the core so that it is strong enough to overcome the tension of the spring that holds the points apart. The points then close, and as long as the generator is charging the battery, the points remain in this position. The charging current flows through the heavy winding and holds the points together. When the voltage of the generator falls below that of the battery, the

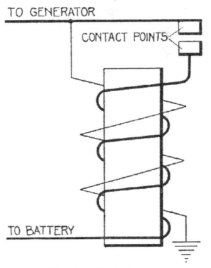

Fig. 23. Simple Cutout

current begins to discharge into the generator, and therefore the current through the heavy winding is reversed. Before the reverse current starts to flow, the core loses its magnetism as no current is flowing in either direction. The spring will then open the contact points, breaking the circuit between the battery and the generator and preventing the battery from discharging into the generator.

Cutout Mounting. On many cars, the cutout is mounted under the engine hood on the right side of the dash, and the base

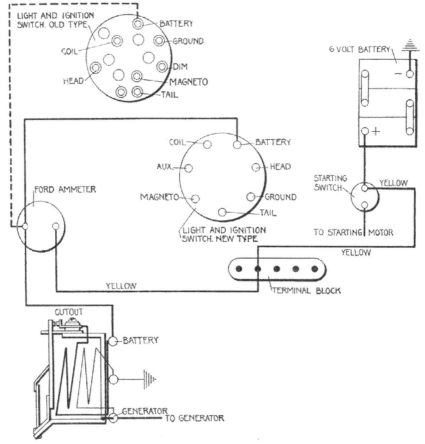

Fig. 24. Cutout Mounted on Dash

of the cutout is grounded to an iron arm projecting upward from the frame of the car. On later cars, the cutout is on top of the generator, and its frame is grounded directly to the generator.

Cutout on Dash. There are three terminals on the base of the cutout, Fig. 24. The two outside terminals are marked **BATT** and **GEN**; the one marked **BATT** is connected to the ammeter, and the one marked **GEN** is connected to the generator terminal. The two outside terminals are insulated from the base of the cutout, while the middle one, which is not marked, is grounded to the base. A movable arm carries one of the contacts, and a flat spring tends to hold the two contact points apart. Passing through an opening on this arm is a brass arm stop, and by bending or straightening this piece, the distance between the two contact points may be changed. The correct distance is about $\frac{1}{32}$ inch.

The stationary contact point is carried on an arm that is insulated from the upright piece to which it is mounted. The distance between the points may also be changed by moving this arm up or down.

Cutout on Generator. The internal connections of the cutout when mounted directly on top of the generator are shown in Fig. 25. The part *A* is bolted to the generator terminal and is connected to *B* by a round-headed machine screw which may be seen by looking at the bottom of the cutout; *A* and *B* are both insu-

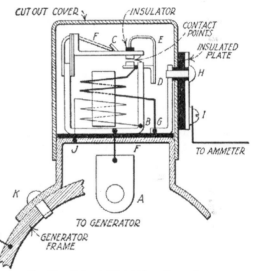

Fig. 25. Cutout Mounted on Generator

lated from the base of the cutout, which is fastened to the base of the generator. The arm *C* is mounted on and electrically connected with *B*, and at one end of the arm *C* is one of the contact points. The other contact point is fastened to *D*, which is insulated from *B* and *C*. A brass hook *E*, which is an extension of *D*, acts as a stop for the arm *C*. This hook can be bent, when the motor is not running, to change the air gap between the points so as to secure proper operation of the cutout when the generator is running. The spring *F* tends to hold the contact points away from each other; and the tension of this spring may be increased or decreased by bending it to secure proper action of the cutout both in opening and in closing the circuit between the generator and the battery.

Voltage-Coil Circuit. The circuit through the voltage coil is as follows: from the ungrounded main brush to the generator terminal, through A to B, through the voltage coil to the base J. through the generator frame, thence to the grounded main generator brush, and back to the armature.

Current Through Cutout. Current from the generator enters the cutout at A and travels into B and C, through the contact points into D, thence through the outside winding, which is heavy wire, and into G which is insulated from all parts except the coil. The current then passes through the screw H into the insulated plate. This screw passes through the cutout cover but is insulated from it. The current then goes to the battery along the wire fastened to this plate under the screw I. The screw H is sealed to the cover and should always be turned down tight as the charging circuit is broken if this screw is removed.

The base of the cutout, which is screwed down to the generator frame, is connected to one end of the voltage coil but is insulated from all other parts except the cover which fits over it; the other end of the voltage coil is connected to B.

Care of Cutout. The contact points should at all times be clean and smooth, and when they are touching each other they should make contact at all points of their surfaces. They may be cleaned by drawing a rag moistened with gasoline between them; to make them smooth, a piece of fine sandpaper or a fine file may be used, drawing the emery cloth or the file between the contacts while the movable contact is pressed down.

The movable arm which carries one of the points is insulated from the base of the cutout; care must be taken to see that it does not become grounded to the base.

Adjusting Cutout. To adjust the cutout, be sure that the generator is generating about 10 amperes. The specific gravity of each of the battery cells should not be less than 1.250. Turn off all the lamps and run the motor on the magneto. With the motor running slowly, close the throttle until the points open. The points may be watched to see when they separate, or the ammeter pointer may be observed. The pointer will swing past the **O** on the ammeter just before the points open, and will then come back to the **O** line and remain in that position. Now gradually increase the speed of the engine, carefully watching the ammeter. When the motor is running at 600 r.p.m., or at a car speed of 10 m.p.h., the cutout points should close. There should be a slight movement of the ammeter pointer when the cutout closes, indicating a charge of 2 or 3 amperes. With a further increase in speed, the ammeter pointer should gradually go to 10 amperes, and this should be the maximum charging rate.

When the cutout closes and the ammeter reads reversed, thus indicating that the battery starts to discharge into the generator, the cutout is closing before the voltage of the generator is equal to or greater than that of the battery. This is remedied by bending the spring on the movable arm of the cutout so that the spring will hold up this arm with greater force. It will then require a higher generator voltage to close the cutout circuit. Another way is to increase the distance between the points by straightening the hook, or the bent-over piece, a little.

If the ammeter pointer does not move when the cutout points close, it indicates that the generator and the battery voltage are equal at this instant. The spring on the movable arm should then be made stronger by bending, or the distance between the points should be increased.

If the ammeter indicates 10 amperes charge when the points close, the cutout does not close soon enough. To remedy this, the spring on the arm should be weakened, or the distance between the points decreased.

Checking Cutout Action. To check the action of the cutout in disconnecting the generator from the battery, gradually decrease the speed of the generator and watch the ammeter pointer. The pointer should not move past the **O** line more than 2 or 3 amperes. Should this pointer indicate a discharge of more than 3 amperes or should it remain below the **O** line for more than an instant, then the points are not opening soon enough, and the spring on the movable arm should be strengthened.

Removing Generator. When it is necessary to take out the generator, the three cap screws that fasten to the front end of the cylinder block should be removed. Then place the point of a screw driver between the generator and the front end cover and gradually force out the generator. Always start prying at the top of the generator and force it backward and downward at the same time. If it is desired to run the car while the generator is removed, the timing-gear-case opening where the generator was removed should be covered with a plate. This plate can be secured from any Ford dealer or service station.

Remove the cover that closes up the opening in the rear-end housing by taking out two screws *B* that hold it in place, Fig. 26.

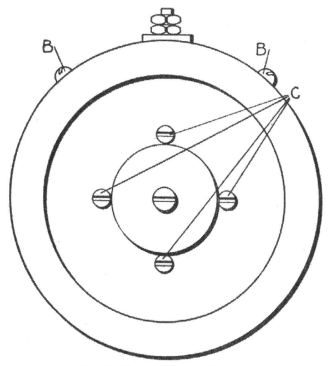

Fig. 26. Rear End View of Generator

Grasp the pigtails on each brush with a pair of long-nosed pliers and pull the brushes up until the brush springs snap from the top of the brushes and bear against their sides. This will hold the brush clear of the commutator. Then take out the six flat-headed screws, *A*, Fig. 27, and insert the point of a screw driver between the front-end cap and the frame and pry the cap loose. Next take hold of the generator and pull out the armature. Remove the rear-end housing by taking out the four screws *C*, Fig. 26, and pry the housing loose with a screw driver. When do this, be careful not to damage the insulation around the generator terminal. When the rear-end housing is loose, it may be pulled back as far as the wires fastened to the brushes will allow. These wires should then be disconnected, or they may be disconnected first, care being taken to note the connections so that they may be correctly replaced. Fig. 18 shows the proper connections.

To remove the brush ring, take out the four screws shown at C in Fig. 26. The main brush-holders are riveted to the ring

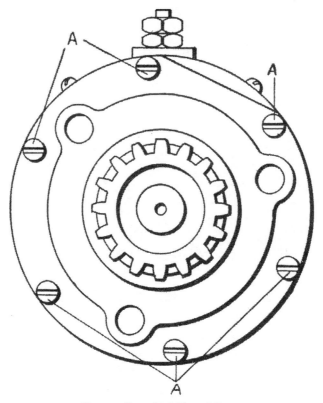

Fig. 27. Front End View of Generator

and cannot be removed from it, while the third brush-holder is removable.

Armature. The generator armature is shown in Fig. 28. It has twenty-one slots and twenty-one segments on the commutator, and the wires are enameled and cotton covered. The only part of the commutator that requires attention is that on which the brushes bear, and this should be kept clean and smooth and free from oil. There will be no trouble caused by a greasy commutator, if the rear-end bearing on the generator is not given too much oil and the oil-retaining washer at the front end of the generator is in good condition. To clean a greasy commutator hold first a dry rag against it, then a rag moistened with kerosene when the generator is running. Do not use too much kerosene on the rag and always run the generator for a few minutes after the rag is removed so that any surplus kerosene may be dried up. The space between the commutator segments should be kept free from oil, grease, bits of carbon, and copper. These spaces may be cleaned with a sharp-pointed tool, scraping out the dirt until the clean mica shows the entire length of the commutator. The mica should be cut down until it is about $\frac{1}{32}$ inch below the surface of the commutator. If the commutator is

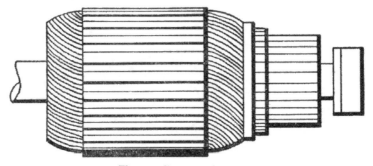

Fig. 28. Generator Armature

rough, it may be smoothed by holding a piece of fine sandpaper against it. *Never use emery cloth!* If there are grooves around the commutator, it should be turned in the lathe until the surface is smooth and of the same diameter at all points.

Wiring Diagrams. A wiring diagram of the complete electrical system of the Ford is shown in Fig. 29. This system is for all cars having the cutout mounted on the dash. A diagram for all cars having the cutout mounted on the generator is shown in Fig. 30.

Generator Troubles. *Generator Reversed.* To test the generator for reversal, a voltmeter should be used, Fig. 31. Hold one test point on the ground on any clean metallic spot of the generator frame and the other test point on the generator terminal. The voltmeter should show a voltage of about 7 to $7\frac{1}{2}$. If the needle moves backward the polarity of the generator is reversed.

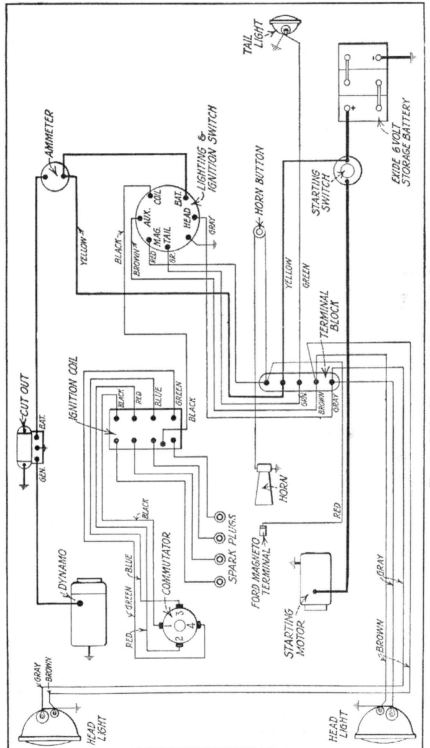

Fig. 29.   Wiring Diagram with Cutout on Dash

375

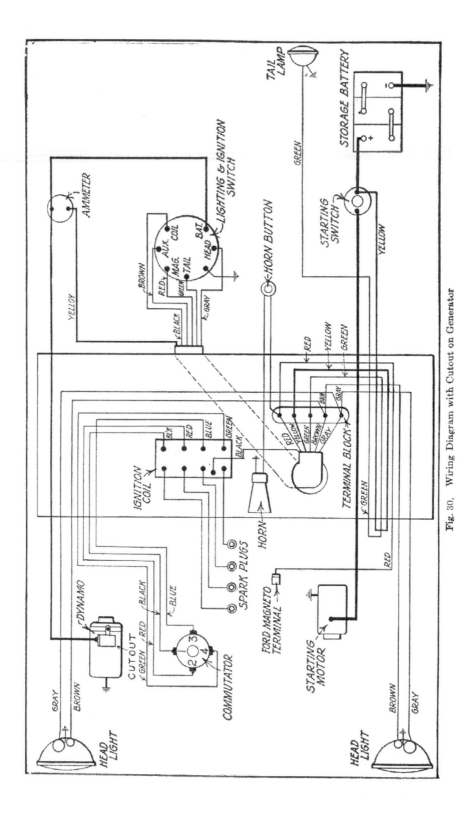

Fig. 30. Wiring Diagram with Cutout on Generator

ELECTRICAL EQUIPMENT

This generally happens when the battery is run down. To remedy this trouble, put in a fully charged battery and hold the cut-out points closed, by hand, for an instant. Then look at the ammeter to see if the generator is charging the battery. If the battery is still discharging, reverse the field connections in the generator.

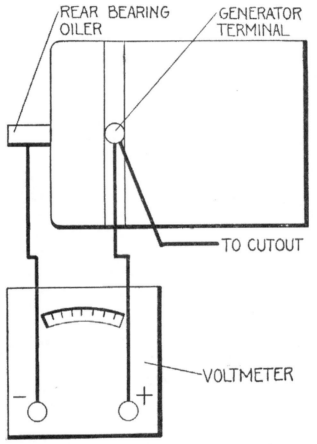

REAR BEARING OILER

GENERATOR TERMINAL

TO CUTOUT

VOLTMETER

Fig. 31. Testing Generator for Reversal

To do this, the field wires that are connected to the third brush and the grounded main brush are exchanged.

Shorts and Grounds. The generator field takes about 2.5 amperes when it is connected to a 6-volt battery if the fields are not shorted or grounded. When the generator runs as a motor, it takes 9 amperes from a 6-volt battery if there are no shorts or grounds in the armature or fields. If there is an indication of a short or a ground, remove the housing cover and inspect the wire leading from the terminal on the generator to the ungrounded main brush and the wires leading from the field coils to the third brush and the grounded main brush. The insulation on these

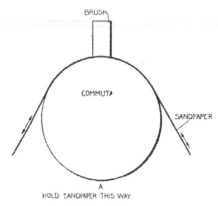

Fig. 32.   Correct Way to Sand-In Brushes

wires should not be cut or torn, and the pigtails should not touch the end housing or the brush ring, although no damage will be done if they touch the brush-holders.

Sparking at Brushes. Excessive sparking at the brushes should be prevented. If the brushes are of poor material or are the wrong size or type of brush, they are likely to spark. A spark will also take place if the brushes are not set in proper relation to the windings. If the armature is loose or the commutator is not running true on the armature shaft, sparks will also develop at the brushes. If some of the armature coils are short, or open-circuited, the sparking will occur only when the commutator segments to which the coils are connected pass under the brushes. If two adjacent segments are blackened or burned, it is plain that there is a short-circuit present between the windings connected

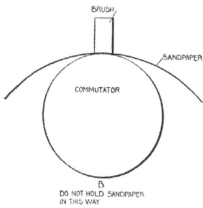

Fig. 33.   Incorrect Way to Sand-In Brushes

to these segments.

Brush Trouble. For inspection the brushes may be removed by the use of long-nosed pliers; pulling on the brush pigtails removes the brushes from their slots. Of course, the dust cover must be removed in order to get at the brushes. After they are removed, they should be examined for dirty, pitted, or insufficient contact surface. The parts of the brush surface that make contact with the commutator will be smooth and polished, while the other parts will be dull and rather rough. If the brush contact surface is not perfect, cut a piece of fine sandpaper and insert it between the brush and the commutator with the sanded side toward the brush, as in *A*, Fig. 32. In Fig. 33, *B* shows the incorrect way of sanding-in the brush. The sandpaper should be drawn back and forth under the brush until all imperfections in the brush surface have been removed when the brush will fit the curvature of the commutator properly. When the brushes are too short, they will give unsatisfactory service, as the spring tension is greatly reduced. Brushes in these conditions should be replaced by brushes secured from the manufacturer of that particular instrument. As a rule, it is not good policy to use any brushes other than those manufactured by a reliable concern and for that particular instrument only.

Improper Spring Tension. If the brush springs are broken, total failure of the instrument may result, or if the brush-holder becomes gummy so that the brush sticks, a great deal of sparking at the brushes will be present. Sparking is sometimes the result of loose brush springs also.

Defective Insulation. If the insulating washers are broken or in any way damaged, they should be replaced with new ones. Any grease or any gummy substance should be removed from the brushes and the brush-holders cleaned with a stiff hairbrush and gasoline.

TESTING

Testing Armature and Commutator. A single dry cell is best to use in testing the armature windings for opens or shorts. The cell should be connected in series with an ammeter, Fig. 34. One post of the cell is connected to one terminal of the ammeter and a wire having a testing point at one end is connected to the other post. If desired, this testing point may be eliminated and the bare wire used instead. A wire is connected on the other terminal of the ammeter and the free ends of the two wires are used to make contact on the various segments of the commutator, Fig. 35. Before making the test, the brushes may be raised from the commutator, or, better still, the armature may be removed from the generator where it will be much more accessible. The test should be started on any point of the armature, the two leads touching the two adjoining segments. Note the reading on the ammeter and then proceed to the next segments.

For example, the wire should be placed on segments Nos. 1 and 2 and then on Nos. 2 and 3, etc. The readings of all segments should be compared, as any great difference is indicative of trouble on those coils which have different readings. It must be remembered that when the wires are on contact, a circuit is completed through the armature, the ammeter, and the dry cell which will fully discharge the cell if contact is held for any length of time; just enough contact to allow the operator to read the ammeter should be made.

If the commutator and the armature are free from short or

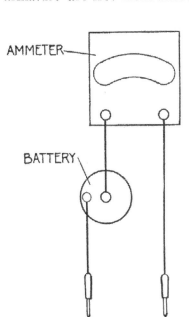

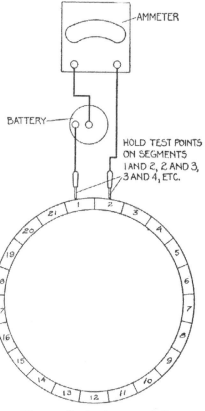

Fig. 34. Armature Testing Set

Fig. 35. Testing Armature Coils

open circuits, the ammeter readings between the various pairs of segments will be about equal. In case the reading becomes much higher with the test points resting on any pair of segments, this condition indicates that either the armature coil attached to these segments or the segments themselves are short-circuited. If the reading becomes much less, this indicates that a broken, burnt-out, or otherwise open-circuited armature coil is present between the two segments where the test points are then touching.

ELECTRICAL EQUIPMENT

Open Circuit. If an open circuit exists, make sure that the wires soldered to the segments are making perfect contact and that they are not broken as far as they can be traced. If no trouble can be detected on the surface, it will then be necessary for the armature coil to be unwound until the trouble is found, when repairs can then be made and the armature rewound.

Short-Circuit. If the test indicates that a short-circuit is present, the mica slots should first be thoroughly cleaned, removing any bits of metal or carbon that may have lodged in them. If any of the commutator bars have been damaged so that the

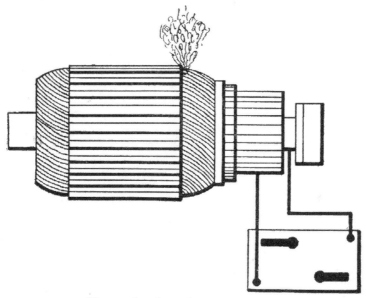

Fig. 36. Locating a Short in the Armature

copper touches another bar, the metal should be cut away until they do not touch. If this does not eliminate the trouble as shown by a record test, the short-circuit is in the armature winding. This short-circuit can generally be located by using a 6- or a 12-volt battery, connecting No. 0 leads to the battery terminals and touching the other ends of these wires to the segments that indicate a short, Fig. 36. In the majority of cases, smoke will be produced at some point on the armature, thus showing where the short exists, and it can often be repaired without removing the winding. It is sometimes possible to burn out this short with a

6-volt battery, although some manner of insulation such as shellac or tape should be made after this kind of repair has been made.

Testing Fields. *Open Circuit.* In making this test, all brushes should be insulated from the commutator by inserting a piece of paper between each brush and the commutator bars. A 6-volt battery should be used to make the test, having a 6-volt bulb in series, Fig. 37. Disconnect the wire from the main brush-holder and touch this wire with one test point while the other test point is placed on the third brush. The lamp should light; if it

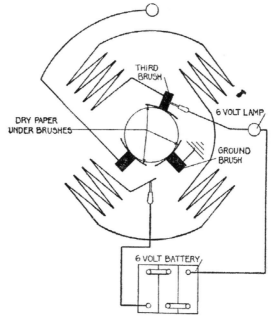

Fig. 37. Testing Field for Open Circuit

does not, this is a certain indication of an open in the shunt winding. The joints between the field coils should then be carefully inspected as the soldering sometimes becomes loosened, causing a poor connection or an open circuit. If the solder on these connections proves to be firm, each coil should be tested by placing the test points on the soldered connections between coils Nos. 1 and 2 and Nos. 3 and 4, etc., Fig. 38. If the lamp does not burn when any coil is tested in this manner, the coil is open-circuited. In order to repair the open, it will be necessary to remove the coil. To do this, take out the screw that holds the pole piece in place and disconnect the coil from the adjoining coil. If the broken circuit is not visible, the coil must be carefully unwound until the break is located. It will then be necessary to make suitable repairs, taking special care to see that each coil is properly insulated.

Ground. To make tests for a ground in the fields, the tester should be used according to the method shown in Fig. 39. With the brushes still insulated from the commutator, one test point should be placed on the third brush and the other point on any

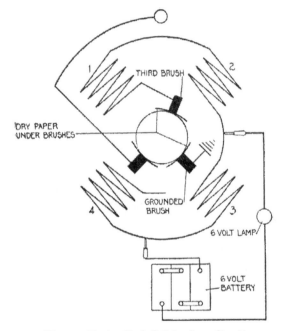

Fig. 38. Testing Each Coil for Open Circuit

part of the generator frame. If the lamp lights, there is a ground in the field coil or the third brush-holder. If the lamp does not light, hold the test point that was on the generator frame on the end housing, this part being removed and not touching the generator. If the lamp now lights, the third brush-holder or the insulated brush-holder mounted on the brush ring in the end housing is shorted. The brush ring must then be removed and the insulation under the brush-holders carefully inspected to locate the ground. If the lamp lights when one test point is held on the third brush and the other test point on the generator frame, there is a ground in the field coils. Connection between the field coils should be carefully inspected for damaged insulation or places where the bare wires are touching the frame. If these connections are in good condition, it will be necessary to disconnect the field coils from each other by unsoldering the joints between them. Each coil should then be tested separately by holding one test point on the generator frame and the other point on a coil terminal. When the lamp lights, the grounded coil has been located. The coil should then be removed as previously

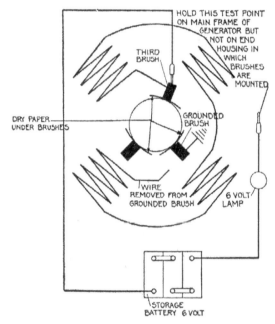

Fig. 39. Testing for Grounds in Fields

described and the ground repaired. The ground in a field coil is much easier to locate than a short, as the ground will generally be present at a point where it touches the field cores, and then it is usually only necessary to retape the coils. This test is shown in Fig. 39.

Short-Circuit. In order to test the coils for a short-circuit in their windings, the tester should be used as shown in Fig. 40. Note the amount of current flowing through the ammeter when the coil is being tested. With a 6-volt battery, a current of about 10 amperes should flow. If any coil takes more than 10 amperes, it indicates that this coil is shorted, and it should be removed and inspected. The field should be repaired, if possible, and carefully reinsulated before replacing.

Reversed Fields. To test the polarity of the fields it will be necessary to use a small compass as in the method shown in Fig. 41. Alternate fields should show opposite polarity. The compass should be held about 1 foot from the generator frame and gradually moved toward one of the screws that hold the field

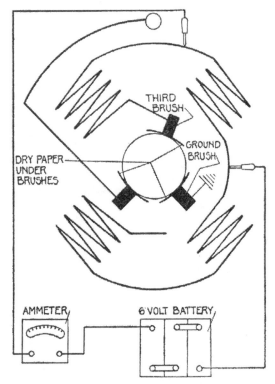

Fig. 40. Testing Coils for Short-Circuit in Fields

poles in place. The compass should then be moved toward another screw and brought nearer, when it should indicate the opposite polarity. If three successive poles attract the same end of the compass needle, the coil on the middle pole is wrongly connected, and its connections should be reversed for proper operation.

Generator Terminal Grounded. Sometimes the insulation around the generator terminal becomes cracked and the terminal loosens. If it is left in this condition, a ground sometimes results.

This insulation should be carefully inspected; if it is broken or cracked so that the terminal might touch the frame, new insulation should be put on.

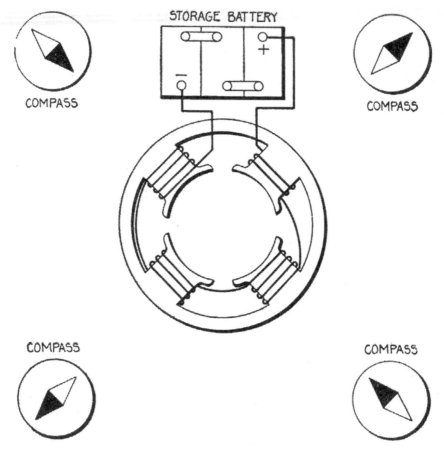

Fig. 41. Testing Coils for Polarity

ELECTRIC STARTER

Construction. The only function of the starting motor is to crank the engine so that it may start under its own power. This motor does not generate any current and is entirely disconnected from the system at all times except when the engine is being started. The starting motor is a four-pole series-wound instrument located on the left side of the engine in front of the flywheel and is fastened to the transmission cover by four $\frac{5}{16}$-inch bolts. The drive is of the Bendix type, which threads the pinion into mesh with the teeth on the flywheel when the starting circuit is complete by the depression of the starting button. When the engine starts, the flywheel, running at a higher speed than that of the pinion, threads the pinion out of mesh with the flywheel gear, thereby preventing any damage to the starter. The motor pinion has 10 teeth and there are 120 teeth cut on the periphery of the flywheel. The gear ratio is, therefore, 12 to 1, the motor turning 12 times to the engine turning once. The starting armature is mounted on plain bearings, and as the starter is used but little, it is not necessary to supply it with much lubrication. The bearing next to the flywheel is lubricated from the flywheel, while the bearing at the commutator end should not be supplied with any lubricant. The front bushing is made of bronze, the rear is of soft bearing metal.

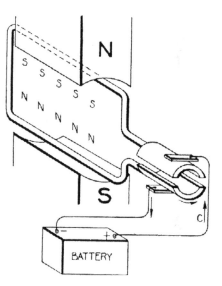

Fig. 42.   A Simple Starter

Principle of Operation. The principle of the starting motor is similar to that of the generator, except that the operation of the starting motor is reversed. It has been previously stated that when magnetic lines of force are cut by a coil, a current is induced in this coil; also that an electromagnet has a strength dependent upon the amount of current passed through the coil. It may also be remembered that like poles repel each other and unlike poles attract each other. For instance, a north pole will attract a south pole of another magnet while it will repel a north pole of another magnet. Keeping these facts in mind, let us examine the illustration, Fig. 42. The current flows from the battery into one side of the loop, causing south magnetic lines of force to be set up in the upper part of this loop. The upper motor field, which is a north pole, will then attract the south pole of the coil, and the lower field pole, which has a south polarity, will also attract the north magnetic field that was set up in the lower side of the coil.

ELECTRICAL EQUIPMENT

TABLE II

Current Consumption of Ford Starter

Condition of Motor	Amperes	Volts	Watts	Horsepower Developed
Running without load	65 to 80	5.75	373	0.5
Cranking new engine at 75 r.p.m.	275 to 300	4.5	1350	1.8
Cranking used engine at 185 r.p.m.	140	5.0	700	0.93

At the same time that this attraction is taking place, there is also a repelling force acting between the upper part of the coil and the south field, and the lower, or north, polarity of the coil and the upper north field. The modern electric motor is composed of a series of loops of wire rigidly mounted and is capable of allowing a large amount of current to flow through its windings. This sets up a strong magnetic pull which produces great turning torque when the starter button is depressed.

Fields. The starting motor is a series-wound machine as shown in Fig. 43. A series winding is used as this type of instrument produces great turning torque at low speeds, which is the result desired from any starting motor. The current consumption of the Ford starter under various conditions is given in Table II.

Brushes. There are four brushes on the starter, one being connected to one end of the series winding and the opposite brush to the other end of the series winding. The two opposite brushes remaining are grounded. The starting current enters the instrument at a connection in the fields shown in Fig. 43. The brushes are of copper composition, and each brush has two heavy, uninsulated, copper pigtails. The free ends of these pigtails are soldered into the copper terminals that are fastened to the brush-holder by a machine screw. The brushes are $\frac{3}{4}'' \times \frac{3}{8}'' \times \frac{3}{4}''$. The brush-holders are made of aluminum and are riveted to the brush ring. The main brushes are insulated from the brush ring by fiber strips, while the grounded brushes are riveted directly to the metal of the brush ring, having no wires except the pigtails. The brush ring is riveted to the housing and therefore cannot be removed. The same care that is given to the brushes and the commutator of the generator is also applicable to those of the starter.

Removing Starting Motor. In order to remove the starting motor from the car, the pan on the left side of the engine must first be taken off. The four small screws which hold the shaft cover to the transmission cover at the back of the flywheel hous-

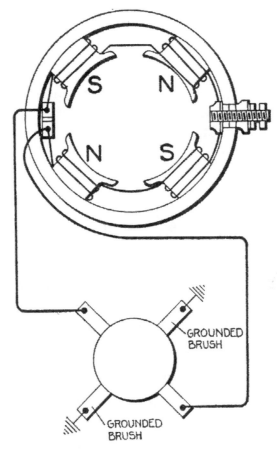

Fig. 43. Series-Winding of Starter

ing should then be removed. Then turn the Bendix drive shaft, Fig. 15, around so that the set screw on the end of this shaft is in a horizontal position with the head of the set screw pointing toward the left, the operator facing the rear of the flywheel. There is a split spring-lock washer having sharp points at the joint between the two halves on opposite sides of the washer, and this washer is located under the set screw to prevent it from becoming loose. One of these points is turned against the Bendix collar and the other is turned against the screw head. The point turned up against the screw should be bent back and the set screw removed. The washer is generally broken when removed, so it will be necessary to use a new one when replacing the starter. After the set screw has been taken out, the Bendix pinion spring and sleeve can be slipped off at the end of the starter. The four screws that hold the starter housing to the transmission cover are taken out, and then the motor can be pulled out at the front; lower the motor through the opening in the chassis made by removing the engine pan. If the car is to be used while the starting motor is removed, the hole in the transmission case should be covered with a plate which can be secured at any Ford parts house. When the starting motor is replaced, make sure that the terminal mounted near the rear end of the starter frame is on top.

Dismantling Starter. As the Bendix drive was removed before the starter was taken out of the car, it is now necessary to remove the cover from the rear-end housing. Force this cover off with a screw driver, grasp the pigtails of each brush with a pair of long-nosed pliers, and pull up until the brush spring snaps from the top of the brush and bears against the side of the brush; this action will hold the brush away from the commutator. The six screws in the drive-end cap should be removed and the cap pried off with a screw driver. The armature can then be removed, and it becomes necessary as well to remove the rear-end housing by taking out the four screws that hold it in place. The two leads from the ungrounded brush-holders are next disconnected and the brushes removed by unscrewing the proper pigtails and then lifting the brushes out. The brush-holders, however, cannot be removed. The relative positions of these parts are plainly shown in Fig. 15.

Starter Troubles. The starter may be tested for shorts, grounds, and opens in the same way as the generator. If a test for ground is made and the lamp does not light, the instrument is in satisfactory condition. If the lamp lights, there is a ground in the field. Then the next procedure is to disconnect, one at a time, the two large insulated field wires from the two insulated brush-holders. Repeat the test as each of these is removed. If the lamp goes out after one of these wires is removed, the brush-holder to which that wire is attached is grounded to the brush ring and must be reinsulated. If the lamp still burns after both wires are removed from the brushes, the ground is in the field coils of the motor. It is then necessary to disconnect each field coil and test it. If the lamp lights when a certain field coil is tested, that field coil is grounded. The coils should be removed and repaired as described on page 34.

Open Circuit. While the field coils are not likely to become open-circuited, still the soldered joints between the coils should be inspected carefully to see that they are well soldered. In making a test for open circuit in the field coils, the connection between any two coils should be opened. The test lamp, Fig. 38, should be used in testing each coil by holding the test points on the bare ends of that coil. If the lamp does not light, the coil is open-circuited and should be removed and repaired as described on page 33.

Bendix=Drive Trouble. Sometimes the starter armature will only spin when the starting button is depressed. This indicates that the spring connecting the pinion sleeve to the armature shaft is broken. This break is sometimes caused by attempting to crank a very cold stiff motor with the starter, or the starter may not be lined up properly. Therefore, it is advisable to loosen up the motor with a hand crank if it is stiff or cold.

Starting Switch. The starting switch is operated by the driver's foot and enables him to complete the circuit between the battery and the starting motor so that the engine may be cranked. A spring in the starter button automatically opens the circuit when the driver's foot is removed, thereby disconnecting the battery from the motor. The switch is located under the floor boards on the left side of the car.

LIGHTING SYSTEM

Bulbs. The headlights contain two bulbs, a 6–8 volt 17 candle-power, and a 6–8 volt 2 candle-power dimmer bulb. The tail lamp has a 6–8 volt 2 candle-power bulb.

It is important to use lamps of the proper voltage as a bulb designed for a lower voltage than 6–8 would be easily burnt out and one with a higher voltage would not give sufficient light.

Bulb Troubles. If the lamps burn out when they are turned on while the engine is running at a car speed of about 20 m.p.h., there is probably a loose connection between the battery and the lighting switch or the generator may be charging at too high a rate; generally the trouble is an open circuit due to some loose or broken connection. If the battery is overcharged, run the starter a few minutes with the ignition switch off or burn the lights over night.

Lighting and Ignition Switches. The Ford sometimes uses a combination lighting and ignition switch, thus enabling the driver to turn the lights on or off and to connect the ignition coils to either the battery or the magneto. This switch is located on the instrument panel in front of the driver. Several types of switches are used. On some of the early models, there is a push-and-pull button for controlling the head lamps, while on the later models, the round-type switch, Fig. 44, is used.

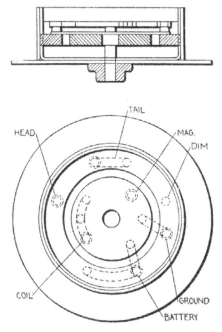

Fig. 44.   Early Type of Round Switch

On the latest models, the round-type switch shown in Fig. 45 is used. Round-type switches have a handle extending downward from the center of the switch that controls the lamps. The ignition is switched on or off by turning the key inserted in the keyhole in the center of the switch.

Switch Troubles. Some troubles found in the early type of the round switches were generally due to short circuits between the wires connected at the back of the switch. The connections on the back of both switches are shown in Fig. 46. It sometimes happens that it is impossible to turn off the ignition, and in this event the engine will continue to run after the switch is turned to the **OFF** position. If the ignition key is then turned to **MAG** position, the battery will discharge into the magneto at a rate of about 20 amperes, while the engine is not running. This indicates that the **COIL** terminal on the back of the switch is shorted with the **BATT** terminal. If when the lamps burn out the ignition key is turned to the **MAG** position with the engine running, the

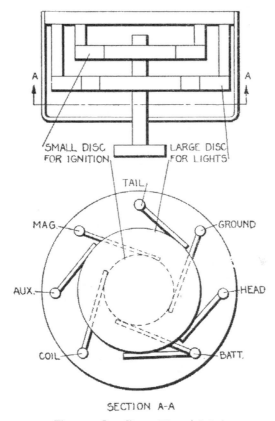

SMALL DISC FOR IGNITION

LARGE DISC FOR LIGHTS

TAIL

MAG.

GROUND

AUX.

HEAD

COIL

BATT.

SECTION A-A

Fig. 45. Late Type of Round Switch

HEAD terminal is short-circuited with the coil terminal. If the battery is used for ignition with this short-circuit present, the head lamps will burn even if the lighting switch is turned off. If the small bulbs in the head lamps burn out, it indicates that the **MAG** terminal is short-circuited with the **DIM** terminal.

With a later type of round switch, these short-circuits do not occur as this switch has two movable round discs, one for the ignition and one for the lights. When the ignition key is turned to the **BATT** position, the battery furnishes the ignition current. When running and when the generator is charging, this current will be furnished by the generator. When the ignition key is turned to the **MAG** position, the ignition current is furnished by the Ford magneto. When the handle controlling the light switch is turned to the **DIM** or the **AUX** position, the tail lamp and the

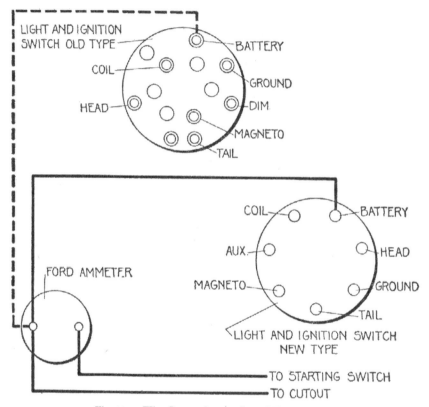

Fig. 46. Wire Connections on Round-Type Switches

small bulbs in the headlights will burn. With the handle in the **ON** position, the tail light and the large headlight bulbs will burn. The late cars are equipped with Tulite or double filament bulbs.

If switch troubles occur, the entire panel on which the ammeter and the switch are mounted may be removed from the front by taking out the four screws in the panel. The entire rear cover may be removed from the switch in order to look for shorts in this instrument; it will also be well to examine all wires leading to the instrument board to see that there are no shorts or grounds present.

HORN

Operation. The Ford horn is operated from the magneto and works on the vibrating principle. Its action is similar to that of

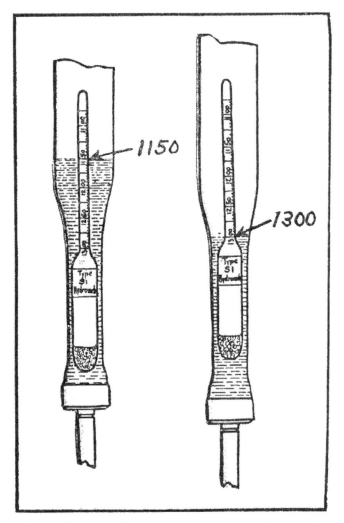

Fig. 47. Hydrometer Readings of a Half and a Fully Charged Cell

the vibrator on the ignition coils, but the vibrator strikes the pin in the center of the horn diaphragm and causes the sound.

ELECTRICAL EQUIPMENT

Charging System. When the car has attained a speed of about 10 miles per hour in high gear, the ammeter on the dash should show **CHARGE.** This ammeter indication will increase until the car has reached a speed of about 20 miles per hour. At higher speeds this charge will taper off, this being a characteristic of the third-brush generator, as described on page 93. When the speed of the car has reached approximately 15 miles per hour, the generator should show a charge of from 10 to 12 amperes with all the lights off. When the lights are turned on, the charging rate as indicated by the ammeter will drop to about 5 or 6 amperes as the generator is furnishing current to the lights.

Care of Battery. The storage battery is a very important instrument in any car and it should be carefully examined and a hydrometer reading taken every week, as this reading indicates the condition of the charge. A hydrometer reading is shown in Fig. 47.

TABLE III
State of Charge of Battery

GRAVITY		AMOUNT OF CHARGE
Tropical Climate	Cool Climate	
1.200	1.275	full
1.175	1.250	three-quarter
1.150	1.225	one-half
1.125	1.200	one-quarter
1.100	1.150	full discharge

A battery charged the same amount will have different readings in tropical climates where water never freezes than it has in other localities. Table III shows the relation of the readings to the amount of charge in the battery.

The hydrometer test should not be taken immediately after the battery is filled with water, as this procedure will not give an accurate reading. It is necessary for the battery to charge some little time after water is supplied before the reading is taken so that the acid will be thoroughly mixed. The battery should not be discharged below one-half charge. When it is in this condition, it should be taken to a battery station and recharged. In case of emergency, it is possible to allow the battery to fall to three-fourths discharge, but this is not good practice and the battery should be placed on charge as soon as possible. If the motor is operated without using the starter, the gravity of the cells will be raised.

If a battery goes dead, the cause of this condition should be located before the recharged battery is installed, as it is quite possible that a short or ground is present in the system; also make sure that the generator is charging properly. When the reading of one particular cell is more than fifty points different from the others, it indicates that this cell is not in good order and the battery should then be taken to a service station for attention.

Distilled water should be added at least once a week if the electrolyte is not covering the plates. During cold weather this water should be added only before the car is to be operated as it is likely to freeze if put in at any other time.

TABLE IV
Magneto Output

| R.P.M. | MILES PER HOUR | | VOLTS | AMPERES | CYCLES PER SECOND |
	Car	Truck			
200	5	2.63	0.5	6.1	26.4
400	10	5.26	9.8	7.9	52.8
600	15	7.89	14.4	8.5	80.0
800	20	10.52	18.8	8.8	106.4
1000	25	13.15	22.8	8.9	146.4
1200	30	15.80	26.2	9.0	160.0

PACKARD MARINE SWEEPSTAKES MOTOR

Courtesy of Packard Motor Car Company

OHM'S LAW

Ohm's law somehow seems to be a stumbling block for many students. In fact, many are frightened by the mere mention of a law or the sight of a simple mathematical symbol. It is for these this talk is given.

Ohm's law is a simple statement which explains the relation of voltage, current, and resistance in a direct-current circuit. By its use we may calculate the size of wire required in a light circuit, size of starting resistance for motors, and numerous other problems which are met every day in electrical work.

The statement of Ohm's law is, *the current in a circuit is directly proportional to the voltage impressed on the circuit and inversely proportional to the resistance of the circuit.* A mathematical statement of the law is that the current in a circuit is equal to the voltage of the circuit divided by the resistance of the circuit. In the form of an equation this statement of the law would be

$$\text{Current} = \frac{\text{Voltage}}{\text{Resistance}}$$

Most people like to make things as simple as possible so electrical men write this expression

$$I = \frac{E}{R}$$

in which I is the symbol used for current or current intensity; E represents voltages, sometimes called electromotive force, potential, or pressure; and R represents resistance. Current (I) is the number of amperes, voltage (E) is the number of volts, and resistance (R) is the number of ohms in the circuit.

There are two other ways of expressing Ohm's law which are just as important as the one we have been discussing. (1) *The voltage between two points in a circuit equals the current multiplied by the resistance.* Or, as an equation,

$$\text{Voltage } (E) = \text{Current } (I) \times \text{Resistance } (R)$$

or, simply, $$E = I \times R$$

(2) *The resistance of a circuit equals the voltage applied divided by the current.* Or, as an equation,

$$\text{Resistance } (R) = \frac{\text{Voltage } (E)}{\text{Current } (I)}$$

or, simply, $$R = \frac{E}{I}$$

When any two of the values mentioned in Ohm's law are known, the third may be determined by use of the proper one of the above equations.

Simple method of expressing Ohm's Law

Since Ohm's law is one of the most commonly used fundamentals of electricity, it is essential that it should be memorized. A very ingenious way of representing and of memorizing Ohm's law is embodied in Figs. 1 to 4. If any one part be removed or covered, the relative position of the other two gives the value of the one covered in terms of the other two.

Fig. 1

Fig. 2

Thus if we cover I, Fig. 1, $E \div R$ is left, Fig. 2. Therefore the value of I in terms of E and R is E divided by R. If R is covered, $E \div I$ remains, Fig. 3, giving the value of R in terms of E and I, which is E divided by I. In the same way, if we cover E, we have its value remaining in terms of I and R, namely, I times R, Fig. 4.

Fig. 3   Fig. 4

Example 1

A voltage of 6 volts is used to force a current through a resistance of 3 ohms. What is the current?

Solution

The voltage (E) is 6 volts and the resistance (R) is 3 ohms, we wish to find the current (I). Using the first statement of Ohm's law we find that

$$I = \frac{E}{R} = \frac{6}{3} = 2 \text{ amperes}$$

Example 2

What voltage is required to force a current of 2 amperes through a resistance of 10 ohms?

Solution

The current (I) is 2 amperes and the resistance (R) is 10 ohms. We want to find the voltage (E).

$$E = I \times R = 2 \text{ amperes} \times 10 \text{ ohms} = 20 \text{ volts}$$

Example 3

A voltage of 20 volts is required to force a current of 5 amperes through a coil. What is the resistance of the coil?

Solution

Voltage (E) = 20 volts.   Current (I) = 5 amperes

$$R = \frac{E}{I} = \frac{20 \text{ volts}}{5 \text{ amperes}} = 4 \text{ ohms}$$

ELECTRICAL EQUIPMENT

Example 4

The voltage between the ends of a piece of wire is 15 volts and its resistance is 3 ohms. What current will flow through it?

Solution

Covering the symbol I in the diagram, Fig. 1, there remains $E \div R$. Substituting the values of voltage and resistance given, we have $15 \div 3 = 5$ amperes.

Example 5

A current of 10 amperes is forced through a conductor by a pressure or voltage of 30 volts. What is the resistance of the conductor?

Solution

Covering R in the diagram, Fig. 3, we have left $E \div I$. Substituting for E and I their values from the conditions as stated, we have $30 \div 10 = 3$ ohms.

Example 6

A current of 10 amperes flows through a resistance of 2 ohms. What is the voltage that is forcing the current through the resistance?

Solution

Covering E, Fig. 4, we have left I times R. Substituting their values as before, we have $10 \times 2 = 20$ volts.

Applications of Ohm's Law

Ohm's law may be applied to a circuit as a whole or it may be applied to any part of the circuit—a circuit being the path through which a current flows from its source through a conductor back to its source. A great amount of caution and practice is required to apply this law correctly in all cases. Accordingly, there is no part of electrical work where so many mistakes are made as in the application of this simple law. Once the principle is firmly grasped, the student is prepared to handle correctly a wide range of electrical problems.

ELECTRICAL EQUIPMENT

Many of the difficulties will be cleared up if the student will keep in mind the following two statements and will use them intelligently.

When applying the law to the *entire* circuit, state the law as follows:

(1) The current in the entire circuit equals the voltage across the entire circuit divided by the resistance of the entire circuit.

Notice that the term *"entire"* applies to current, voltage, and resistance. Not to one of them, but to *all* the factors of the equation.

When applying the law to a part of the circuit, state the law as follows:

(2) The current in a certain part of a circuit equals the voltage across that same part divided by the resistance of that same part.

Notice here again that the values for current, voltage, and resistance are taken from the *"same part"* of the circuit. By far the greatest number of mistakes in applying Ohm's law come from dividing the voltage across one part of the circuit by the resistance of some other part of the circuit and expecting to get the current in some part of the circuit.

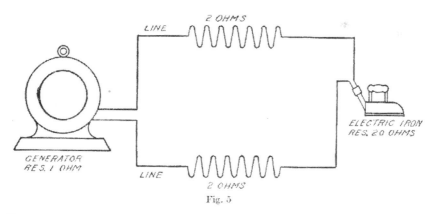
Fig. 5

Example 7

Fig. 5 is a diagram of a typical direct-current circuit. The generator has a resistance of 1 ohm and generates 150 volts at no load. Each line wire has a resistance of 2 ohms. The iron which represents the load has a resistance of 20 ohms. What is the current in the circuit?

ELECTRICAL EQUIPMENT

Solution

The resistance of the entire circuit is the resistance of the generator plus the resistance of the lines plus the resistance of the load, or

$$R = 1+2+2+20 = 25 \text{ ohms}$$

The total voltage produced is 150 volts, therefore the current is

$$I = \frac{E}{R} = \frac{150}{25} = 6 \text{ amperes}$$

IR Drop

The electromotive force of a generator, such as a dynamo or a battery, is the potential difference maintained between its terminals when no current is being taken from it. When current is taken from the generator, the terminal voltage—that is, the voltage applied to the line—is less than the open circuit voltage by an amount equal to the resistance drop or *IR* drop in the generator. The potential difference existing between two points in a circuit is called drop in potential, potential drop, fall of potential, voltage, and the like.

By Ohm's law the voltage drop in any *part* of a circuit is equal to the current in that part multiplied by the resistance of that part of the circuit.

$$E = I \times R \text{ volts}$$

in which E is the voltage, I the current, and R the resistance of *that part* of the circuit.

Thus the fall of potential in a portion of a circuit whose resistance drop is R is often called the "*IR drop*", as the *IR* drop applies to any *part* of the circuit it will also by proper use apply to the entire circuit.

Example 8

What is the *IR* drop across the electric iron shown in Fig. 5, when 6 amperes are flowing through it?

Solution

$$IR \text{ drop} = 6 \times 20 = 120 \text{ volts}$$

ELECTRICAL EQUIPMENT

Example 9

In Fig. 5 what is the voltage drop in the line when a current of 6 amperes flows through the circuit?

Solution

The total IR drop in the line will be twice that in one of the wires. The total line drop is

$$IR \text{ drop} = (6 \times 2) \times 2 = 24 \text{ volts}$$

Example 10

What is the IR drop in the generator when it is delivering a current of 6 amperes?

Solution

$$IR \text{ drop} = 6 \times 1 = 6 \text{ volts}$$

Example 11

What must be the open circuit voltage of the generator in order that it deliver a current of 6 amperes to this circuit?

Solution

Electromotive force $= 120 + 24 + 6 = 150$ volts
Or, total resistance $= 1 + 2 + 2 + 20 = 25$ ohms
Total IR drop in circuit $= 6 \times 25 = 150$ volts

ELECTRICAL INDICATING INSTRUMENTS

Volt=Ammeter. With an electric, it is important to watch the volt-ammeter. An example of this type of combined instrument is shown by the accompanying illustration, Fig. 1. It will be noted that the indicating needle of the ammeter does not go to the end of its scale, but reads both ways, the scale to the left hand being for the charging current, and that to the right for the discharging current. These instruments are manufactured in various forms, one type very much in use having the voltmeter and ammeter scales parallel in a vertical plane. Some also have the voltmeter scale so divided that the reading of the individual cells may be taken.

ELECTRICAL EQUIPMENT

By becoming familiar with the readings of the instrument and by realizing their significance, the driver of an electric automobile is in a position not only to judge whether the battery is giving the proper service, but he also has an accurate gage on the condition of the running gear and transmission of the vehicle itself. The instrument is capable, therefore, of giving ample warning by its deflections of any weakness, electrical or mechanical.

Ampere=Hour Meter. While the volt-ammeter affords a constant indication of the working of the battery, as well as the effi-

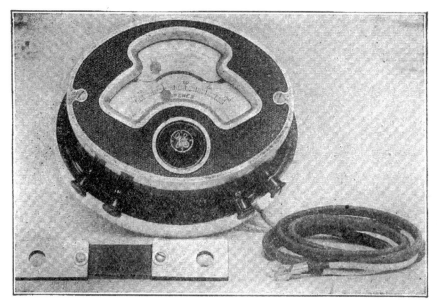

Fig. 1.   General Electric Volt-Ammeter

ciency of the transmission, and is accordingly indispensable, it does not permit of the direct reading of the state of charge nor indicate off-hand how much of the energy has been utilized and how much remains available at any given time. For this purpose the Sangamo ampere-hour meter has been developed and generally adopted by the builders of both pleasure and commercial electric cars.

Method of Use. To keep the battery plates in good working condition, it is necessary to give the battery a certain amount of charge, so that under normal conditions more ampere hours must be put into the battery than can be taken out of it. This difference is the overcharge, and it must be taken into account in figuring the number of ampere hours in a battery available for useful work. Since the only information desired by the driver is how much energy can be taken from the battery, the Sangamo ampere-hour meter is designed to compensate for the overcharge, and indicates at all times the current available without the necessity of resetting the pointer every time the battery is charged. This is accomplished by means of a differential shunt, as shown by the diagram, Fig. 2. Two shunts are employed, and the relative value of their resistance

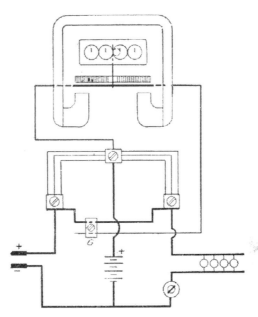

Fig. 2. Circuit Diagram of Differential Shunt
Type Sangamo Ampere-Hour Meter

is adjustable by means of the sliding connection G, so that the meter can be made to run slow on charge or fast on discharge, as desired. The usual method is to allow the meter to register less than the true amount on charge and the exact amount on discharge, the difference representing the loss in the battery, or overcharge.

Readjusting the Meter. However, over long periods of use under varying conditions, the battery losses will vary and in time the meter and battery will get out of step. Therefore, it is good practice to give the battery an extra overcharge at stated intervals and reset the meter, a simple device being provided for this purpose. Moreover, in vehicle work the batteries are frequently subjected to excessively high discharge rates and, under such conditions, the battery suffers an actual loss of capacity, which requires further compensation, as otherwise the meter will give a false indication of the number of ampere hours available. The variation in the capacity of the battery with its discharge rate is shown by the curves, Fig. 3.

In the Edison battery, the transfer of active material does not take place between the electrolyte and the plates, but from one

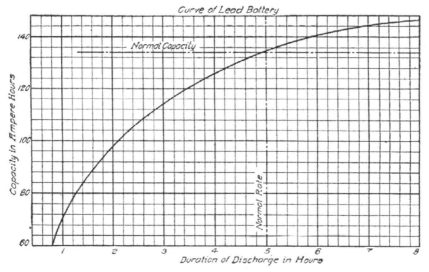

Fig. 3. Variation of Useful Ampere-Hour Capacity of Lead Battery with Discharge Rate

plate to the other, as in the ordinary electrolytic cell, commonly known as a primary battery. Therefore, the specific gravity of the electrolyte does not change with the state of charge and, consequently, the only direct way to measure the state of charge is with an ampere-hour meter, the hydrometer being of no use. But the loss of capacity due to high discharge rates is not a characteristic of the alkaline cell as it is with the lead type, so that an Edison battery does not require a compensated meter as just described. However, the drop in voltage of the Edison cell under high discharge rates is such that, from the user's viewpoint, the result is practically the same as with the lead-plate cell.

Started in Volume 1

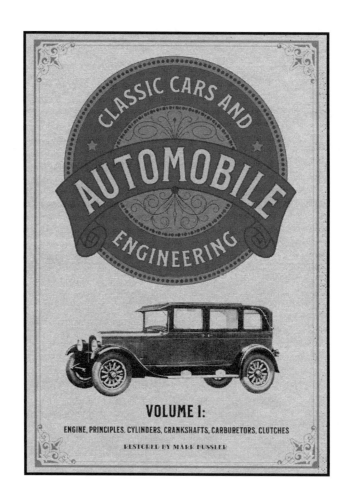

Continued in Volume 5

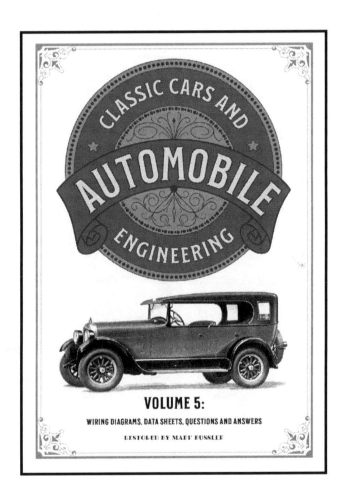

OTHER BOOKS FROM CGR PUBLISHING AT CGRPUBLISHING.COM

1939 New York World's Fair: The World of Tomorrow in Photographs

San Francisco 1915 World's Fair: The Panama-Pacific International Expo.

1904 St. Louis World's Fair: The Louisiana Purchase Exposition in Photographs

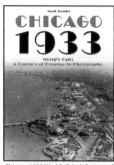

Chicago 1933 World's Fair: A Century of Progress in Photographs

19th Century New York: A Dramatic Collection of Images

The American Railway: The Trains, Railroads, and People Who Ran the Rails

The Aeroplane Speaks: Illustrated Historical Guide to Airplanes

The World's Fair of 1893 Ultra Massive Photographic Adventure Vol. 1

The World's Fair of 1893 Ultra Massive Photographic Adventure Vol. 2

The World's Fair of 1893 Ultra Massive Photographic Adventure Vol. 3

Henry Ford: My Life and Work - Enlarged Special Edition

Magnum Skywolf #1

Ethel the Cyborg Ninja Book 1

The Complete Ford Model T Guide: Enlarged Illustrated Special Edition

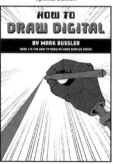

How To Draw Digital by Mark Bussler

Best of Gustave Doré Volume 1: Illustrations from History's Most Versatile...

OTHER BOOKS FROM CGR PUBLISHING AT CGRPUBLISHING.COM

Ultra Massive Video Game Console
Guide Volume 1

Ultra Massive Video Game Console
Guide Volume 2

Ultra Massive Video Game Console
Guide Volume 3

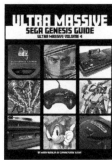

Ultra Massive Sega Genesis Guide

Antique Cars and Motor Vehicles:
Illustrated Guide to Operation...

Chicago's White City Cookbook

The Clock Book: A Detailed Illustrated
Collection of Classic Clocks

The Complete Book of Birds: Illustrated
Enlarged Special Edition

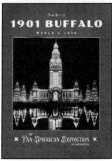

1901 Buffalo World's Fair: The Pan-
American Exposition in Photographs

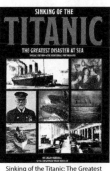

Sinking of the Titanic: The Greatest
Disaster at Sea

Gustave Doré's London: A Pilgrimage:
Retro Restored Special Edition

Milton's Paradise Lost: Gustave Doré
Retro Restored Edition

The Art of World War 1

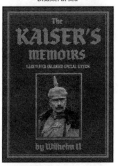

The Kaiser's Memoirs: Illustrated
Enlarged Special Edition

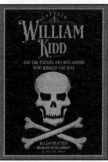

Captain William Kidd and the Pirates
and Buccaneers Who Ravaged the Seas

The Complete Butterfly Book: Enlarged
Illustrated Special Edition

Made in the USA
Monee, IL
11 September 2024

65388502R00227